EXPLAINING HEALTH AND —ILLNESS—

An Exploration of Diversity

Wendy Stainton Rogers

HARVESTER WHEATSHEAF

New York   London   Toronto   Sydney   Tokyo   Singapore

First published 1991 by
Harvester Wheatsheaf,
66 Wood Lane End, Hemel Hempstead,
Hertfordshire, HP2 4RG
A division of
Simon & Schuster International Group

Printed and bound in Great Britain by
BPCC Wheatons Ltd, Exeter

Set by Photoprint, Torquay
in Garamond 11/12½

British Library Cataloging-in-Publication Data

Rogers, Wendy Stainton
  Explaining health and illness: An exploration of
  diversity.
  I. Title
  362.1

ISBN 0–7450–0765–1
ISBN 0–7450–0764–3 pbk

---

1 2 3 4 5 95 94 93 92 91

This book is dedicated to
the memories of my mother,
Margaret Patricia Giles, and my
father, Peter Eric Giles

Contents

Acknowledgements

This book is based upon my doctoral thesis (Stainton Rogers, W., 1987). I started as a graduate student when my daughter, Rebekah, used to sleep in her carry cot outside my office window, and finished more or less by the time she got her driving licence. She, and Amanda, my foster daughter, deserve more than my thanks for having spent so much of their childhoods putting up with a mother who was often totally preoccupied. Nobody can write a thesis or a book while trying to hold down a full-time job and helping to bring up a family without enormous amounts of practical help and support. These were given by my sisters, Sally Brown and Pamela Sherlock, my friends, especially Susan Ashby and Margaret Veros, and my daughters and husband. Rex not only did all the things dedicated housepersons do to enable authors to write, he was my constant and most demanding critic and adviser and stopped me each time I tried to put the manuscript on a bonfire. And without the encouragement of Stan and Dee, it would simply never have been possible.

I am also grateful for the kindness and support of those who have offered academic encouragement and advice, particularly Mildred Blaxter, Kate Gleeson, Ivana Markova, Rory Williams, Celia Kitzinger, Roisin Pill, Steven Brown, and especially Will Stephenson, who was a very special inspiration. I also received considerable support from the people with whom I work, from Carole Jeffery, who constantly copes when I 'panic for two', Rae Smyth and Carole Hewett, who deciphered my scribblings and keyed in the text, and Malcolm Johnson, who promised I would finish it, and made it possible for me to do so. I would also like to thank Farrell Burnett, my editor, who was extremely patient as well as enormously supportive, and Rupert Hughes of the Judicial Studies Board and the Children Act 1989, without whom she would not have had to wait so long.

Despite the cliché, however, my most heartfelt thanks must go to the people who participated in the studies. They spent a great deal of time talking to me and shuffling around scraps of paper, and they must have wondered what on earth it was all for. Without them it *really* would have been impossible.

CHAPTER ONE

Introduction

There is always something you can do to help your health. The very fact of taking a positive action can help by improving your state of mind. . . . We must be the person who knows our own body best – what exercise it needs, food it needs, rest it needs, etc. etc. No one else can take responsibility for these things.

Looking out over my Fen in the summer sun, I realise that the farmer sprays herbicides regularly in the field next to my house, my tap water comes from surface water heavily polluted with nitrates and there's radioactive dust in my allotment.

Illness acts as a reminder that I shouldn't take all the good things in life for granted.

Health in general boils down to you yourself leading as healthy a life as you can. If you are fat and unfit you are more likely to have illness.

Economic resources are one of the major sources of feelings of security and well-being, or insecurity and stress.

There are more important things to worry about than the state of my personal health, given that Man and Nature between them will eventually finish me off anyway.

It is through the Lord Jesus that we are given our health and wellbeing.

It's my body, my risk to die young, my lungs, and I reserve the absolute right to decide, and not be dictated to by a doctor or so-called expert from the Health Education Council.

All of these statements were made in interviews or written comments by people who participated in two research studies I carried out in 1985 and 1986. Their range and diversity give some flavour of what I set out to achieve, and what I discovered. I wanted to find out about

1

how people explain, to themselves and to others, what it is that makes them healthy, why it is they get ill and, when they are ill, what enables them to recover. I was interested in all kinds of explanations, including those usually viewed as 'expert knowledge' *and* those often called 'lay beliefs'. I could see no justification for assuming they are necessarily different *kinds* of knowledge, so the research methods I used were ones which enabled all sorts of different people to participate in and contribute to the studies, and a diversity of views and perspectives to be made apparent.

I based my work upon the assumption that, given the appropriate opportunities, people are highly proficient at weaving explanations to suit particular circumstances, or to answer certain questions. The warp and weft of their explanatory fabric are the ideas, images and stories they know and think about and which are shared among their immediate social circles and in their work, and made available to them more generally by their culture and social location. The main thrust of my research was to try to understand this process better, both in terms of the endeavour of explanation itself and the kind of knowledge it operates upon. What are the ideas, images and stories that people work from? And what are the theoretical implications of construing people as active weavers rather than just passive users of explanations?

Therefore in this book I will be telling you about some of the ideas, images and stories that I identified as the basis for people's explanations of health and illness. Throughout I have used the word 'account' as a generic term for these. I chose this word (lifting it from Harré, 1979) rather than terms like 'social representation' (Moscovici, 1961), 'schema' (Bartlett, 1932) or 'personal construct' (Kelly, 1955) because it is simple and has explicitly story-like qualities. Although it can also imply an explanatory function, as I have used the term, an account is not so much an explanation itself, but the knowledge and understanding base upon which an explanation can be formed. Used as such, an account incorporates aspects of meaning, of moral evaluation, and of broader ideology or worldview. Yet because it is not pinned down by the prefix 'social' or that of 'personal', it is able to accommodate much more comfortably the sense of being both individual and collective property. I wanted to discover what kinds of accounts are available – in the marketplace of ideas in everyday life, and in the more restricted arenas of professional, religious and ideological discourses – for the weaving of explanations about health and illness.

I think it is important to make explicit from the beginning that my motivations were in no way neutral. The work I did had an expressly rhetorical purpose. I wanted to challenge the perception, currently prevalent among many psychologists and health professionals (less so among medical sociologists and anthropologists), that the 'lay health beliefs' held by ordinary people are at best only watered-down and simplistic versions of proper professional medical knowledge, and at worst 'old wives tales', superstitions and quackery. I also wanted to dispute another commonly held notion, that people's understandings are sufficiently artless, lawful and common property that they can be expressed along some simple dimension, or be encapsulated within a small number of pre-ordained categories. In promoting the view that people draw upon a range of alternative accounts to 'make sense of' their worlds, I wanted explicitly to confront theories which variously claim that the way people think is determined by specific, enduring personality traits, or by psychological mechanisms or by social forces. I believe such formulations are not only wrong, they are ideologically suspect in the extreme.

Take for instance a typical example of a personality theory approach, Mischel's (1966) portrayal of self-control as a characterological attribute:

> At one extreme is the person who predominantly chooses larger, delayed rewards or goals for which he [sic] must either work or wait. This person is more likely to be orientated towards the future . . . and to plan for distant goals. He (or she) also is apt to have high scores on 'ego-control' measures, to have high achievement motivation, to be more trusting and socially responsible, to be brighter and more mature, to have a high level of aspiration, and to show less uncontrolled passivity. . . . At the opposite extreme is the individual who predominantly prefers immediate gratification and rejects the alternative of waiting or working for larger, delayed goals. Correlated with this is a greater concern with the immediate present than with the future, and greater impulsivity. (p. 37)

Apart from its obvious dressing up of the wolf of value-judgement in the sheep's clothing of psychological theory, this kind of description portrays people as unthinking, unaware and driven solely by dispositional trait. It assumes that they are insensitive to situational and contextual influences. By treating self-control as an 'essence' hermetically sealed into individual heads it pretends that people never argue about it, gossip about it, read about it in books, or watch it portrayed in movies. It denies it is a theme that is culturally articulated in aphorisms and fables (such as Aesop's 'The Ant and the Grasshopper'). It assumes that it is only *experts* who are aware of such a

3

dispositional tension, and that ordinary people lack any reflexive self- or other-awareness.

Brown's (1985) description of 'perceived control as a coping mechanism' for reducing anxiety is a typical example of the psychological mechanism approach. This portrays people as at the behest of an objectified psychological force. The underlying model is of thought as a kind of psychodynamically pre-programmed control routine that, once triggered, runs systematically through its sequence. Threat, fear and worry, in this analysis, start up the sequence, and in order to reduce the ensuing anxiety, the person is driven inexorably to construe themself as 'in control'. This kind of theory makes people look like automata, the only real difference from the disposition model just described is that it is one which works on a short-acting fuse rather than following a permanently wired-in program. In many ways, the sociological forces approach is not that different either. For example, Friedson's (1970) assertion that doctors are the 'architects of medical knowledge' portrays ordinary people as equally mindless. It is just that this time they are the passive recipients of understandings moulded for them by others. Thinking, in this analysis, is a vapid, automatic response to the string-pulling of puppeteers.

I think all three kinds of theorization fail to do justice to the complexity and self-awarenes of people's experience, and to their capacity to argue and disagree. They all fail to address the subjectively familiar experience of thinking based upon confused and contradictory images, ideas and possible understandings: states of 'being in two minds' or 'having half a mind to . . . ', of feeling *both* 'in control' *and* 'controlled'. An approach which treats people as proficient weavers of stories offers a way out of these conceptual strait-jackets. In construing accounts as both things that individuals may consider subjectively in their thinking, and as things that are debated about and communicated within interpersonal discourse (spoken and written), the 'text' from which people 'make sense' is neither conceptualized as writ, immutable, inside the head, nor is it seen as being read, uncritically, from external canons. By proposing that such 'texts' are many and varied, offering people (individually and collectively) a range of alternative knowledge sources from which to choose, the kinds of contradictions, confusions, half-formed thoughts and half-believed explanations that form the basis of experience can be accommodated within a perception of social cognition that none the less reflects its constructive, organized, effort-after-meaning qualities. This is the image of the person with which I began my work.

4

This first chapter is intended to 'set the scene' for the book, and for the work upon which it was based. It begins with a brief overview of my theoretical starting points, in particular my response to recent postmodernist and post-structuralist trends within social psychology specifically, and the social 'sciences' more generally. I also use this opportunity to define some of the terms I will employ, some of the axes I want to grind, and indicate some of the questions I consider important. When I have done that, I provide a brief review of the various chapters in the book, and how they fit together.

NEW PARADIGMS FOR OLD

Just as the term 'nouvelle cuisine' has been used repeatedly for at least two hundred years to describe whatever was the latest fashion in cookery, psychology, even in its much shorter history, has been continually confronted with 'new paradigms'. Each one has been presented as a dramatic refutation of a worn-out previous order, offering fresh insights and innovative solutions. It is almost as though theories, like washing machines, have built-in obsolescence, so that after a period of constant use they cease to work efficiently and need to be replaced by a new model.

Until very recently the most ubiquitous 'new paradigm' in social psychology was that of 'interpretational social psychology', offered in slightly different versions in the early writings of people like Kenneth Gergen and Edward Samson in the USA and Rom Harré and John Shotter in Britain. Their 'new improved brand' of psychology was most notable in its denunciation of the kinds of theories I have just described, of austere and artificial laboratory experimentation, and the image thus created of people as 'idealized automata in bland, anomic environments' (Harré, 1979). They wanted to put the 'social' back into social psychology, and the 'person' back, more generally, into psychology. They thus proposed a 'new psychology' in which the purposive, rule-making and rule-following, constructive aspects of personhood and social interaction formed the subject of study.

This new psychology was launched in the late 1960s and early 1970s at a time of major social upheaval in Western society; an upheaval comprising paradoxical tensions between a renewed interest in socio-logical and cultural influences upon behaviour and experience, and commitment to 'social responsibility'; and at the same time an increasing interest in the uniqueness of the individual, and commitment to self-expression and self-actualization. On the one hand emergent feminist, Marxist, politically radical and civil rights groups were questioning what they saw as the 'psychology of the "good guys"' dominating theorization in a way that portrayed women, ethnic minorities and the poor as 'deviant', and which failed to recognize the effects of inequality and disadvantage. On the other hand, the humanistic and self-actualization movements were questioning the mechanistic aspects of behaviourism that portrayed people as passive and mindless, denying individual creativity and spiritual values. These tensions were reflected by pressures, from the former, to forge links with sociology (and less often with anthropology) in order to acknowledge the societal and cultural determinants defining and limiting action and constructing and constraining experience; and pressures from the latter to develop a new, emancipatory psychology which recognized the importance of self-determinancy and the individual's capacity for self-definition.

Today these tensions between 'the social' and 'the individual' have emerged as perhaps *the* major theoretical problem that psychology has to face. How can we develop theories that do justice to the singularity of each individual's unique experience, while at the same time recognizing the importance of shared culture and common social experience?

The solutions adopted for the central individual/social problem have been varied. Attempts to meld the two within a single theory have been articulated within both sociology and psychology. The sociologists Berger and Luckmann (1966), for instance, offered a social construc-tionist framework within which people are seen to construct their realities within a cyclical interplay of three 'moments' (internalization, objectification and externalization). Within psychology Riegel (1978) and Buss (1979) proposed different versions of 'dialectical psychology' combining the two theoretical polarities of 'person' and 'society' within reflexivity, and Pribram (1986) has suggested that the duality can be elided over by simply assuming that they are alternative facets of a single entity.

However, Henriques et al. (1984) and Doise (1986) have argued that such a 'democratic fusion' of theories is impracticable because they are 'different universes of discourse' (Doise, op. cit.) and therefore cannot merely be combined or added together. Henriques et al. argue the case strongly in their criticism of the questions raised by interpretative socialization theories (such as those of Shotter, 1974 and Richards, 1974):

None of these questions can be addressed while psychology brackets off content into the domain of the social and defines it as outside of the boundaries of its theories, to fall within the domain of sociology, for example. In socialisation theory it is implicitly assumed that, if they are added together, the ideas of psychology and sociology will produce a full explanation. But this assumption is itself based upon the idea that the theoretical objects of the two disciplines – individual and society – are commensurable. In fact in psychology they are two kinds of theoretical objects produced in different discourses through different disciplines, destined to by-pass each other in the addition as they do in the interaction. (Henriques *et al.* 1984, p. 20)

The basis of this assumption of incommensurability was the growing conviction (cf. Devereux, 1972; Potter, 1984) that the articulation of new theories is not the product of Kuhnian (1962) 'paradigm shifts' of sequential overthrow, each new paradigm replacing the last. Rather, what we see is a situation where at any moment there will be competition between a number of mutually contradictory theories. The anthropologist Press (1980) has suggested the term 'sympatricity' for such a situation, drawing an analogy between theories, and species in a biological ecosystem. Sympatric species are those that compete, within any ecosystem, for resources and ultimately for survival, but at any point in time will be seen to be co-existing and more or less equally viable. The image is of sympatric theories that operate in parallel, at one and the same time competing and co-existing. This is a philosophy of science which argues that what researchers and theorists should be doing is not seeing theory testing and building as some evolutionary game of epistemological 'survival of the fittest', but instead should be exploring a theoretical ecology (cf. Adam, 1990) within which each theory implicates (but at the same time excludes) the others.

These ecological notions are themselves not innovative. In the nineteenth century William James introduced a number of new and fascinating concepts that have recently received renewed attention (e.g. Stephenson, 1986a,b). Possibly his most striking idea was that of theoretical 'complementarity' (James, 1891), where phenomena require separate and different theory-bases to be understood. Stephenson (citing the physicist Bohr) offers the wave and particle theories of light in physics as an example. Applied to present day psychology, the principle of theoretic complementarity proposes that no single theory will ever be able to 'make sense' of the social phenomena that we are seeking to understand. Just as both wave and particle theories are necessary to 'make sense' of the properties of light, so too must more than one theory be used to 'make sense' of people's thoughts and actions. They cannot be subsumed, because the very basis of complementarity is that there are – and always will be – alternative universes of meaning and explanation. What something 'means' in one universe is quite different from what it 'means' in another (what Barnes and Law, 1976, call 'indexicality').

THEORIZATION IN THE POSTMODERN ERA

Theories do not spring fresh and new within a single discipline. They arise within a historical context, products of a whole 'Zeitgeist'. The origins of ideas like those of sympatricity and complementarity can be traced to the broader shift heralded by postmodernist (more usually called post-structuralist in the social sciences) thought. This is an immense subject, and one I have neither the knowledge nor time to get embroiled in at this stage. But to set the scene for the work I will cover in this book, we do need to spend a few moments here seeing what postmodernism means for the topics I am going to cover.

Tomás Ibañez (1991) defines 'modernity' as 'the joint outcome of the technical achievements of scientific knowledge, and the rhetoric of scientific truth'. (It may be worth noting that this is not a consensual definition, its meaning being somewhat different within the study of literature, for example.) Modernity, by Ibañez's definition, began in the West in the sixteenth and seventeenth centuries, a social movement to replace the irrationality and superstition of earlier orders by scientific rationality and empiricism. Throughout the eighteenth and nineteenth centuries modernist thought was socially and culturally legitimated, not just in the domain of science itself, but more broadly by the promotion of ideas of progress, democracy and individual freedom throughout the institutions of society (e.g. the law) and within portrayals of the kinds of values to which people should aspire. At the very core of modernity is a rhetoric of scientific truth. Mulkay (1991, p. 27) identifies as the central tenet of scientism the belief in a 'a single coherent factual world which can be accurately and consistently represented'.

Postmodernism, by contrast, denies there is any single, coherent, real world. It assumes instead that there are a multiplicity of alternative realities. In broad terms, this is what is implied by Berger and Luckmann's 'social construction of reality', Press's 'sympatricity' and James' 'complementarity', and, as such, all are postmodernist theories. All argue for there being 'many potential worlds of meaning that can be imaginatively entered and celebrated, in ways which are constantly changing to give richness and value to human experience' (Mulkay, 1991, pp. 27–8).

A POSTMODERN THEORY OF EXPLANATION

Postmodernism offers not just a conceptual framework for formulating theories, but a basis for theorizing itself about, say, psychological phenomena like attitudes, opinions and beliefs. This kind of theory proposes that the way we make sense of our world in everyday life is (as is academic theorizing) a process of making explicit, at any precise point in time, one from a number of co-existing complementary explanations. From this perspective, when an individual marks an item on an attitude scale, they are not expressing 'their' opinion (i.e. making explicit a single implicit and enduring 'essence'), rather they are selecting *one* from a range of contradictory 'attitudes'. They are choosing which one to express at a particular moment. Their choice is made according to such influences as situational demands, 'mood', what is at the 'top of my mind', and so on. But in a different state of mind, or different situation, or following a different set of prior events, they might well express a different 'attitude' and tick a different box on the scale. Like the physicist who selects which of the wave or particle theories to draw upon depending upon what is to be achieved, people select which of the opinions at their disposal to draw upon according to the function to be served by its expression.

This kind of formulation has been the basis of a number of recent approaches in social psychology. The best known is discourse analysis (Potter and Wetherell, 1987), which stresses the constructive and variable nature of discourse, and seeks to study what people say in conversations in terms of the discursive functions of the variability to be found. The image is of the person as a 'capable negotiator of reality', able to perform a range of functions by their talk, ranging, say, from self-presentation management to social 'grooming' (when in interaction with others), and from, say, rationalizing to problem-solving (when engaged in private thought). We can see how such ideas developed from the earlier formulations of 'constructive alternativism' (cf. Kelly, 1966), 'social constructionism' (cf. Berger and Luckmann, 1966) and 'invented realities' (cf. Watzlawick, 1984). They propose not just that social realities are constructed, nor just that different people (as

9

individuals and groups) construct different realities, but that each individual and collective draws upon and lives constantly within *multiple* realities. The image, however, is not one of personal or collective 'schizophrenia', of living and operating within a complete muddle of unmanageable confused and contradictory thoughts and selves (although it is a much more multifaceted image than most other perceptions); rather, it is one of people as clever weavers of stories, whose supreme competence is that they can and do create order out of chaos, and moment to moment make sense of their world amid the cacophony.

THE AUTHOR'S DILEMMA

This perception of people as story weavers, drawing upon complementary and sympatric discourses to 'make sense' of their social world and social being, makes things difficult for me writing this book. By convention my job as author is to weave a coherent, plausible, user-friendly story for you that will stimulate and retain your interest over the next couple of hundred pages or so. Yet, as Mulkay (1991) put it, the best I can do is *parody* the texts that I tell you about, whether these are actual texts (i.e. the books and papers I read and will describe to you) or the 'texts' I obtained in my studies (i.e. what people said and wrote when they took part). In order to weave my story, I must inevitably do violence to the ideas and understandings as they were originally expressed. I cannot, within a postmodernist approach, pretend to be merely mirroring their reality. I cannot assume the legitimacy of a science which says these texts exist independently and all that I am doing is recounting them. I must, at one and the same time, caution you that the story you will read is a distorted and partial version that I have deliberately constructed for you in a particular way, for particular reasons; and try to convince you that I have something important and worthwhile to say. I am not, then, setting out to 'tell it like it is', but rather saying 'look at it this way'.

Part of my problem is that, even given this caveat, the linear structure of this book, and its textual singularity, are not particularly appropriate for conveying ideas in a postmodernist endeavour. Other more innovative ways of undertaking the task are not available to me. I lack access to a film camera or television studio, the skills of an artist, or even my usual resources (as a teacher in the Open University where texts are produced collectively by a team that includes artists and designers). So this book, and its format, is the limit of what we have available, and we will have to do our best with them. All I will say is that if at any point you find yourself being thoroughly gripped or inspired by my story (however pleasing that may be for my ego), beware. Its ability to convince you that what I am saying is 'insightful' or 'true' will be because I have succeeded in telling a good story. Remember, there are always other stories that could be told!

OVERVIEW OF THE BOOK

In the next two chapters I trace the historical development of theories in this area in more detail than I have done so far. As well as for conventional reasons (it is considered rather arrogant, particularly for a relative novice, to base a book just on your own work), I have begun with these theoretical chapters for practical purposes too. I justify them out of my own experiences as I gradually got to know about this whole field of explaining health and illness. At first I worked with what I knew – psychology. I did the usual things in the usual ways, and scoured the books and journals listed under 'psychology' for work similar to my own. I found virtually nothing. By chance a friend told me about a conference run by people called 'medical anthropologists' about a topic called 'lay beliefs' and I went along. It was an eye opener, for here were people whom I thought all spent their lives in Papua New Guinea, studiously working away in Bethnal Green, Cardiff and Oxford, Tucson and Toronto. And they were interested in almost identical issues and questions to the ones I wanted to explore. By this point I became rather adventurous, and began to attend sociological conferences too. My trips to the library became marathon occasions, as I gradually learned to look into *three* discipline areas to see what was new. My arms grew longer and my wrists stronger (until they gave up altogether, but that is another story).

As I gradually learned about and got on top of the literature of these two new disciplines, two things struck me forcibly. The first was just how much we all had in common. The second was how ignorant we were of each other's work. At other conferences I found anthropologists grappling with areas which had become 'old hat' in psychology. At the same time I noticed just how little the work of anthropologists and sociologists had permeated into psychology, and in many ways how tardy psychology had become in theorization about such areas as 'medical pluralism' (the study of account sympatricity in cultures, such

11

as the co-existence and competition between biomedicine and traditional medicine in places like Mexico and India). What I have tried to
do in this book, therefore, is bring together some of the fruits of my
labours, so that psychologists can gain access to the wealth of work
available in anthropology and sociology; and so that sociologists and
anthropologists can find out about some of the main areas of
theorization in psychology. Consequently in Chapter 2 I look at the
ways in which anthropologists and sociologists have sought to
understand how people explain health and illness. In Chapter 3 I
undertake a similar task for psychology, although here I have tended to
concentrate upon broader theorization, including social learning
theory, attribution theory and other theories of social cognition. In
part this emphasis is because this is an area which social psychology
regards as central to its discipline, unlike the situation in sociology and
anthropology, where such work has been important but ultimately of
only limited concern. In part too, social psychology (from my
perspective anyway) has had little to offer at a theoretical level in the
specific area of health and illness, with the exception of the inspiring
work of Claudine Herzlich and Janine Pierret (1985, 1987). It may be
worth noting that I have also included a more specific theoretical
review of psychological theorization in Chapter 7, when I proceed to
report studies about blame, responsibility and locus of control. As the
reader you will need to choose how best to tackle these theoretical
components of the book.

At this point in the book I begin to move from theory to research.
Chapter 4 weaves a story (highly selectively) around the various studies
that have been conducted to discover people's beliefs about and
understandings of health and illness. Here I have combined work from
all three disciplines to provide an overview of the different kinds of
research that have been conducted, and the different findings obtained.
In Chapter 5 I briefly consider the kinds of methods that were used in
these studies, and the question of what methods of research are
appropriate and available for gaining such understandings. Postmodernist thinking has been conceptually highly productive, but it has
been notably less successful in discovering research methods suitable
for pursuing empirical support. Included in this chapter is a brief
description of a method well known in political science and market
research, particularly in the USA (although its originator, William
Stephenson, was British, and its formulation occurred in Oxford and
London in the 1930s within the group led first by Spearman and then
by Burt). Q methodology offers, I believe, not *the* ideal social

constructionist method, but certainly a useful addition to the repertoire of anybody wanting to identify and describe accounts. In this chapter I argue that we need to use a variety of methodologies in conjunction with each other if we are to do justice both to the richness and complexity of accounts themselves, and to their cultural and social as well as psychological articulation and development. Most of all, we need to combine methods which can tell us about both the ecological and the historical features of account diversity, construction and change. The conventions of postmodernism already pay due regard to the archaeologies of knowledge; I would argue that we must also consider its tectonic properties, and need to discover methods that will enable us to do so.

The next two chapters report my own research. Chapter 6 describes my first study, which adopted a broad, taxonomic approach, of trying to identify and describe as many and as wide a diversity of accounts for explaining health and illness *in general terms* as I could. My second study, described in Chapter 7, focused in on more personal accounts, those involved when people seek to explain what it is that makes *them* healthy or ill, or enables *them* to recover. In this area, issues of responsibility and blame are particularly salient, and I looked especially at these. As well as exploring the accounts themselves, I also wanted to challenge existing approaches, in particular the 'Health Locus of Control', and so the study includes work done to deconstruct the concept itself, and demonstrate the inadequacy of the scale devised to 'measure' it.

Finally, in Chapter 8 I bring my research results together into a cultural analysis of alternative accounts of and for health and illness. To weave a coherent story I have been somewhat selective and chosen eight of them to explore in more depth. Within the space available, I have spent a little time expanding upon each one, and looking at its origins and history, and some of the ways it has been changed over time. Together these eight accounts offer a rich mosaic, and I complete the chapter and the book by speculating about some of the ways the approach I have taken may contribute both to our understanding of how people explain health and illness, and of the process of explanation itself.

CHAPTER TWO

Anthropological and Sociological Approaches

In this chapter I will look at the ways in which anthropologists and sociologists have sought to understand how people make sense of health and illness – the explanations used, processes involved and the influences upon them. I have brought these two disciplines together (and I will go on to link them in with psychology in the next chapter) because I believe we need to examine all three approaches if we are to get a theoretical handle on a very complicated area of interest. I begin by considering the overall theoretical field of anthropology and sociology, and then show how specific formulations about health and illness have been accommodated within them. In some ways the two disciplines have paralleled each other in the development of their theories and approaches. This is in part because academic thinking reflects the broader 'spirit of the age', so theories developed at similar times, albeit within different disciplines, will usually be influenced in similar ways. In part, too, the parallel development is due to at least some workers in each field taking the trouble to look over their shoulders to find out what is going on beyond their own intellectual back fence – though this has been far from the common state of events. More usually, anthropologists and sociologists have worked in isolation from one another, occasionally dipping into the more generally available texts from completely outside of the social 'sciences', but seldom troubling themselves to see what other disciplines were up to, and even, at times, displaying sufficient antagonism to ignore each other deliberately.

I have started with theory for more than just scholarly convention. In Chapter 5 I will go on to consider the vexed question of how our understandings, as theorists, are moulded by the methodological approaches which we take as researchers. To do that it is necessary to

14

begin with theory, as this – in principle at least – sets the scene for empirical endeavour. We can make sense of the research only if we know about the theory-base from which it originated.

ANTHROPOLOGICAL THEORIES

The first anthropologists to consider explanations for health and illness were not specialists. They looked at these concerns in the context of general studies of the beliefs, understandings and practices of specific cultural groups. These were typically small-scale and intensive studies of particular tribes, indigenous to areas which were relatively untouched by Western influences. However, even when, somewhat later, anthropological studies were conducted which focused specifically on a tribe's understandings about health and illness, the studies seldom distinguished between descriptions of medical practices, and of beliefs and explanations. Consequently it is often hard to disentangle them. Most early theorization, therefore, was couched in terms of the 'medical systems' of different cultures.

Distinguishing between 'civilized' and 'primitive' medical systems

Anthropologists, working in the 1920s and 1930s – eras still of Empire and Imperialism – and largely drawn from upper-class academic backgrounds, saw the peoples of the world as divided into two kinds: 'civilized' and 'primitive'. It was in this context that Rivers (1924, 1926) first asserted what soon became a common assumption about the difference between 'civilized' and 'primitive' medical systems: that whereas in the West, medicine was based upon objective and rational science, 'primitive' medical systems were all founded upon ideas of magic and religion. Rivers wrote that illness was universally seen by 'primitive peoples' to be caused by sorcery and the actions of the spirit world. In this primitive worldview, preventing illness was seen to depend upon respecting taboos and religious rules of conduct, and cures were ones of ritual or magic. Somewhat later Clements (1932) described such 'primitive' medical systems in more detail, classifying them according to three kinds of explanations for disease: intrusion into the body by disease objects, intrusions by spirits and the capture of the soul. Ackerknecht (whose work spanned from 1942 to 1971), argued that although 'primitive' medical systems differed greatly from one cultural group to another, they were none the less all

15

fundamentally magico-religious in form. To early anthropologists, then, explanations of health and illness fell into two classes: those adopted by orthodox medicine in the West (scientific, rational and grounded upon empirical evidence); and those adopted by 'primitive' cultures elsewhere (mystical, magical and religious, grounded upon faith, myth, dogma and tradition).

The introduction of ecological and systems theories

By the 1950s and 1960s this division became increasingly unacceptable, seen as judgemental, racist and elitist in its dismissal of alternative explanatory systems as not just exotic and strange, but (implicitly if not explicitly) 'a load of mumbo-jumbo' (the everyday use of this term to mean 'nonsense' is evidence of the scorn with which such ideas were – and still are – regarded). In an attempt to ameliorate this situation a number of anthropologists (e.g. Paul, 1955 and Dunn, 1968) adopted 'systems theory' in order to try to make comparisons fairer. Within a systems theory approach, however strange to Western ideas, magico-religious explanations of health and illness can be seen as rational and indeed inevitable, given that they are embedded and articulated within an *overall* cultural worldview based upon magic and religious belief. In other words, if your whole world is imbued with religion, and your actions guided by social rules of taboo, respect for your elders and the need to propitiate your gods, how else could you make sense of falling ill *but* as the consequence of rule-infringement, or the wrath of God?

At about this time medical anthropology began to emerge as a recognized, separate discipline of its own. However, despite attempts to be more 'culture fair', medical anthropologists continued to maintain a strong conviction that while all other medical systems *did* require explanation (i.e. they were seen as 'systems of beliefs'), the underlying assumptions of Western biomedicine did not, since they were based upon 'scientific facts'. They continued to be so beguiled by the literally 'outlandish' rituals, taboos and practices they observed when studying the medical systems of 'alien' cultures that they found it difficult to tell where magic ended and medicine began, whether in large-scale ceremonies or, say, everyday rules about food preparation. What has distinguished more recent anthropology (see, for example, the work of Guess, 1984, and Kleinman, 1984) is its determination not to claim any superiority for Western thought. This has enabled contemporary anthropologists to recognize that beliefs in magic and religion and ritualistic behaviour abound in Western culture. They are so familiar to us that we fail to recognize them as just as much superstitions and rituals as those enacted by, say, the !Kung in Africa. Equally, they are able to observe that non-Western medical systems involve large numbers of practices which are not in the least magico-religious, such as prescribing straightforward herbal remedies for everyday aches and pains. From a contemporary perspective, whatever the differences between systems, they are most certainly not ones of 'rationality' versus 'magic' that were assumed at the beginnings of medical anthropology.

This recognition began to emerge as a number of more ecological theories were formulated (see, for example, the work of Alland, 1966, 1970, and Wellin, 1978). These examined each culture's medical system within a broad context of other influences. Despite a continued ethnocentrism, these theories expanded the scope of medical anthropology and made it much more sophisticated. It enabled anthropologists to begin to consider cultural influences in the context of, for example, sociological, political and psychological influences; and the importance of taking account of the biological, environmental and technological settings in which explanatory systems were constructed and used. Theorizing thus became much more outward-looking, gained insights from other disciplines and began to recognize that all explanatory systems (including those of the West) need to be viewed within the ecology of the environment, prevailing ideologies and society within which they operate. The new eclecticism also introduced the concept of time and raised questions about how medical systems develop and change historically.

The kinds of thoroughgoing analyses that emerged within medical anthropology in the 1970s (such as Fabrega's, 1974) provided rich and detailed theory-bases within which to study explanations for health and illness. In their sheer range (as well as elegant descriptions of empirical work carried out in a whole host of different cultures) they had a substantial impact upon medical anthropology, making it a discipline that has come strongly to influence medical sociology and, less so, psychological work in this field. Perhaps the most important new idea to emerge within this interdisciplinary approach was the recognition that explanatory systems differ *intra*culturally as well as *inter*culturally; that within any society or community there will operate a number of sympatric systems, which co-exist and compete in dynamic interplay, varying in the extent to which they are culturally sanctioned and endorsed. This kind of study, termed 'medical pluralism', is of growing interest to medical anthropologists, and I will return to it later.

Challenging the dominance of biomedicine

Thus we can see medical anthropology today challenging the assumption that Western biomedicine is in any fundamental way different from the explanatory systems of other cultures. It is regarded as just one of many ways of explaining illness and health, as well as directing medical treatment. This perspective has been promoted within a framework of social epistemology drawing heavily on the work of cultural analysts such as Foucault (who saw his task as one of 'an archaeologist of knowledge', digging up clues from the past in order to discover how contemporary ideas are constructed); Habermas (who focused on the links between language, knowledge and culture); Berger and Luckmann (whose analysis of the social construction of reality offered ideas about the nature of the process by which individuals and groups construct their taken-for-granted worlds); and Douglas (who focused particularly on the way in which anthropological concepts such as ritual and taboo offer useful insights into the workings of Western culture, and its sytems of knowledge production).

Central to the social epistemology approach has been an exploration of sign systems and language, particularly the codes and representations by which knowledge is portrayed, shared, interpreted and constructed. This has included the approaches of semiotics (i.e. the study of signs and symbols) and hermeneutics (i.e. the study of the interpretation of text). Both are fundamentally postmodernist, treating all forms of knowledge representation, encoding and decoding as based upon shared, intersubjective qualities of meaning, for which we can seek empathetic understanding (sometimes termed *verstehen*) but can never objectively define. Since this paradigm is so critical to the subject of this book, and spans across the disciplines of anthropology, sociology and psychology, I will take it up later in the next chapter, where its implications can be explored more generally, and in greater detail.

Medical anthropologists have been particularly concerned with the way that the dominance of biomedicine reflects a relationship between the status of different *forms* of knowledge concerning health and illness in any society. Similarly they have been interested in the distribution of *power* within society, as derived from religious, economic, political or institutional sources (see, for example, the work of Logan and Hunt, 1978). From this perspective a combination of economic and professional dominance, and the threat posed by illness, enable healers *in all societies* not only to gain status and material advantages, and control access to resources, but also to promote their own explanatory

18

systems. Within this analysis, theorists like Friedson (1970, 1976) refer to doctors and shamans as the 'architects of medical knowledge'. Their assumed superior skills, expert knowledge and high status provide them with the power to dispense healing or withhold it. Hence they gain the power to *construct* knowledge for others.

This is not just a simple matter of medical professionals assuming that their explanations are more correct, more accurate and more predictive than the alternatives. It goes a lot further, as the anthropologist Alan Young has described so neatly: 'these beliefs appear to the people who use them . . . to merely reflect "empirically observed" facts of nature . . . taken for granted, commonsensical, and admitted without argument: they attract no epistemological scrutiny and receive no formal codification' (Young, 1980, p. 136). Another influential anthropologist in this field, Michael Taussig (1980), went even further and argued that biomedicine, as practised in the West, 'reproduce[s] a political ideology in the guise of a science of (apparently) "real things"'. This process of turning 'ideas' into 'real things' within the language that we use (both for thought and communication with others) is termed 'reification'. Reification is the process of taking a complex and amorphous mixture of observed events, experiences, accounts and ideas, conceptually turning them (or having them turned) into a 'thing', and then giving that 'thing' a name (e.g. anorexia, premenstrual tension and post-traumatic shock syndrome). What both Alan Young and Michael Taussig argued persuasively, from within anthropology, was that processes like reification do not happen randomly or in a neutral fashion – they are not mere practical solutions to practical problems (such as finding a convenient name for a new phenomenon). While they may seem commonsensical, 'merely mirroring the real conditions of existence' (Young, 1980, p. 133), what they are in fact doing is constructing and then promoting a particular version of reality. In other words, they are *ideological* in their impact, not just 'naming names' but, more powerfully (and indeed, in some cases more insidiously and subversively), constraining people to see the world in a particular way.

Young used the illustration of the concept of 'stress' to argue that ideas like this allow the medical establishment to emphasize and highlight certain features of our social world. By treating 'stress' as a *personal* problem (requiring individual solutions), it becomes possible to deny and cover up other possibilities – such as being exploited in the workplace or in one's relationships. By believing themselves and presenting to others an image of their own explanatory system as 'incontrovertible fact', the dominant healers in a society can marginalize rival systems, treating them as not just inferior, but 'not really medicine at all'. In Western culture, this takes the form of a medical establishment that regards other healers as charlatans and quacks, to which only the foolhardy would turn, and portraying other explanations as dangerous and needing to be corrected. For example, over the last couple of years some members of the medical establishment in Britain have set themselves up as a group, calling themselves 'QUACKBUSTERS', with the specific aim of undermining and counteracting forms of treatment that do not conform to current medical orthodoxy.

Possibly one reason for all this medical Angst is that in the 1980s and 1990s, the dominance of biomedicine has been under attack popularly as well as intellectually. Aakster (1986) has argued that in the West, doctors as well as 'ordinary people' are becoming increasingly convinced that orthodox medicine is failing to solve their health problems. Their first reaction was to interpret this as merely a problem of resources – and to pour more and more money into the medical system. But as that has been seen to fail to stem the tide of 'more cancer, more mental disease, more heart infarctions, traffic accidents, suicides, addictions' (Aakster, 1986, p. 271), they have increasingly turned to various forms of 'alternative medicine', such as homoeopathy, acupuncture and naturopathy; or, as Levin and Coreil (1986) call it, 'New Age Healing'. Thus within both the world of academic anthropological theory and in popular discourse in the West, medicine is ceasing to be seen as

> the administration by doctors as a group of morally neutral, essentially benign and effective techniques for curing disease and reducing pain and suffering. The techniques themselves are frequently useless and all too often actually physically harmful. The 'scientific' knowledge of doctors is sometimes not knowledge at all, but rather social messages (e.g. about the proper behaviour of women) wrapped up in technical language. And above all, both the doctor–patient relationship and the entire structure of medical services are not mere technical relationships, but social relationships which express and reinforce (often in subtle ways) the social relations of the larger society: e.g. class, racial, sexual and age hierarchy. (Ehrenreich, 1978, p. 15)

The medical anthropological attack upon conventional biomedical knowledge does not imply that there has been a deliberate conspiracy on the part of the medical profession to dupe the public, using an

Orwellian kind of 'newspeak'. While there are undoubtedly times and circumstances in which any professional group will deliberately use specialist terminology to confuse, persuade or even to mislead others, it would be mistaken to suppose this is all that is happening. Medical professionals are themselves persuasively indoctrinated by the 'reality' of the world in which they work and have been educated. The whole ethos of biomedicine is modernist and positivistic, a world of 'real things' and of 'scientific truth'. To challenge this is to run the risk of the certainties on which they work coming tumbling down like a house of cards (a pretty frightening thought). My brother-in-law, who is a surgeon, once got very angry with me when I criticized doctors as acting like 'god almighties' who knew it all. 'Of course we act like gods', he said. 'How the hell else do you think we can cope with making decisions, day after day, that, when they go wrong, kill and maim people!' Medical professionals are prey to the same worries and concerns that beset the rest of us (and carry more life-and-death responsibility than most of us do). The problem is not their motivation, by and large, but the *effects* of their assumption of superior knowledge.

It also needs to be acknowledged that biomedicine is a highly effective curative system for many kinds of illness. Its epistemological basis may be less firm than is often assumed, but that does not mean it is ineffective. The arguments of contemporary medical anthropologists are not that we should overthrow biomedicine altogether, nor that we should see medical professionals as power-hungry propagandists, pulling the wool over the unsuspecting eyes of their patients. Rather they seek to challenge the assumption that biomedicine is the *only* valid medical system, that it has some natural superiority, or that it is universally benign, morally neutral and merely 'mirrors reality' without distortion.

Medical pluralism

The field of medical pluralism is concerned with the ways in which alternative medical systems co-exist and compete together within a culture; how they jostle with one another for dominance; and how they interact with each other. Within this field there have been numerous suggestions for classifying medical systems. Dunn (1977), for example, proposed the use of geographical divisions, identifying medical systems according to their sphere of influence: cosmopolitan, regional and local. He classified *local* medical systems as those restricted to small geographical areas, based upon the systems indigenous to that area. An example would be the practices and beliefs relating to health and illness of the !Kung people of the Kalahari desert (Lee, 1978, offers a comprehensive description). *Regional* medical systems, in Dunn's analysis, are also indigenous, but where a single paradigm (often linked to religious and moral ideologies) extends its influence over a wider geographical area. An example would be Ayurveda medicine, arising from within classical Indian philosophy and religion, which is to be found throughout the sub-continent of India. Finally Dunn suggested that *cosmopolitan* medical systems were those imported and adopted world-wide, biomedicine being the most notable example, but including other systems with fundamentally different theory-bases, such as homoeopathy and traditional Chinese medicine.

Other classifications have focused upon the nature of the belief systems themselves. The most comprehensive division is between attributions of *exogenous* (external to the person) or *endogenous* (internal to the person) causes of illness (Valabrega's 1962 account is a good example). Clements' classification of 'primitive' medical beliefs can be accommodated within this framework: intrusions of disease objects or spirits being exogenous explanations; soul capture endogenous. However, many other content-specific classifications have been suggested. For example, Foster (1976) distinguished between personalistic and naturalistic systems; a *personalistic* system being the attribution of illness as arising from the intended and motivated intervention of another person or being, whereas a *naturalistic* system is where illness is assumed to be the product of naturally occurring processes. Other anthropological theorists (e.g. Jones, 1977) worked from the assumption that explanations of health and illness arise within the overall worldview of the culture, and classify alternative systems accordingly. Jones distinguished between *Naturwissenschaft* (N-tending) and *Geisteswissenschaft* (G-tending) worldviews. Western scientific thought, including the accounting system of biomedicine, is firmly based within a N-tending worldview, whereas, for example, homoeopathy and traditional Chinese medicine arise from within a G-tending worldview.

Leslie (personal communication) has more recently suggested a framework which brings these various elements together into a simple but comprehensive classification that can be applied to all explanatory systems. He argues that they all include (though in varying degrees of salience) three different kinds of explanation: *mechanistic* theories, which construe health as the correct functioning of a machine-like body, and illness as its breakdown; *equilibrium* theories, that regard health as a matter of balance and harmony, and illness as their

22

breakdown; and _ethical_ theories, linking health to 'right living' and seeing illness as a punishment for misdeeds or transgression of moral codes. He stressed that there is considerable diversity within each of these, and the different ways in which they are incorporated together into the particular explanatory system of a specific culture or group; a diversity that biomedicine (particularly in its training) undervalues and attempts to reduce and control.

Cognitive aspects

Although anthropology tends to focus upon cultural processes, it is interesting that in the last ten years or so there has been a growing interest within medical anthropology in an area of theory which is usually regarded as the domain of psychology – that of the cognitive (thinking) processes which may operate, at an individual level, in the formulation of explanations of health and illness. These include the work of Good, Kleinman and Young. They all begin by distinguishing between three meanings of discomfort or dysfunction to make explicit the difference between what the person experiences, and what the medical system defines as a breakdown of normal healthiness. Overall, these states are called forms of _sickness_ (note that all the theorists were North American, and this word has a different meaning in the USA from Britain, where it often refers specifically to feeling nauseated, and/or vomiting). _Disease_, in this terminology, is what doctors diagnose, is written about in medical textbooks, and biomedicine treats. _Illness_ is what people experience as bodily and psychological dis-ease.

Within this framework, Good (1977, see also Good and Good, 1981) devised a theory based upon what he termed _core symbolic elements_, where the capability of dominant symbols to convey multiple meanings within a culture allow for different applications in different contexts. For example, when we talk of a 'cold', it implies both an illness, and the way it makes us feel. In this way different domains in our explaining of the world get linked together (for example, colds become explained as the result of too rapid changes in body temperature). Good suggested that these core elements are organized into a _semantic illness network_ of linked ideas, definitions and relations, which enable people to make sense of their bodily experiences, not just in terms of their biological 'reality' but also aspects such as personal morality, social relationships and obligations, and so on.

Kleinman (1978, 1980) proposed a similar model, concentrating upon what he called *core clinical functions*. These, he suggested, are what enable people to know what to do when they are ill, to devise strategies for seeking health care and healing, and to respond to the outcomes of therapy. He regarded these functions as attempts (which are not always successful) to adapt to the worry and concern that illness poses, within a social context in which only some forms of disturbance are sanctioned as 'disease' (i.e. *real* sickness). For example, in medieval society it was considered perfectly reasonable to view 'being in love' as a form of *real* sickness. To be 'love-sick' was not just a form of words but a condition with symptoms (rapidly beating heart, lack of appetite) in need of treatment (medical advice varied from avoiding the object of desire to making use of concubines). These days we would be much more likely to deal with such a state by attributing our experiences and feelings to something other than sickness. They are to be experienced (and maybe even enjoyed) and, if necessary, controlled, but they are *not* something needing *medical* treatment.

Kleinman suggested that people generate, in their thinking, *explanatory models* which contain knowledge about the kinds of sicknesses that may befall them, what to expect about the onset of symptoms, courses of sickness episodes, appropriate treatment, and so on. We know, more or less, what hayfever, 'flu and a hangover are like because we have learned how to recognize their symptoms, and what it is appropriate to do when we have got them. However, Kleinman's formulation went well beyond the assumption that individuals and groups adopt particular sets of explanations for illness, which provide instructions for understanding and action. He argued that cultures provide people with ways of thinking that are simultaneously models *of* and models *for* reality. The explanatory models of a culture also *create* order and meaning, and produce the conditions required for their own perpetuation. Explanatory models for becoming and being ill also define roles, norms of conduct, expectation of one's own actions and the actions of others when illness is seen to occur. These are not merely aids to understanding, but also powerful components in the act of constructing the events themselves.

Young (1982, 1987) also interpreted semantic networks as the basis of explanatory models. They are, he argued, abstract representations from which an explanatory model can be generated to respond to a particular episode or set of events such as the occurrence of bodily disturbance. They act as conceptual templates onto which we can map our experience, in order to recognize what it is that we are experiencing. By mapping events in our lives onto the templates of explanatory models, the person identifies what is going on. In this way they are able to answer questions like 'Am I ill, or just feeling under the weather?', 'Should I ignore this ache, or is it a symptom?' 'Is there a link between the way my stomach feels, and what I ate for lunch?', and so on. Explanatory models also provide a basis for communicating with others in shared attempts to analyse and explain (including situations where a researcher is asking a person to explain what causes illness). We can understand each other to the extent we have access to each other's explanatory models.

Whereas Kleinman regarded explanatory models as essentially specific to the individual, Young saw them as culturally articulated and shared; as the means by which individuals can draw upon cultural wisdom to make sense of their own personal experiences. He contrasted these with other more individual kinds of internal representations of knowledge which people can draw upon: *prototypes* (derived from the work of Hallpike, 1979) and *chain complexes* (taken from the formulations of Vygotsky, 1962). Prototypes, in Young's theory, consist of memories of strings of events and circumstances recalled from a person's biographical past, conceptually connected by cause-and-effect assumptions or in terms of sequentiality, closeness, or resemblance. They are typically very personal, though they may be shared between a small number of people closely connected by friendship or kinship. Chain complexes, he suggested, are similar to prototypes, but are not explanatory, simply strings of recalled events, sensations and episodes that cohere and persist in the mind of the individual because of their importance to the mental life of the person concerned. Young proposed that people make sense of sickness by drawing upon a variety of different kinds of knowledge simultaneously. He based his ideas on observations that people, when asked to provide explanations of something, seldom express abstract semantic explanations. Rather they weave explanation within a fabric of episode-specific and biographical reminiscences, comments about similarity and analogy, about social relations, norms of behaviour, emotions and feelings.

SOCIOLOGICAL THEORIES

Medical sociologists are particularly interested in exploring how different groups in society explain health and illness in different ways, and why this is so. They want to know how these differences have been moulded by social forces, particularly power relationships. Like medical anthroplogists, their work has been conducted within broader conceptual frameworks, in particular the major competing theories of societal action (structural functionalism versus dominance theories), and of social epistemology (knowledge as constructed for or constructed by particular groups of people).

Structural functionalist and dominance theories

Sociology has been, throughout its history, permeated by a theoretical tension between structural functionalism, on the one hand, and a number of versions of dominance theory on the other. They each portray a persuasive – but quite different – model of how society operates. Structural functionalism sees social institutions as evolving and surviving (in an almost Darwinian sense) because they serve society's needs: promoting the overall good, maintaining social order and enabling people to live together in relative harmony. They make effective use of the available resources and provide the conditions for children to be brought up, for the old, the sick and the vulnerable to be cared for, for law and order to be maintained and for the moral values of society to be upheld. In this context social divisions are regarded as necessary and functional. They are the mechanisms by which the different tasks, roles and responsibilities within society can be shared out and thus accomplished.

Dominance theories (sometimes called conflict theories) come in a number of versions, although the best known is Marxism. All variants are in opposition to structural functionalism. They deny that social forces, social institutions and social divisions have evolved in order to serve the needs of *all* members of society in a mutually benign and functional manner. Instead they propose that the processes involved have been ones of conflict, exploitation and oppression, whereby the more powerful groups in society have used their power and influence to dominate the weakest and most vulnerable. From this perspective, social divisions arise, not as a result of a functional 'division of labour', but as a consequence of various power inequalities – the rich who own the means of production dominating the poor, who have only their labour as a commodity to be hired; the patriarchal power of men used to dominate women: the imperialism of the West dominating the exploited peoples of the Third World, and so on.

In early Marxist formulations, there was a concern with how wealthy property owners could dominate by the way they controlled the allocation of the material resources necessary for human existence (food,

26

housing, etc.). However, the debates soon extended to encompass more subtle mechanisms of control, over such things as information, knowledge and the moral agenda, by way of social institutions such as education, the law, the mass media, and so on. One of their major themes has been the notion of 'deviance'. Both structural functionalists and dominance theorists see deviance as a threat to social order. But, not surprisingly, their interpretations have been different. Functionalists have concentrated on how to limit and control deviance. Dominance theorists want to promote it, seeing dissidence and social disorder as the means by which the old, inequitable order can be overthrown. Our understanding of deviance and dissidence has become much more complex recently, when it has been Marxist–Leninist regimes which have themselves been overthrown. But the observation remains that conflict theories argue that knowledge and power are intimately connected.

Illness as deviance

It was Talcot Parsons, one of the most influential structural functionalist theorists, who first directed the attention of sociology to issues of health and illness. He introduced the term 'sick role' into our language (Parsons, 1951). Because illness had been regarded as a 'naturally occurring event' and therefore unmotivated, it had up until then tended to be excluded from the sociological analysis of deviance. But Parsons argued that since illness interferes with the performance of normal social roles, albeit without deliberate intent, society has had to set up mechanisms for channelling and controlling it, to prevent it straining social order and the smooth functioning of the social system. He suggested that whereas, say, criminal deviance is controlled by institutionalized law, the deviance of illness is controlled by assigning approved roles to ill persons and those who care for them.

Society, from this perspective, has developed a complex of functional, 'self-evident' socially sedimented beliefs upon which our responses to illness are predicated. First, beliefs have evolved about the 'sick role', exempting ill people from some social obligations (e.g. from having to work) but enforcing others (e.g. staying in bed). Ill people are believed to lack any moral culpability for their illness, and to be incapable of overcoming it themselves. Second, beliefs have evolved about the relations between society and ill people; that the well have a responsibility to 'care for' the ill, and offer them sources of expert and effective help. From the interplay between these two sets of beliefs has arisen the third, about the role of the medical profession and services provided for the sick. These include the assumption that medicine offers effective treatment, and consequently that medical practitioners must be given the social status and resources to make sure patients follow their orders.

Subsequently dominance theorists have disputed whether these sedimented beliefs are merely 'functional'. They suggest instead that they operate as a system of social control. While in functionalist terms, they ensure that society meets the needs of its more dependent members, in dominance theory terms, they enable the powerful groups in society to promote their interests by exploiting or marginalizing others. (This is, of course, another version of the argument that contemporary anthropologists such as Young and Taussig have made.) In sociology the most influential account of this 'social control' viewpoint was Zola's (1972) essay, in which he argued that medicine has become

> a major institution of social control, nudging aside, if not incorporating, the more traditional institutions of religion and law. It [has become] the new repository for truth, the place where absolute and often final judgements are made by supposedly morally neutral and objective experts. And these judgements are made, not in the name of virtue or legitimacy, but in the name of health. (p. 487)

Zola argued that the functionalist analysis allows people to convince themselves that modern medicine is a benign and humanitarian force which replaces 'punishment' (e.g. of alcoholics) by 'treatment' and thus absolves the individual from responsibility for their own misfortunes. This supposedly liberal discourse, argues Zola, is not benign at all. Condemnation is not avoided but merely displaced. The result of such processes is that they 'bring man [sic], not bacteria to the centre of the stage and lead thereby to a re-examination of the individual's role in his own demise, disability and even recovery'. Zola suggested that there are four main ways in which our lives have become 'medicalized':

1. by the expansion of medicine into our private lives (e.g. by telling us what to eat, how much exercise to take, and how many sexual partners to have);
2. by its expansion into public life (e.g. demanding constraints upon the advertising of tobacco and alcohol);
3. by extending its control over procedures like prescribing drugs and performing surgery (making doctors the arbiters of, for

example, who should get a kidney transplant, or a 'test tube baby');

4. by gaining dominance of 'taboo' areas (such as drug addiction, alcoholism, and more recently, child abuse).

Zola summed this up persuasively by arguing that:

> From sex to food, aspirins to clothes, from driving your car to riding the surf, it seems that under certain conditions, or in combination with certain other substances or activities, or if done too much or too little, virtually anything can lead to certain medical problems . . . every aspect of our daily life has in it elements of risk to health. (Zola, 1972, p. 498)

This 'medicalized' version of social reality, and the presumption of the medical establishment that they have the right to control our lives in the name of 'health', has been criticized by dominance theorists of every persuasion: by Marxists (Navarro, 1977, is probably the best known, though difficult to read); feminists (Scully and Bart, 1978, is a good place to start, if for no other reason than because they use such a fun title: 'A funny thing happened on the way to the orifice'); humanists (Illich, 1976, is the best known); and more broadly politico-economic theorists (e.g. Ehrenreich 1978; Doyal 1979).

Each approach offers alternative accounts, providing compelling arguments about the ways in which, variously, capitalism, professional and corporate self-interest, the patriarchy, Third World exploitation, industrial pollution, economic and social inequalities, etc. are the true culprits for ill health. All hold in common the idea that ordinary people are duped into a 'false consciousness' which prevents them from challenging the construction provided for them by the medical establishment. All see medicine as a powerful hegemony – a dominant and dominating power-base which, in order to protect, perpetuate and expand its influence, exploits and oppresses others.

Social control epistemological theories

What functionalist and dominance versions of social control theory have in common is that they both tend to assume that people's understandings – most notably those at the bottom of the power hierarchy, but to some extent everybody's – are constructed *for* them and imposed *upon* them as the product of social forces, and generally to serve the purposes of others. Robert Dingwall (1976) has described this as an image of people as the 'puppets' of dominant groups (whom Becker, 1963, refers to as 'moral entrepreneurs'). Essentially this analysis is concerned with the legitimation of knowledge – the way in which some forms of knowledge are socially sanctioned by powerful groups in society, and thus promoted as *the* 'truth', whereas other forms of knowledge are denied, devalued, marginalized and made obscure.

The sociologist who has argued this case most comprehensively in relation to explanations for health and illness is Friedson (1970, 1986). He focused attention specifically on the way in which specialist medical knowledge and expertise provides doctors with the authority to decide who is ill and who is not, and hence to enforce their definitions of 'disease' upon the lay public. Friedson was most concerned with explaining the disparity between the esoteric body of knowledge which constitutes the professional explanatory system (i.e. the knowledge-base of biomedicine) and what he saw as the ignorance, misconceptions and irrationality of ordinary people's understandings, particularly those of the 'lowest social classes' (his terminology). According to Friedson, by their ignorance and lack of understanding of medicine (in professional terms), patients with lower-class backgrounds acquire, in the eyes of doctors, a level of deviant status. Their understandings become discountable, and so doctors respond by giving up attempts to communicate with them in any meaningful way, and palm them off with half-truths, or, more often than not, by keeping them in ignorance 'for their own good'. These patients, Friedson argued, then respond by distrust, suspicion and, not unsurprisingly, anger at the way in which they are mistreated. The result is that their ignorance is at best untouched, and at worst increased. Their own explanatory systems become marginalized and increasingly regarded not just by doctors but also *by themselves* as invalid. In this way, Friedson suggested, working-class patients are not allowed to develop and use their own explanatory systems, but rather have another – that of the doctors – foisted upon them. Doctors thus become the 'architects of medical knowledge', knowledge that fails to serve a functional role for the working class, but rather becomes yet another mechanism to reinforce their exploited and marginalized social role at the bottom of the class hierarchy.

It would be easy to respond to such theories simply in terms of their elitist terminology and rather dismissive portrayal of people as 'puppets'. To do this is to miss the point they are making about the enormous pressures placed upon particular social groups by the dominance of the more powerful 'architects' of knowledge. As Young

30

made clear, professional orthodoxy does not only assume that its knowledge is better, it also dismisses other explanatory systems as 'not really medicine'. It thus creates a situation in which lay people find it very difficult to be taken seriously, or indeed, to take themselves and their own understandings of the world at all seriously. The power relations within medical encounters are thus major influences not only in the way professionals construct the knowledge that their patients use within the consulting room and the hospital, but also within day to day conversations among family and friends.

Social constructionist epistemological theories

A social constructionist analysis, while it acknowledges the impact of social forces, says that people are more than just passive recipients of handed-down knowledge; they are also themselves continually engaged in its construction. Illness, from this standpoint, is not a simple, 'natural' biological occurrence, but a human product – something people *make*! Some states which have been defined as 'ill' are easy enough to see as deceptions. My favourite example is drapetomania – a disease, discovered and described by Cartwright in 1851 (you can read his paper in reprinted form – it makes fascinating – if horrifying – reading). Basically, according to Cartwright, drapetomania was a disease of Negroes. It was to be found in Negro slaves, its symptoms consisting of escaping from their masters and its cause attributed to over-indulgent treatment and insufficient discipline. However, such self-evidently ludicrous, ideologically-motivated labelling (translation – it conflicts with our contemporary worldview) apart, social constructionists maintain that *all* illness is a matter of social definition. The point was elegantly illustrated by Sedgwick (1982, p. 30), when he argued that:

> The fracture of a septuagenarian's femur has, within the world of nature, no more significance than the snapping of an autumn leaf from its twig: the invasion of a human organism by cholera germs carries with it no more the stamp of 'illness' than does the souring of milk by other forms of bacteria.

In other words, when we label ourselves or other people as 'ill', what is happening is a process of social definition in human terms. Illness – any illness – is meaningful *as illness* only to the extent that it has particular implications for us, as people, and not just as biological organisms.

31

Indeed, such social labelling extends beyond people. We do not regard the action of yeast upon grapes as a disease, but as 'winemaking'. Only when the process goes wrong (and, say, vinegar is produced) do we regard the grapes as 'infected' (except of course when we are making vinegar). Illness is thus a product of the particular social reality we have constructed for ourselves. This is not to say that somebody will not feel queasy and terrible when they have food poisoning, or in pain with an infected tooth cavity; it is to say that such symptoms have no meaning as and of themselves. They are only symptoms of illness (rather than, say, spirit possession or being in love) because we so define them. In other circumstances, their meaning might be quite different.

The broad theory of social constructionism was popularized, in particular, by Berger and Luckmann's book: *The Social Construction of Reality* (1966). Berger and Luckmann proposed that knowledge in any culture is distributed within 'socially segregated sub-universes of meaning'. These are developed within specialized groups (differing according to such things as social class, profession or religious affiliation) negotiated, carried and continually produced in individual and social processes within the group. Such universes of meaning compete within society, vying against each other for plausibility and hence dominance. The example which Berger and Luckmann gave to illustrate competition between alternative sub-universes was one of medical knowledge. They described the kind of rivalry that exists between orthodox medical systems (e.g. biomedicine) and various 'alternative medicines' (e.g. homoeopathy and Christian Science). They suggested that in advanced industrial societies like ours, with the conditions and resources to allow large numbers of people to devote themselves to the pursuit of quite obscure areas of knowledge, 'pluralistic competition between sub-universes of meaning becomes the normal state of affairs'. They argued that as these sub-universes multiply and become more complex, they become sealed off from one another, with all manner of techniques used (such as mystification and propaganda) to keep insiders 'in' and outsiders 'out'. Once more adopting an illustration from biomedicine, they suggested:

> It is not enough to set up an esoteric sub-universe of medicine. The lay public must be convinced that this is right and beneficial, and the medical fraternity [sic] must be held to the standards of the sub-universe. Thus the general population is intimidated by images of physical doom that follows 'going against doctor's advice'; it is persuaded *not* to do so by the pragmatic benefits of compliance, and by

its own horror of illness and death. To underline its authority the medical profession shrouds itself in age-old symbols of power and mystery, from outlandish costume to incomprehensible language, all of which, of course, are legitimated to the public and to itself in pragmatic terms. Meanwhile the fully accredited inhabitants of the medical world are kept from 'quackery' (that is, from stepping outside the medical sub-universe in thought or action) not only by the powerful external controls available to the profession, but by a whole body of professional knowledge that offers them 'scientific proof' of the folly and even wickedness of such deviance. In other words, an entire legitimating machinery is at work so that laymen [sic] will *remain* laymen, and doctors doctors, and (if possible) that both will do so happily. (p. 105)

Legitimation is a central construct in Berger and Luckmann's theorization (they devote a whole chapter to it in their book). They divide it up into four levels. The first is legitimation built into language (and other symbols by which people transact meaning) where the constant use of words like 'doctor', 'patient', 'cure', continually bolsters these particular constructs as meaningful, real and merely mirroring the way the world is. The second is the impact of everyday explanations, examples being the proverbs and clichés of ordinary conversations – such as 'doctor knows best' or 'a little knowledge is a dangerous thing'. Thirdly there are the explicit theories of any body of knowledge, such as the germ theory of disease (i.e. that tuberculosis and 'flu are caused by infectious organisms). Finally there are symbolic sub-universes themselves, whole bodies of knowledge which integrate different provinces of meaning into coherent wholes – what anthropologists call 'worldviews'. By legitimation, the sub-universe of biomedical knowlege becomes the property of individuals (by a process Berger and Luckmann label internalization) and the property of collectives (in their terminology by a process of institutionalization). Hence a particular sub-universe of this kind becomes a social and psychological construction of reality, available (albeit, at times, in mystified or distorted form) to all in the culture who have access to it, and consequently acting as a powerful frame within which people individually and collectively make sense of their world. Berger and Luckmann also wrote about variability in experienced 'reality', which they attributed to differences in the underlying 'plausibility structures' which produce and maintain them. As sociologists, though, their discussions of moment-to-moment changes in reality within individual construction were less well articulated than their extensive and rich theorization about the construction and negotiation of realities in the social domain and long-term shifts from one individually experienced reality to another (such as following religious conversion).

Robert Dingwall (1976) was one of the first theorists to promote the social constructionist viewpoint specifically within medical sociology. He went from the notion that illness is a socially determined state, to argue that there is no reason to claim that one way of explaining it is necessarily or inevitably more accurate or more valid than any other. Hence he argued that the lay explanatory systems of ordinary people should be recognized as functional within their own domain, and accorded equal epistemological status with other systems. (This is a parallel argument to the anthropologists' claims that the medical systems of other cultures are, at an epistemological level, equal to biomedicine.) In this Dingwall was not arguing that all explanatory systems are *functionally* equal, nor denying that they are in part constructed for people by other groups; what he wanted to do was to redress the balance, by reminding us that people from all social groups engage in the active construction and interpretation of reality for themselves. The explanations they hold are arrived at, in part at least, by thoughtful and purposive analyses.

Dingwall suggested that central to the way ordinary people make sense of health and illness is the concept of 'ordinariness', within the context of general social norms. To be ordinary is to do usual, expected, normal things at usual times in usual places. Dingwall saw efforts to make sense of health and illness as always occurring within the context of broader explanatory systems (particularly those to do with personal morality) which enable people to theorize, to themselves and others, in terms of estimates of ordinariness and its various antitheses – deviance, unusualness, discontinuity, and so on. A great deal of how we explain health and illness is, he argued, concerned with managing the body in ordinary ways that are consistent with the social norms of our reference group (i.e. people like us – the same age, gender, social class, etc.). This creates a definition of health that is somewhat tautological – healthy people are normal, and normal people are healthy. The concept of social norms enables the notion of normality to be context specific; it will differ, say, between the young and old, between men and women (particularly in terms of gender-specific states such as pregnancy and menopause).

Dingwall adopted the term 'discontinuity' as the most useful way of describing the kinds of states, events and phenomena which demand consideration of 'ordinariness' and 'abnormality' in order to decide between judgements of whether we are 'healthy' or 'ill'. To be and to

34

remain 'ordinary' is highly socially desirable – who, in the general way of things, wants to stand out as 'odd', 'unnatural' or 'abnormal'? When faced with discontinuity – when something upsets the smooth fabric of our lives – this strong desire to be seen, none the less, as still 'normal', or to get back to normal as quickly as possible, acts as a compelling motivational framework for explaining how and why we become ill.

Being 'ordinary', he suggested, involves a great deal of fluency with 'commonsense knowledge' (this idea is well argued and illustrated by Cicourel, 1973). Central to this is the notion of 'theoreticity', which Dingwall adapted from the work of a number of other theorists, particularly that of Voysey (1975). Voysey defined theoreticity as involving two elements: 'intelligence' (having access to and being able to invoke some symbolic conceptual scheme), and 'morality' (the incorporation of moral symbols). A person who is operating within a theoretic mode is somebody who is aware of the social norms and rules (both explanatory and morally prescriptive) involved, and intends and interprets their action in the light of this knowledge.

In this framework, deviance is not just a status foisted upon some people by powerful groups within society; it also involves deliberation on the part of the people involved, who are well aware that they are being deviant, and its implications for them. An individual's understanding of their own illness is not, therefore, simply arrived at by passively interpreting some or other form of bodily discontinuity. The self-labelling of 'being ill' is actively constructed. It is arrived at after posing questions about responsibility, blame and culpability. When biological discontinuity fractures normality, and so needs to be explained, we ask 'Why this?', 'Why me?', 'Why now?' These are issues of personal morality, seen in relation to a complex and sophisticated understanding of what constitutes 'ordinariness' in the everyday world.

In other cultures, and at other times in history, Dingwall argued, there were a range of alternatives for explaining discontinuity in ways that were socially acceptable. But, he has suggested, in the West today, personal morality has largely become overshadowed by the imposition of public moral values. This is a consequence of the widening gap between work and home, the State taking over many responsibilities previously undertaken by families, and the increasing importance of large corporations and the impact of social planning. The blurring of the distinction between private and public morality has thus reduced our freedom as individuals to define discontinuity for ourselves. It also limits the ability of our immediate social group (such as our family or religious community) to define it as anything other than illness: 'Other possibilities – witchcraft, spiritual intervention, sin, bad taste, poor manners and the like – are less and less frequently available' (Dingwall, 1976).

Thus, in the West at least, illness has come to represent the overriding attribution that can be proffered to exonerate a person from the stigma of deviance. So long as people can establish that they have not behaved in ways that brought it upon themselves, illness is an explanation that ordinary, (theoretic) people can legitimately, and socially acceptably, proffer (to themselves and to others) for behaving in unusual ways or demonstrating unusual bodily manifestations.

I was made very aware of this recently when my friend came to visit with her sister. I invited them in for coffee and mince pies, and my friend and I sat down at the kitchen table. Her sister remained standing, continually shifting rather awkwardly from one foot to the other. It rapidly became evident that she was not going to sit down, and it was surprising just how tense the situation became. Then she explained. She had a back injury, which made sitting down very painful, so she never sat down except when it could not be avoided. She described how embarrassing it was, and how it made things like attending meetings and eating in restaurants very tricky. I could *feel* the embarrassment, even from her description. As she said, it was all right once people knew why she was standing, but in public places she looked very odd, as if she was being deliberately – and tactlessly – awkward. 'I've even thought of having a badge, you know, saying: "I have a bad back"', she said.

What was very noticeable was that, despite her explanation, her standing continued to feel very uncomfortable. Dingwall argued that the tension between ordinariness and deviance means that illness cannot be regarded as an easily accepted part of everyday life. It must be divorced from it by its seclusion as 'private trouble' within the family, or, if it is more serious, contained within institutions like hospitals which insulate public awareness from the deviance in its midst. I suspect it is more subtle than this. Some forms of discontinuity can be relatively easily accommodated in public, for example, physical injuries that are obvious, but have clearly been treated (such as a broken leg in plaster) and minor conditions, which pose no threat of infection (such as a 'hangover'), so long as they do not unduly disrupt the smooth flow of whatever else is going on. However, the point Dingwall made is generally valid. We expect people, when they are ill, to remove themselves from public view, and although this also has a degree of pragmatism (we do not want them spreading their 'germs' around), it also reflects an unease with trying to accommodate the rule-breaking of illness into 'normal life'.

Illness as stigmatizing

Goffman, who introduced the term stigmatization into popular vocabulary, argued that when we institutionalize illness, its deviance becomes exaggerated, both by the impact of institutional regimes themselves, and by its separation from the world of normality. Thus illness is a very restricted escape route from the attribution of 'deviance' available only for non-serious illness of short duration. Permanent illness and disability are stigmatized:

> people expect . . . the cripple to be crippled; to be disabled and helpless; to be inferior to themselves, and they will become suspicious and insecure if the cripple falls short of these expectations . . . [the] cripple has to play the part of the cripple. (Goffman, 1963)

Indeed, some life-threatening illnesses acquire, in popular imagination, the status of social metaphors for all that is evil, undesirable and needs to be destroyed. We talk, for example, of getting rid of 'sicknesses' in society (like poverty and delinquency) as 'cutting out a cancer'. When this happens, those who suffer from the illness so labelled become stigmatized themselves – they become social outcasts, and their misfortune acquires a whiff of blame, of maybe, possibly, having done something bad to have deserved it, and the illness itself acquires a threatening and menacing image.

The best-known account of this kind of process is Susan Sontag's (1977) description of cancer. Until very recently this was *the* terrifying illness in the West, often mentioned in hushed tones, or even only by its initial 'C', as though even to speak its name was dangerous (an example of magical thinking in Western 'civilized' culture!). The French theorists Claudine Herzlich and Janine Pierret (1985) have carried out a number of detailed historical investigations into 'scourges' of this kind, and have concluded that once they acquire this kind of popular imagery, they stop being seen in terms of individual cases, and come to represent very menacing forms of *collective* adversity which threaten the equilibrium of the whole community.

Today, of course, AIDS has rapidly acquired the status of the most powerfully stigmatized and stigmatizing disease (Sontag's new book on this subject takes up her arguments about cancer, and applies them to AIDS: Sontag, 1989). AIDS provides a good example of how once an illness has acquired a metaphorical status as a 'scourge', its attribution loses any ability to protect the sufferer from attributions of deviance and blame. Having AIDS arouses immense antagonism, not just because it is, in itself, horrifyingly threatening (due to its lengthy incubation period, our poor understanding of mechanisms of infection, and the fact that AIDS leads to disfigurement and slow, painful and, at present, inevitable death) but crucially, because of its associations with other forms of deviance (i.e. drug addiction, homosexuality and sexual promiscuity). Clear evidence of this is provided by the way haemophiliac AIDS sufferers are so often referred to as 'innocent victims' (implying that other categories are in some way 'guilty').

AIDS will inevitably have an impact upon medical sociological theory, since it brings the very real fear of infectious disease back into public awareness. In order to redress positivistic explanations of illness, social constructionist analyses of illness have tended to underestimate the biological threat of illnesses that are contagious and consequently menacing. It is here that perhaps the ethnocentric bias of contemporary sociological theorization is most apparent. In Third World countries the biological reality of sickness, famine and high infant mortality has always been highly salient. AIDS is re-introducing into the West the need to develop socially functional responses to a sickness that, so far, biomedicine cannot tackle. Its means of infection demand reconsideration of the 'social control' thesis; for, within our current understanding, *only* changes in lifestyle and behaviour can alter its spread.

Medical sociological challenges to social constructionism

Not all medical sociologists regard social constructionism as either all that helpful or valid. Bury (1986), for instance, has criticized it for failing to deal with relativism (a contention which, more generally, Mulkay (1991) denies) and because he says it 'rests on contradictory intellectual and value premises' (p. 137).

Certainly sociological theorization is now having to look for ways of accommodating biological 'reality' back into its formulations, a case argued by John Ehrenreich, in the introduction to his book (1978), which is that, while we need to recognize that medicine is a social — and not a technical, or commercial — endeavour, we still have to tackle

the fundamental *social* question of how a good society deals with human *biological* interdependency; with death, birth, pain; with care of the young, the sick, the disabled, and the aged . . . . [T]he major problem of the medical system now is not that it generates dependency; the problem is the kind of dependency it generates, and its social impact. What we have to develop is a medical system which acknowledges our need for autonomous control over our bodies and which accepts our need for dependency; which enhances autonomy but, when we do feel the necessity to give up and be dependent, can deal with that need in a signified and nurturing way. (pp. 27–8)

The question to be answered is how we can create the conditions under which such a system would be possible — where the medical establishment is able to recognize the ideological traps of reification, medicalization and the dogmatic assumption that 'we know best', and yet is not so paralysed by these challenges to its basic tenets that it becomes unable to deal effectively with biological catastrophes, whether personal or collective.

CHAPTER THREE

Psychological Theories Concerning Explanation

In this chapter I will examine some of the main kinds of theory that psychologists have devised concerning the way in which people explain their own behaviour and experience, as well as those of others, and the things that happen to them. These theories have become influential in a number of applied fields (e.g. health education), but are often poorly understood. My aim here is to provide a reasonably clear description of each one, as a foundation for considering what insights psychology may have to offer into people's explanations of health and illness.

SOCIAL LEARNING THEORIES

Within psychology as a whole, learning theory is the application of behaviourism to the way in which organisms learn. It is a vast area, and I can do little more than summarize it very briefly here. To oversimplify, the theory holds that behaviour arises from two main processes. First is instinct – behavioural repertoires 'wired in' to the brain, programmed from genetic information. Instinctive behaviour (e.g. a baby suckling to the breast) is not learned, but present in every member of the species, from birth. Otherwise, behaviour is most usually the product of responses to stimuli impinging upon the organism, and their consequences. When a response is followed by a reward (i.e. a hungry animal gets food) then that response is reinforced and more likely to be repeated. When the response is followed by a punishment (e.g. pain) then it becomes less likely to be repeated. In this way, the behaviour of the organism becomes moulded – learning occurs.

A number of highly articulated learning theories have been devised, specifying a variety of learning processes: classical conditioning, operant learning, autoshaping, imitation, and so on. Mainly these were developed by the study of animal behaviour (rats and pigeons were the most popular, but dogs, mice and monkeys were also common; less often much simpler animals such as woodlice and worms were used). Many experiments were also conducted with humans, though these were often harder to devise in ways which were sufficiently rigorous (see Chapter 5). Generally, then, the theories about human behaviour were extrapolated from the principles gained from observations of the systematic ways in which animals responded to punishments and rewards.

Applying this theory to social situations, social learning theory assumes that people learn to tackle their lives according to the rewards and punishment they have received, particularly in childhood. One well known example is the theory of learned helplessness (Seligman, 1975, is the standard text) devised from observations of rats in the laboratory. They were exposed at first to a regime where they were repeatedly punished without being able to do anything to prevent it. When, later, the regime was altered (so that they could now avoid the punishment) instead of changing their behaviour, the rats remained passive. They seemed to have lost the capacity to do anything to save themselves. They had 'learned to be helpless'. Analogies were drawn by Seligman and his followers to suggest that people may react to parallel situations in similar ways. People who grew up in environments where, whatever they did, they were treated badly, become, according to this theory 'eternal victims'. Either they become completely passive, seeing themselves as totally incapable of gaining life's rewards, or they blame themselves whenever harmed by misfortune, beset by feelings of recrimination and guilt. This theory of learned helplessness has been used, for example, to seek to explain symptoms of depressive illness (e.g. Seligman, Abramson and von Baeyer, 1979. Wortman and Dintzer, 1978, provide a critique of this analysis).

Another, similar example is Rotter's locus of control construct (see Rotter, 1966, and Chapter 7 for more detailed accounts). According to this formulation, the way in which adults explain the things that happen to them is a product of their learning experiences as children. Those with early experiences of good behaviour being consistently rewarded, and bad behaviour being consistently punished, come to see themselves as 'in control'. Their successes are construed as just rewards for hard work and diligence; failure is that which they must expect if they are lazy, or do not try hard enough. Thus they learn to site control

41

within themselves, and within their own actions. These people are termed 'internals'. In contrast, those who have had inconsistent experiences as children – who were rewarded and punished indiscriminately, irrespective of their behaviour, come, as adults, to see the things that happen to them as the consequence of chance. Their own behaviour is, from this standpoint, irrelevant – success is a matter of 'good luck', failure a matter of 'bad luck'. They site control in the vicissitudes of the outside world, and are labelled 'externals'. (Note the parallel with the exogenous/endogenous division in anthropology, described earlier.)

This construct has been adopted by Wallston and Wallston (see for example their 1978 review article, described in more detail in Chapter 7) as the basis of the Health Locus of Control construct, specifically applying social learning theory to the way people explain health and illness. Their original formulation was based on Rotter's ideas (though they subsequently expanded upon this), dividing people up between 'internals' (who see their health and illness as the outcome of their own behaviour) and 'externals' (who see them as the consequences of chance). This theorization, and the empirical work which resulted from it, are clearly central to the subject matter of this book, and I have devoted a whole chapter to this work, and my own criticisms of it. So we will leave this story for now, and take it up again in Chapter 7.

THEORIES OF SOCIAL COGNITION

Within social psychology, the study of how people explain and make sense of the world around them, the events in it and how it works, their experiences, their own actions and those of others, is generally tackled under the heading 'social cognition'. Although a simple de-jargonization turns this into 'how people think about the social world', the use of the word 'cognition' (also found more generally in the phrase 'cognitive social psychology') signifies something more than that 'thinking ' is involved.

Cognitive psychology, more generally, is an approach usually attributed to Ulric Neisser (the standard text is his 1966 book of that name), although he acknowledged its historical roots in the work of Frederick Bartlett (1932). Neisser introduced and promoted the cognitive approach, in reaction to the then-popular approaches of behaviourism and information processing, as a more accurate and more functional way of construing the way people think – the way they

42

perceive the world, remember, divide their attention between various inputs from the environment, and so on.

Those earlier formulations of the 1950s and early 1960s, Neisser argued, were overly mechanistic. They portrayed people as passive responders to stimuli or passive receivers and processors of information. They were what Buss (1979) has termed reality-constructs-person paradigms, in which it was assumed that people play a very small role in the *making* of the realities they experience, but are dependent upon the world-picture constituted *for* them by the way events-in-the-world impinge upon their sensory apparatus.

Behaviourists, according to Neisser, modelled people as automata, machine-like beings, pre-programmed (by instinct) to respond in pre-ordained, specific ways to particular stimuli, or re-programmed (by processes such as conditioning) to adjust their behaviour, according to highly systematized learning routines dependent on the effects of punishment and reward. The information processing approach drew upon systems theory from the world of computing (remember how this also broke into anthropological theorization, around much the same time), and information theory (then currently being developed by engineers working in the field of telecommunications). Together they introduced greater complexity into the rather simple stimulus–response formulations of behaviourism, a process soon boosted by the rapid growth of computers, so that the model swiftly moved from mind-as-telephone-switchboard to mind-as-computer. None the less, the fundamental machine-like analogy remained, together with its depiction of people as passively interpreting and responding to a real-world-out-there, with little themselves to offer in the way of world-making.

It was this mechanistic image of human thinking that Neisser's brave new cognitive psychology was drawn up to challenge. The shift was towards a person-makes-reality perception of thinking, which stressed the capacity to construct the world in our own heads, as well as have it constructed for us by events and stimuli in the world outside. Neisser did not claim that thinking is always a matter of construction, but that the two go hand in hand. Sensory data from the outside are both processed 'bottom-up' (one of psychology's more unfortunate phrases!) and 'top-down'. The world we perceive, understand and with which we interact is a product of our taking in the signals it sends to us, and interpreting them via our own internal models-of-the-world. Fundamental to this approach is a refutation of the claim that people process raw data per se, or even just simple transformations of data.

What happens is that sensory input is imbued with meaning, and it is this meaning that gets processed. The eye, for example, cannot be seen as a camera that merely encodes patterns of light into film-like mental pictures in the brain for some internal homunculus to 'see'; rather, seeing is a process profoundly affected by our active striving to make sense of what we see around us – beauty truly is in the eye of the beholder.

Cognitive social psychology was thus a reaction, paralleling the shift in other realms of psychology, against the simplified machine-like models of the person, as formulated by a social psychology that had adopted behaviourism (and, less so, information processing theory) in, for example, its theories of social learning. Its intention was to reconstruct our image of people away from one of mere pawns of social conditioning, towards one which considers people to be active, purposive thinkers, who strive to make sense of their social world, and bring to this endeavour complex, sophisticated models-of-the-world, which are used to interpret it, and construct a social reality. In the process, the analogies used shifted away from ones based on machines, towards ones based upon human beings; people were portrayed as 'scientists' (testing out hypotheses) or 'statisticians' (computing the interplay of different variables), clever, insightful, folk who used their brains in clever and insightful ways.

Herein lay a trap. While more humanitarian in their theorizing, early formulations in this field tended to model the thinking of their subjects as 'naive science' and avoided getting embroiled in the stuff of ordinary, everyday social life like the tenets of religious faith, myths, traditions, folklore and the messages of the mass media. This kind of person seems never to have exchanged shaggy dog stories in a pub, watched television, read a newspaper or attended a political rally. So social cognition put the thinking back into the person, but in the process seems to have isolated the individual, and made them strangely cardboard, unimaginative and lacking in originality. These truly come over as the 'puppets' which Dingwall suggested that sociologists have portrayed, their strings pulled by the scientists who studied them, who could act and think in only highly constrained ways, hardly socialized or enculturated like real people at all. As we will see, even in their later formulations, this imposed severe restrictions on their capacity to offer insights into how people explain health and illness.

There are three main kinds of social cognition theory: attribution theory, models of decision making and schema theory. I will examine each of these in turn.

Attribution theory

Charles Antaki (1988) has called attribution theory the 'jewel in the crown' of the social cognition paradigm. Certainly it became the most common approach in experimental social psychology in the 1960s and 1970s. Attribution theorists acknowledge Heider (1958) as their 'founding father'. Apparently Heider devised his theory as a result of spending a very cold and hungry period just after the First World War writing up his PhD thesis. This experience got him wondering why people become 'touchy and petulant' with one another (perhaps not the grandest basis for theory making, but certainly a reaction that many of us who have written PhDs – and those who have put up with us during the process – can sympathize with very sincerely). Although the overall term Heider used for his theory was 'phenomenological causality', he carefully distinguished between attributions of 'causes' and of 'agents'. He thus set the scene for a continuing debate about the nature of 'naive' forms of explanation, and the extent to which they are different from scientific explanation based strictly on notions of cause and effect. Although he did not express himself all that clearly, he made reference to distinctions between specific and general explanations; and between analysis of 'what happened' in the past, and predictive explanations which link ideas about 'how things happen' to 'what is likely to happen' in the future. Although he was primarily concerned with social perception (i.e. the ways people explain their own actions and those of others) he reviewed theories of the way in which people account for events and influences from the physical environment too.

Even though Heider's work has been the basis for attribution theory, Heider himself was much broader in his theorizing, and much more philosophical in his approach. He regarded the process of explanation as something which both differs *between* people according to particular personal characteristics (for example, suggesting people differ in whether they site blame externally or internally according to personality), and something that is dynamic *within the individual*, changing according to circumstances (for example, that attribution depends upon mood). His formulations were, in fact, highly reflexive, stressing that the explanations individuals use to explain the world are both products of the way they 'structure the world' and at the same time contribute to that structuring. They may serve, for instance, psychodynamic needs like providing an external focus for aggression, wish-fulfilment or self-justification.

He argued strongly for studying explanation at a 'commonsense' level, stressing that people do not respond directly to how 'the world works' but according to their *perceptions* of the workings of the world. The explanations that individuals use to structure their world are crucial to making sense of the strategies they adopt in responding to it. He argued that we can begin to develop psychological theories about the way people act only once we have gained access to the explanatory framework within which they operate. Psychology, he asserted, needs to study people as 'naive physicists' who have theories to predict and understand events in the physical world; as 'naive psychologists' who have theories to predict and understand the behaviour and experience of others; as 'naive sociologists' who have theories to predict and interpret social forces, and so on. It is easy to see how this kind of approach attracted those psychologists who wanted to adopt the cognitive approach.

Heider distinguished between two main kinds of attribution for an event: *personal* (where a particular individual is seen as responsible, or to blame) and *impersonal* (where nobody is blamed or held responsible). Impersonal attributions may be naturally occurring events (e.g. being struck by a branch falling from a tree), but could also arise from unintended actions (somebody accidentally knocking the branch off the tree). Personal attributions, however, always carry the implication of intended action (i.e. somebody deliberately throwing the branch at you).

Heider used a great deal of visual analogy. Fascinated by art, he described attributions using metaphors from visual perception. By his analysis, for example, when Joan tries to understand why Mary did something, she tries to separate the 'figure' (Mary) from the 'background' field of the social situation in which Mary acted. Heider suggested that people have a tendency to misperceive actions, because they confuse figure and ground. They conceive the figure (i.e. the person acting) as dominating the conceptual ground (the social situation) in parallel fashion to the way in which figure can dominate ground in visual perception. Thus people tend to be more willing than is justified to assume that actions are the *deliberate* intentions of the people involved, and less willing to attribute causes to what is going on in the social scene at the time. Applied to explanations of illness, this would suggest that people are more prone to ask 'what did that person do to bring this upon herself?' than is justified, and less likely to acknowledge that something in the world around might have been the cause. An example would be the way in which Edwina Currie, when she was a junior Minister of Health, blamed the poor health of northerners on their bad diet and smoking, rather than acknowledging that poverty and bad housing might have been responsible.

This propensity to blame the individual formed the major plank upon which attribution theory was built. Later workers expanded upon it, and drew up a number of more detailed and complex formulations about the kinds of information people use to make inferences, and the ways in which they are calculated against one another. The first moves were made by Jones and Davis (1965), who proposed the notion of *correspondent inference*. Basically, this concerned the degree to which the actor – the person whose behaviour is being judged – is seen as behaving according to a stable and enduring disposition. Examples are: anger expressed by a person who is usually grumpy and bad-tempered and laughter from a person who has a well developed sense of humour. People make correspondent inferences in these circumstances (i.e. inferences which correspond to the assumed disposition), attributing the cause of the action – the anger or the laughter – to the person, rather than the situation.

Jones and Davis theorized about the sorts of knowledge required for making correspondent inferences, and suggested that one element was connected with role expectations. When people act in-role, according to preconceived notions of what their role should be (e.g. when nuns are devout, Australians brash, and professors scholarly) their behaviour will be seen, they argued, as role-driven, and thus less likely to be a product of personal qualities. When people act in ways that are counter to their assumed roles (e.g. when a nun is brash, an Australian scholarly, or a professor devout) their behaviour is much more likely to be accredited to something peculiar to them as individuals.

Experiments were able to confirm these suppositions. A good example is one conducted by Jones, Davis and Gergen (1961) (see Chapter 5, p. 115). Unlike Heider's formulations, the concept of correspondent inference makes no claims about intentionality – all that is at issue here is whether attribution is about cause 'in the person' (intended or not) or 'in the situation'. A good example is where people explain why somebody has a heart attack. If the person is seen as 'an ideal candidate' (they are overweight and take little exercise) then it is the overweight and laziness that will be seen to be the cause. But when a person who is a paragon of virtue health-wise gets struck down, then the explanation given will need to be more singular – they must have had some specific susceptibility or have suffered some unexpected unique risk.

Harold Kelley (1967) devised an even more complex and sophisticated series of parameters to the attribution process. He suggested that people base an attribution about a particular action upon estimates of three main kinds of information:

1. **Distinctiveness:** the extent to which the person in question normally behaves in this kind of way.
2. **Consistency:** the extent to which the person in question has, in the past, behaved like this before in similar situations.
3. **Consensuality:** the extent to which other people normally behave like this.

This is where the 'naive statistician' notion comes in, since Kelley saw attributional judgements as a process of weighing the different sources of evidence available in relation to each other, and carrying out a technique which in statistics is called 'analysis of variance' (ANOVA). The different estimates of variability in the situation are computed together, the attribution a product of this calculation. When asked, for example, why Maxine ate a lentilburger for lunch, the calculation might follow something like the cartoon sequence in Figure 3.1:

Figure 3.1   Schematic illustration of attribution theory

The other set of well-known formulations were about the mistakes people make in their attributions; the ways in which 'naive statisticians' (i.e. ordinary people) are not as clever as psychologists. Nisbett and Ross (1980) describe three kinds of error:

1. **The fundamental attribution error**, an enlargement of Heider's notion that people tend to over-emphasize the personal, and under-emphasize the situational causes of actions.
2. **The actor-observer error** when people (either as individuals, or as groups) assume their own behaviour to be more likely to be situationally determined, and the behaviour of others more likely to be a product of personal intentions.
3. **The false consensus effect** where people tend to assume that others are more likely to behave like them than they really are.

Basically, this set of principles construes people as imperfect logicians, unable to overcome their own prejudices when making judgements. More recent attribution theorists (e.g. Hewstone, 1983) have suggested that in order to understand why this should be, we need to consider the functions – both social and psychological – of attributions. Hewstone claimed that there are (guess what!) three:

1. The need to assume **control** over the physical and social world by being able to explain and predict what will happen. This is particularly salient with regard to misfortune, where blaming personal misbehaviour offers the hope that such misfortune can be avoided in the future, either (if you see yourself to blame) by mending your ways, and not behaving like that again; or (if you blame somebody else) by denying that you would ever do anything so foolish.
2. To promote **self-esteem**, by seeing yourself as competent, taking credit for your successes, and dismissing your failures as caused externally.
3. As a means of **self-presentation** in which the act of attribution is one of portraying yourself (to yourself, and to others) in a good light.

Despite the apparent commonsensicality of these functions, attribution theory's formulations have been much criticized. Firstly, attribution theory has been portrayed as a 'psychology of the good guys'. Evidence for these processes and phenomena can be reliably found so long as the participant samples on which the ideas are tested consist of American college students, or even 'Middle America'. Indeed, as you will see when we come to the next chapter and consider studies carried out by Jocelyn Cornwell with Eastenders in London, psychologists would have no trouble confirming their hypotheses with these kinds of people too. Cornwell (quite independent from psychological theorization) documented their worldview as one in which individuals see themselves 'in control', responsible for their health, and able to protect it; and yet not to blame for illness.

The problem is not that attribution theorization or its findings are invalid, but that they are not what they are purported to be. They are not universals, describing 'how people explain the world'. They are merely confirmations that the people who conduct such studies share a collective understanding of 'how the world works' with the subjects chosen for their experiments, both of them drawing on a shared store of the 'commonsense knowledge' of their culture and society. Would you expect less from scholars who devote their lives to the study of human psychology? But what these results fail to do is offer an account that can be transported elsewhere. Take just one example – where in all this talk about self-justification and esteem is the influence of fate that is so important in other worldviews? I will take up this argument again in Chapter 7.

The second criticism (see, for example, Semin and Manstead, 1983) is that attribution theory excludes from its frame of reference any consideration of the way in which people's understandings are moulded by the explanatory 'stories' of their culture. Maxine's lentilburger lunch, for example, only makes any real sense in the context of the rich set of ideas in late Western twentieth-century culture about vegetarianism (and the ideologies behind it about the immorality of killing animals for food, both from an 'animal rights' perspective and from ideas about the waste of resources of using animal protein as a food source), about 'healthy eating' and the pressures (particularly on young women) to strive for a slim body, and thus eat low-calorie meals. Very soon the question of her lunch begins to take in all manner of subtle complexions – such as ideas about the marketing of lentilburgers and the effects of mass media advertising, of health education and of youth culture. In other words, attributions in the real world are much, much more complex. They are seldom if ever purely matters of internal 'psycho-logic', but are also the product of complex cultural and social forces providing 'texts' within which attributions are made.

This leads us to the third criticism, which is that attribution theory generally assumes that a 'cause' can unequivocally be attributed to a single site. We could ask whether it is Maxine's vegetarianism (or whatever) that led her to eat the lentilburger, or the qualities of the burger (i.e. its vegetable and not meat base)? Surely it is both. But the criticism goes further than this, for, as Ragnar Rommetveit (see, for example, his 1980 article) has pointed out, when we try to make sense of any action, there are many stories we can tell, all of which may have validity. He used as an illustration explanations about why Mr Jones was mowing the lawn. Was it to get exercise, to avoid his wife, to beautify his garden or to annoy his neighbour? Maybe it was all of them! If we turn once more to Maxine, I can think of the following reasons for her behaviour, in just a few minutes:

She ate the lentilburger because:

- She was on a diet.
- To be polite to the friend who cooked it for her.
- Because she was hungry.
- To conform to social rules about taking a meal at lunchtime.
- It was the only vegetarian food served up at the meal.
- Lentils are good protein food.

and so on . . .

There is every reason to believe that *all* of these could be true, and although most of these reasons can be regarded as internal-to-Maxine (in that they say something about her motives), each also has elements of the social context such as social rules about meal-eating and politeness. These are not unique qualities of Maxine, but products of her socialization and enculturation. Even if we add them all up, the person/situation distinction simply fails to capture what is really salient.

Finally, attribution theory has been criticized as portraying people as living in an experiential world constantly beset by ambiguity and confusion about what is going on, desperate to know the causes of each event and constantly needing to calculate alternatives and come up with answers. Semin and Manstead (1983) argued that this is nonsense. Most of the time people go through life experiencing it as a reasonably smoothly flowing series of events, that need to be explained or justified only when something unexpected comes along. To even ask the question 'Why did she do that?' changes things dramatically, since it implies that the action needs to be explained (i.e. was an unwarranted action, or one that broke the rules). Consequently, simply asking people to explain an action comes across as accusatory, and so invites particular kinds of response: justifications, denials of blame, excuses. If what you want to do is to study these kinds of explanation, fine. Asking the 'why' question would be legitimate. But what cannot be done is to assume that the answers given in any way represent anything general or universal about the way people understand the reasons for things, when not called upon explicitly to *explain* them.

Models of decision making

Probably the best known of these is the modelling contained in the theory of reasoned action (see, for example, Ajzen and Fishbein, 1972; Fishbein 1980). This was in part derived from Dulany's (1961, 1968) theory of propositional control, firmly based within a learning theory framework. The main concern of the Ajzen and Fishbein model is to predict the behavioural intentions which are assumed to mediate *actual* behaviour. According to this model, an individual's intention to perform a given act can be worked out mathematically, by calculating the contributions to decision making from two sources:

1. **Attitude** towards performing the act, defined in terms of perceived consequences of the behaviour (beliefs) multiplied by the evaluation of those consequences (values).
2. **Subjective norms** in terms of an estimate of what others expect them to do (normative beliefs) multiplied by motivation to comply.

The model is illustrated in Figure 3.2.

Klein (1988) has criticized this model because of its pompous dressing up of a trite formulation in the emperor's clothes of a mathematical equation:

$$B \cong BI = \left(\sum_{i=1}^{n} b_i e_i \right) w_1 + \left(\sum_{j=1}^{m} nb_j mc_j \right) w_2$$

This use of mathematical expression Klein describes as 'the sacred language of science, the mystic script known only to those few who have undergone the dreaded rites of initiation' (Klein, 1988, p. 24). It is certainly the case that by converting ordinary commonsensical ideas into a 'scientific model', using seven point scales to estimate the variables (i.e. b_i, e_i etc.), and empirically (i.e. not in terms of theory but *post hoc* predictive utility) constructing weightings (W_1 and W_2), Ajzen and Fishbein's formulations have been successful in using estimates of behavioural intentions to predict actual behaviour in

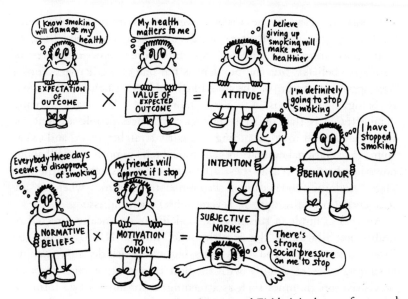

Figure 3.2   Schematic illustration of Ajzen and Fishbein's theory of reasoned
action (after Gergen and Gergen, 1981)

several studies, including some concerned with health related behaviours. Examples are: cigarette smoking (Chassin *et al.*, 1981), drug use (Budd *et al.*, 1983) and contraception (Fishbein *et al.*, 1980). But for all this predictive accuracy, there are a number of reasons why this kind of modelling is highly unsatisfactory. The most obvious is a criticism made by Leventhal and Hirshman (1982): '[I]t is questionable that we greatly advance our understanding . . . by concentrating on the measurement of factors so proximate to action that we are practically using measures at the beginning of the act to predict the action itself' (p. 199).

It is hardly surprising that you can predict fairly accurately what somebody will do if you ask them just before they do it whether they think doing it is a good idea, if they think other people will approve and whether they care about what other people think. It is even less surprising that you can improve predictability by introducing mathematical variables (i.e. weightings) to do just that. But getting consistent answers does *not* mean that you understand very much about their thinking except at a very trivial level, and then only under highly constrained circumstances. Predictability can even be further improved by adding extra variables into the equation (e.g. ideal behavioural intentions, Budd and Spencer, 1985), or by making the mathematical relationships between the various components more complex (e.g. Grube, Morgan and McGree, 1986, used computer modelling to incorporate interactive effects, and multidimensional estimates of normative beliefs). But the problem is not one of predictive accuracy (i.e. upping your score on the academic machismo scale), but that what is being predicted is not very informative. All that is being demonstrated is that under certain circumstances people account for what they intend to do according to a fairly straightforward and (what seems to us) rational evaluation. The model tells us nothing at all about how they have arrived at these attitudes and assessments in the first place. And the model cannot accommodate the times when we are frequently 'in two minds' (or several more) about an issue.

Another example of this kind of modelling, specifically directed to health and illness, is the Health Belief Model (HBM) devised by Rosenstock (1974). The HBM sets out to model decision making (about whether to comply with medical treatment or participate in preventive programmes such as screening) according to two forms of evaluation operating in dynamic interplay: readiness to comply; and motivations and enabling factors for compliance. Assumed influences on readiness to comply are: motivations (e.g. concern about health matters in general); value of illness threat reduction (e.g. subjective estimates of general vulnerability); and estimates of potential threat reduction (e.g. of the likely effectiveness of the regimen). Motivations and enabling factors include demographic (e.g. being old); structural (e.g. cost); attitudinal (e.g. to facilities available); interactional (e.g. doctor-patient relationship); and enabling (e.g. social pressures).

The Health Belief Model has been criticized (e.g. by Oliver and Berger, 1979) as 'more a collection of variables than a formal theory or model' (p. 113). Although they argue that it might be expected to be more functional than the Ajzen and Fishbein model for predicting preventive health behaviours because it includes non-rational elements (such as fear about the threat of illness) it is in fact less predictively successful. This is because it makes much more simplistic assumptions – that, for instance, all cues to the taking of preventive action are seen to be equally salient; that all benefits are evaluated as equally good, and all barriers evaluated as equally bad. But their most destructive criticisms are about *all* models of this kind, because they are inherently constrained by their methodology in requiring that the attitudes to be judged must be pre-specified by the experimenter, and can be measured only according to point positions along single dimensions. I will take up these criticisms in Chapter 5.

My own criticisms are more profound, and similar to those I have made about the kinds of cognitive algebra used in attribution theory. Models based on lists of potential influences (whether upon understanding or decision making), however complex the mathematical relationships proposed between these variables, have, for me, two unsurmountable flaws. Firstly, in having (by their nature) to pre-determine what is to be included and what excluded, they are inevitably culturally and historically highly specific and constrained. Not only, therefore, do they fail to do justice to the rich diversity of human experience, they also reify the worldview of the researcher as a powerfully real 'reality', in contrast to which all other worldviews are made 'alien' and even not actually 'real' at all. This is not just a problem of inaccuracy or inadequacy, for within such reifications are the seeds of ethnocentrism (or worse) sown. Models of this kind are not just pretentious, they are dangerous. They accord the musings of the powerful the status of superior knowledge, bolster this superiority with the trappings of mathematical hieroglyphics and/or scientific language, and, thus located in a position of dominance, act as potent tools which enable the powerful to mute and deny other forms of knowledge or understanding.

Their second defect is that such models are inevitably *dis*integrative. They assume the 'whole' is no more than the (albeit complex) 'sum of the parts'; that actions are informed and chosen via analysis of a set of conceptual components isolated from one another. They have no place for the kinds of interwoven, articulated arguments and stories which form the fabric of conversation and of media messages. At best they portray people as statisticians or accountants, sifting and computing data, rather than the 'competent negotiators of reality' (cf. Potter and Wetherell, 1987) I described in Chapter 1. What these models do, then, is portray thinking as a passive, mindless activity rather than an active striving after meaning; and portray people as thinking-machines rather than as aware and insightful, open to being beguiled by convincing tales and rhetoric, and inventive story-tellers themselves. So I see this approach as ultimately condescending in its image of what it means to be human, and pretentious in the way in which it tries to pass off really very banal ideas as high-blown theory, simply by dressing them up in the cloak of mathematical mystique.

Schema theory

Schema theory does at least try to paint a more flattering image of the person, and a more sophisticated portrayal of the way in which people make sense of the world, than either attribution theory or the models of decision making described above. Moreover, while schema theory is much less well known, it better deserves its 'cognitive' label. The theorists who have worked in this field have more comprehensively adopted into the realms of social psychology the ideas of Bartlett, Neisser and other 'straight' cognitive psychologists. It was Bartlett who devised the concept of 'schema' as the basis by which people represent their knowledge about the world. Schemata are much more than 'mental photocopies' of originals which have been sorted into a 'filing-cabinet' kind of brain. They are the product of complex processes of organization and categorization that imbue the incoming information from our senses with meaning, and thereby turn the information into true 'knowledge'.

Bartlett's ideas came in part from a study he undertook in which he asked people to read a rather strange story, from Native American folklore, called 'The War of the Ghosts'. Having read the story, they told it to another person, who told it to another, rather like the game of 'Chinese Whispers' (another version of Bartlett's experiment was when people had to recall the story, over and over again, often after gaps of several months or even years). He found that each telling of the story distorted it in certain systematic ways. Firstly, the story was always told *as* a story, retaining its narrative structure. However, detail was gradually lost, particularly about themes and ideas that were unfamiliar (i.e. to the Western conception, the more magical and 'illogical' elements). As the story was retold, new interpretations were put onto the sequence of events, and these became gradually introduced into the story as rationalizations for what was going on. What was happening, Bartlett argued, was an 'effort after meaning'. As people strove to make sense of the story from their own perspective, they changed it so that it became more 'rational' and made better sense.

Schema theory thus asserts that when we observe an event, we perceive it through a process of making the event meaningful. The way we do this is by relating it to the schemata already established within our cognitive system. For example, to labour poor Maxine once more, her behaviour is suddenly made more explicable as soon as you know she is a 'vegetarian' (assuming, of course, 'vegetarianism' is a concept for which you have a schema). This pigeon-holing of Maxine immediately makes available to you a whole network of knowledge about the kind of person she is, the kinds of things she is likely to eat, what her motivations are likely to be, and so on. You can, straight away, 'go beyond the information given' and begin to make all manner of surmises about what else Maxine might do, and why she might do it. (I once heard a social worker described as 'all knitted lentil, laddered tights and good intentions', which neatly encapsulates the kind of thing in question.)

It is not surprising, therefore, that schema theorists have tended to tackle areas such as prejudice, seeking better to understand why people explain the world in ways that are distorted by their preconceived ideas. They have taken up cognitive psychology's formulations about the following:

- **Selective attention:** the processes by which people focus upon some aspects of the world as it impinges upon them, while ignoring others.
- **Prototypes:** schemata which represent an 'ideal image' of a particular category of thing, against which we judge other examples or instances.
- **Categorization:** the process of matching new information against various schemata, to label it, and hence make sense of it.
- **The confirmation bias:** the propensity to look for evidence to confirm our pre-conceptions, and ignore contrary evidence – even to perceive what we observe *as* confirmatory, by the way we make sense of it.

Certainly these notions have considerable resonance with concepts from social epistemology, including, in particular, 'reification'. They may help us to understand how certain events or manifestations acquire the sense of 'thinghood'. Once we have the concept of 'stress' and its accompanying schema, for example, we can use it to make sense of certain events in our lives and manifestations of bodily discontinuity. Where we see 'stress' as salient, the attribution of 'stress induced disease' becomes highly plausible – it becomes so real that it is difficult to deny that this is what is indeed happening. New events and new manifestations easily become encompassed within the story, acting as confirmatory evidence, and we can all too easily become so beguiled by the apparent reality of the story, that it becomes *the* only one. Other understandings fall from view – their stories muted and ignored, and hence they remain unexplored: our problem is stress – end of story.

The drawback, of course, is that the focus on prejudice and bias has itself tended to emphasize a particular model of reality, in which people are still portrayed in a highly unflattering light, as prey to entrenched pre-conceptions, unable to break out of the conceptual blinkers so imposed. Within this perspective there is little room for innovation, for people to be able to challenge the old and create any new way of seeing the world. Schema theory is helpful in its theorizing about the impact of existing schemata upon our current perception, but has little to say about how new schemata are constructed, and hence new insights gained. Critics (see, for example, Billig, 1987) have said it generates an image of the person as a mindless bureaucrat, obsessed with efficiency and taking mental short-cuts. This may be the way in which people behave some of the time, but, once more, it offers only a partial (and therefore distorted) picture of the richness of thought and creativity of which people are capable.

However, probably the most telling criticism is that schema theory assumes a very one-dimensional mental apparatus, in which a person's view of the world is painted on a very flat canvas, offering a simple, unified set of understandings. Billig suggested that one of the best ways of studying how social cognition works is to look at how people argue, since this is more likely to encourage them to demonstrate their flexibility of thought, and their capacity to be 'in two minds' (or even more). Also, as we will see, criticisms have been made about the individualizing bias of schema theory, with its assumption that schemata are biographically generated, and hence unique to individuals. In parallel with concerns about the inadequacy of attribution theory to accommodate the influence of culturally and socially mediated knowledge, schema theorists have been exhorted to expand their concepts, and to introduce into them intersubjective as well as subjective elements.

PERSONAL CONSTRUCT THEORY

A more widely known and rather different paradigm is George Kelly's Personal Construct theory. This is usually accorded the status of a school of its own, rather than being thought of as a branch of social cognition. This label is rejected by Personal Construct theorists as too limited. It is, they argue, a much more global theory of human emotion and action as well as thinking, where its suggestions about explanation are not so much 'parts' of the theory, as its basis. Personal Construct theory takes as its fundamental assumption that 'making sense of the world' is *the* basis of what it means to be a person, and underpins all of what constitutes human behaviour and experience. The basic idea (postulate) behind the theory is simple enough – that people

58

interpret the world by way of a series of 'personal constructs'. Kelly and his followers have drawn up a list of descriptions of what these are like, and how they operate (their 'corollaries' – Personal Construct theory is replete with specialized jargon, which makes it difficult to penetrate until you have learned its mystery language). Kelly's own account (Kelly, 1966) and Bannister and Fransella's reviews (the 1986 third edition is currently the most up to date) offer more detailed descriptions, if you want to know more than the summary I provide here.

Personal Construct theory is a specifically *person*-constructs-reality model, where people are viewed as 'scientists' who approach life by constructing a 'best estimate' set of working hypotheses about what is going on and what is likely to happen, in order to plan how to proceed. This constructed reality is continually tested against what *indeed* happens. It is then modified and is refined, so that at any point individuals can approach their lives in a functional, self-aware and self-controlling manner. The taken-for-granted reality they construct thus gains for them a functional 'objectivity' that enables them to see their world as 'real'. In this way it becomes possible for them to tackle the complex demands of living in society, making decisions, planning action and understanding their own actions and emotions and the actions and emotions of others. In emphasizing the person-as-scientist, Kelly was careful so say that this is just one aspect of many forms of 'constructive alternativism' that occur within explanation. His followers, (see for example Swift, Watts and Pope, 1983) have argued that Kelly's notion of 'scientist' has often been misinterpreted as an entirely rationalizing, unemotional image, whereas Kelly chose the term for its liberating properties – its ability to overcome the dehumanizing 'person-as-passive-organism' image of prior forms of theorization such as behaviourism.

In Personal Construct theory the uniqueness of each new event is made understandable by comparing it with the appropriate construct(s). However, the fragmentation corollary states that there are sometimes constructs which contradict one another. Thus the theory recognizes that people can be 'in two minds'. The commonality corollary asserts that people can and do experience the world in similar ways, to the extent that their construct systems are similar. And the sociality corollary asserts that people have access to each other's construct systems, which enables them to 'inhabit each other's worlds' even where they are very different. These aspects are crucial to allow people to operate effectively within a social world, success as a social being depending upon how predictive those constructs are, and how appropriately they are applied. Thus while 'personal constructs' have a lot in common with schemata, the theorization transcends some of the limitations of schema theory; it portrays people as more sophisticated, as sometimes confused and indecisive, as sharing common understandings, and as able to empathize with and understand each other.

However, the theory is ultimately limited in three main ways. First, it is primarily a *personal* construct theory. In stressing the uniqueness of each individual construct system, it has very little to say about the ways in which people may construct and negotiate meanings *collectively*, or how *shared* understandings operate within the medium of culture. It does not deal in any depth, for example, with social processes, such as the influence of social control and the construction of knowledge by powerful groups, which is then foisted upon the less powerful as described in the previous chapter. Basically, it is an *individualizing* discourse, which reifies the individual 'subject' (see, for example, the criticisms of Henriques *et al*, 1984) and operates almost entirely within the domain of intrasubjectivity, to all intents and purposes ignoring the considerable importance of intersubjective processes.

Secondly, although Kelly himself argued that theories (including his own) should be treated as aids-to-understanding rather than as dogmatic assertions that they are (or ever can be) descriptions-of-what-really-is, his focus on construct bipolarity is highly specific and open to question. There are arguments for suggesting that features of reality cannot be understood just in terms of their own qualities, but must also take account of those negative dialectic qualities which make them distinctive (i.e. 'good' makes sense as a concept because it is in opposition to 'bad' – but that also is in opposition to 'fresh', to 'virtuous', to 'valuable' and so on). These arguments date back as far as the earliest psychologists such as Wundt and are currently coming back into vogue by drawing upon some of the ideas of quantum physics about explication and implication (see, for example, Graham 1986). However, the constraints imposed by bipolarity are a serious problem for any theory which seeks to represent the full complexity and sophistication of human thinking. I would argue that this is yet another example of theorization which has fallen into the trap of assuming that the Western worldview has some fundamental superiority, allowing privileged access to human universals. The contrast of opposites is, certainly, a conceptual framework built into the structure of the English language, and deeply sedimented in Western thought. But, for example, it is much less thinly woven into the *Geistwissenschaft* worldview of the East, concerned more with complex interrelationships, holism, and concepts of balance and equilibrium (as described in the previous chapter).

Thirdly, the assertion that people can determine the accuracy of their constructs only by acting upon them and thus testing them out can lead to some highly nonsensical implications. Wiggins *et al.* (1971) provide a telling example. They describe the constructs of a parent in relation to their child crying, that either the child is in pain, or wants 'candy'. If the parent acts, in a particular situation, on the second of these, the child may become violently nauseated, faint, develop a high temperature and die. The parent has tested the construct and found it wanting, and may indeed modify their constructs. But the child would still be dead. This is obviously not what happens. Parents do not just draw upon their own constructs (derived from past experiences) but upon a whole host of knowledge about how to respond to children who are sick and have temperatures, gleaned from books, advice from family and friends and health professionals. All manner of other ideas influence their actions, including ones about risk-taking (encapsulated, for example, in aphorisms like 'better safe than sorry'). Most crucially, people do not simply choose between alternative constructs within their own cognitive system. Anybody who has ever cared for a sick child knows the enormous amount of effort put into working out what is going on, what all the possible reasons may be, and what are the most prudent responses (including seeking advice, calling a doctor out at night if necessary or taking the child to hospital, even at the risk of being thought over-anxious). The process is much more than an analytic search within *individual* thought, it is an active, insightful search after meaning which draws upon advice from others, directly and from the store of commonsense knowledge available within the individual's social and cultural milieu.

Thus while the theory is certainly dynamic (in that it has built-in formulations about change) and it accommodates contradiction, it cannot be viewed as genuinely dialectic. This notion is one which, for example, portrays people as constantly, moment by moment, in a state of dynamic tension between the person-constructs-reality and the reality-constructs-person modes of understanding, always poised between being 'subjects' and 'objects' of the processes in which they are engaged. I will now move on to consider such dialectical theories, which I believe are more useful ways of making sense of how people explain the world in general, and better aids, more specifically, to enabling us to understand how people explain health and illness.

DIALECTICAL THEORIES

Dialectical theories are concerned with the interface between reality as constructed *by* and as constructed *for* the individual, and are gradually growing in importance in social psychology (see, for example, Buss, 1979). Where other psychological theories regard explanation as the *product* of a person's thinking (i.e. arising inside the person's cognitive system, and then being externalized in the process of expression into the public domain), dialectical theories assume a different relationship. They see explanations as occupying external as well as internal 'space' – as operating in the domain of cultural and social *intersubjectivity*, as well as the domain of individual subjectivity. An analogy might be explanation as a 'commodity' (as in 'Yes, I can buy that idea', 'I got sold the argument that . . . ', and so on), bargained in the marketplace of rhetoric and debate, indoctrination and propaganda. The image is less one of explanations as the creations of individual thought, arrived at anew each time they are experienced or expressed by an individual, and more as whole sets of ideas, bound together as tightly integrated packages, which operate in culture within ideological frameworks that can be read *by* people as 'texts', told as stories or appreciated as images. Dialectical theories recognize that explanations are moulded by social and cultural forces as well as the cognition of individual thinkers. They have a life outside – as well as inside – the person. Thus instead of trying to classify people according to the explanations they express (e.g. individuals as 'internals' or 'externals' in their attributions), dialectically informed theorists seek to elucidate the different explanations themselves.

To give one example, Claudine Herzlich (1973) described three main images of illness – as 'destroyer', as 'occupation' and as 'liberation' (these are described in more detail in the next chapter). Herzlich argued that these three ways of construing illness are available to everybody in the culture in which these ideas are sedimented. They are recognizable in literature, in the television programmes we watch, and in the advice given by doctors, as well as in our conversations and our quiet musings. Some people may lean towards one or other of them – say, a preoccupation with regarding illness as a destroyer, as a challenge to their self-esteem and, in its capacity to prevent them fulfilling their obligations at work and at home, something to be feared and avoided. Yet everybody will, at times, draw upon each one to make sense of their world, according to particular circumstances, to mood, to the social context, and so on. These images of illness are thus as much properties of culture as they are properties of people. Further, while we may differ, as individuals, in our interpretation of them, and the circumstances in which we will adopt one rather than another, except in very unusual circumstances, the images available in any particular culture represent the fixed 'menu' from which we must choose – they are in the usual way of things the *only* means by which we can understand and explain the world.

Very seldom can any of us come up with a totally novel explanation that we have thought of for ourself. The best we can do is a new elaboration or variant upon the 'texts' that are knocking around at the time and place in which we find ourselves. Ideas that had currency in the past – and those that will have currency in the future, or that are available in other places and in other cultures or social milieux – are, quite simply 'unthinkable'. They are bizarre and alien notions which we may (or may not) know about, but cannot take seriously. Those past conceptualizations, for example, which we have 'grown out of', gain the status of what Gleeson (1991) has termed 'cultural artefacts' – ideas fossilized or archived into our past, only thinkable-of *as* 'misperceptions from the past' and having no contemporary usage or function, other than interesting historical items to be talked and written about but which no longer have any explanatory power. Rex Stainton Rogers (1989), for instance, has argued:

> That we no longer hang children, burn them as witches or brand them as vagrants is not the victory of a few reformers, it is the victory of a whole society which has overcome the constructions that made such actions possible. (p. 29)

Consequently, dialectical theorization within psychology is as interested in the ecology of explanations, and in seeing how they operate in dynamic interplay with each other *as* explanations-in-culture, as it is in exploring how people use them, and the influences upon the different uses made in different circumstances. Similarly, it is fascinated by the historical development of ideas – how some kinds of explanations become fossilized, whereas others gain in importance and in influence and hence come to reconstruct the whole worldview of an entire culture. In this they have drawn upon, in particular, the work of Michel Foucault.

The three main areas of psychology that can be thought of as taking a dialectical approach to explore the way in which people explain the world are: social representation, discourse analysis, and the study of 'everyday explanation'.

Social representations

The term social representation was adopted by Serge Moscovici in the 1960s as one which could form a bridge between the sociologist Emile Durkheim's concepts of 'collective' and 'individual' representations, and allow for an examination of explanations from a perspective 'at the crossroads of anthropology, sociology and psychology' (Moscovici and Hewstone, 1983). Potter and Wetherell (1987) have said that the theory-base of this concept is difficult to describe, because Moscovici's writings are fragmented and contradictory, and his followers have interpreted them in different ways. Certainly in its details it has much of the terminological awkwardness of Personal Construct theory, with little of its specificity, using labels like 'figurative nuclei' 'informative processes' and 'ontologizing' (even Moscovici himself admitted that this last was 'barbaric'!) but eliding between one and the other and shifting from very broad generalizations to highly speculative specifics from one account to the next.

However, for all its theoretical inexactitude, the concept of 'social representation' has had a very substantial impact upon social psychology, particularly in mainland Europe. This has been, I believe, because as a concept (rather than an articulated theory) it offered psychologists a mental 'coathanger' on which to hang a lot of ideas that were being debated at the time, but had – up until then – little in the way of theory to give them shape and substance. In particular, it enabled ideas about the social production and manipulation of 'knowledge' to be linked up with ideas about individual thinking – it sought to span the subjective/intersubjective gap. It forced home the point, lost from much of psychological theorization of the time, that explanations are as much constructed within the 'unceasing babble and . . . permanent dialogue between individuals' (Moscovici, 1985) as within individual minds and hearts. It stressed the importance of shared understandings, both as a medium for communication between people, and as a basis for social groups to participate in a common social world. Indeed, Moscovici has claimed that it is the sharing of common social representations among a number of people that *makes* them a cohesive social group rather than a collection of individuals, and that the boundaries between one social group and another can be identified by finding out where the influence of their different social representations begin and end.

Moscovici has speculated extensively about the ways in which the knowledge which constitutes the social representations of one group get taken up and incorporated into the social representations of another, and changed in the process. In particular, he has been interested in the ways that the commonsense representations of 'ordinary people' draw upon – and distort – expert knowledge (e.g. scientific knowledge). Common themes with Bartlett's ideas can be discerned, where the appropriation of knowledge from one group by another consists of processes of over-simplification, of categorization and of rationalizing. His own earliest work (Moscovici, 1961) explored the way in which psychodynamic concepts (e.g. 'complex') were appropriated from the domain of professional psychiatry into the discourse of everyday life. A more recent example (Moscovici and Hewstone, 1983) is the way in which ideas of brain lateralization have been taken up (particularly by 'new age' pundits) and promulgated as a full-blown theory about our 'intuitive' right-side, and 'analytic' left (perhaps the most striking index of this is the inclusion of the idea by Paul Simon in one of his songs on the *One Trick Pony* album!).

One of the main problems with Moscovici's theorization is that it lacks any well identified means for empirically testing its formulations. Many aspects are tautological, such as the idea of social representations defining groups. If the only way you can define the separation between social groups is in terms of them having different social representations, how then do you test the theory that different groups *do* have different representations? Other problems arise because of the difficulty of how to tell whether people are speaking for the collective, or for themselves, when they report their explanations. How do you tell whether they are reporting from a 'social representation', or from their own idiosyncratic understanding? This issue is crucial if you are claiming that people share understandings in common. Potter and Wetherall have argued that the commonality discovered in purported demonstrations of the shared nature of social representations is a product of homogenizing methods of data analysis, not true commonality of understanding (i.e. the research methods used did not *uncover* the similarity – they *create* it).

Moscovici has claimed that *all* mental experience is based upon social representations. As a theory this just will not do, as there is no way of disputing it and no way of testing it. Certainly it has some large gaps, since Moscovici has focused his work almost exclusively upon the 'watering down' of expert knowledge by lay people, without looking in any detail at the process in reverse – the moulding of expert knowledge by culturally and socially sedimented ideas. Nor has he taken into consideration the arguments about the role of social forces in the transmission of knowledge, and its use to bolster dominance and maintain power inequalities. It is better, then, to see his formulations as helpful metaphors rather than a full-blooded theory, which at least forces us to always keep the subjectivity/intersubjectivity dialectic in mind when we consider explanation.

Discourse analysis

It is hard to disagree with Potter and Wetherell's (1987) claim that discourse analysis – the study of social texts in functional terms – is fascinating, and can help psychologists to learn a great deal about the way people think about themselves and the world in which they live. What they have devised is a particular way of examining 'talk', which can help us gain understanding, but does not offer the kind of complex, structured theory-base that, say, George Kelly provided in Personal Construct theory (although this is not necessarily a bad thing!).

Essentially they were concerned with process rather than structure – more interested in exploring what people are doing when they talk, and what they are trying to achieve, than in specifying what intrapsychic basis there may be for explanations. The cornerstone of their argument has been that when people talk to each other, they use language purposefully. What they say always has a function, although this is not always explicit or obvious. The function will often have more to do with what individuals want to achieve, than with what they are overtly expressing. So, for example, when my guest says 'there are never any buses round here at this time of day' is unlikely to be meant seriously as an analysis of transport provision in an Oxfordshire village late at night but, rather, as an oblique request for a lift. Working out the function of talk is always a matter of interpreting it in its context, since interpreting such a statement would depend a lot on its social setting, and the tone of voice, and facial gestures that accompanied it.

This idea is not in any sense new. What Potter and Wetherell have contributed is a new focus on inconsistency. They strongly criticize the assumption which implicitly, if not explicitly, underlies most research as well as theory in psychology, which is that an individual's views, opinions and beliefs remain constant, and, indeed, that people are highly motivated to make what they say consistent over time and in different situations. If we accept that talk is functional then, Potter and Wetherell point out, what people say will vary according to the particular end they are seeking at the time. So we should not be surprised if people say contradictory things in different situations. In

66

fact, even within most ordinary conversation of any length, the talker's purpose is likely to shift and change as the talk proceeds. And hence, so too will what is said. From one moment to another, a person may well express quite different and even contradictory views in order to achieve different purposes.

Conventionally, contradictions have been regarded as disruptions to the norm – as mistakes, failures in communication, or as attempts deliberately to decieve, to flatter or be tactful. They are seldom regarded as indicating a genuine inconsistency of thought. They are 'blips' in the data, to be ignored or smoothed over if qualitative methods (e.g. content analysis of interviews) are used. Quantitative methods (e.g. attitude scales) simply do not provide any scope for recording uncertainty, varied reactions, or shifts in opinions from one moment to another. You cannot both agree and disagree with a scale item. Both approaches, Potter and Wetherell claimed, ride 'roughshod over subtle distinctions that may play a crucial role in the participants' discourse' (1987, p. 45). Yet it is these very features of flexibility and ambivalence, they argue, that are the most interesting features of discourse. People are 'competent negotiators of reality' and what we need to explore are the complex and sophisticated ways in which they negotiate it. Potter and Wetherell have proposed discourse analysis as a technique for making these variations open to observation.

They noted that although people continually construct alternative versions of an idea, argument or account, they are often quite unaware of them. This is because each one creates, in effect, a different version of 'reality', and hence people slip into and out of alternative 'realities' all the time, usually without any awareness that they are doing so. In other words, while 'reality' is experienced by the individual as a constant – because at any one moment each version is compellingly *real*, in fact it is much more fluid, shifting and changing, as the individual's frame darts from one purpose to another. This point is crucial, for it states that people are continually constructing versions-of-reality and re-describing events as a matter of everyday talking, not just when they are showing prejudice or distortion – all versions are 'distortions', since there is no benchmark of single, undeniable 'truth'.

What this theory proposes, then, is that the explanations which people proffer will vary according to the purpose of what they are saying or even thinking at the time. In the act of expression they will construct a particular version of reality that makes sense and is functional at that moment. Thus as expressed explanations shift, moment by moment, so too will experienced reality. The explanations themselves are drawn from a repertoire of texts available via the person's broader culture, or their closer social group, used as commodities in social transactions, where people engage in complex processes of negotiation with each other over meanings and purposes. Discourse analysis thus assumes a truly dialectical theory-base, portraying individuals in dynamic tension between constructing reality and having it constructed for them.

Potter and Wetherell have not claimed that their approach is comprehensive, so it would be unfair to criticize it for what it excludes (i.e. everything except language), although I do wonder whether it is entirely satisfactory to seek to base a theory solely on the linguistically expressed features of human experience. I am also concerned about the basis upon which they can be so sure that, as researchers, they can always identify either the function of a portion of talk, or the boundaries of the different discursive storylines. And certainly the approach (at a methodological even if not at a conceptual level) suffers from psychology's obsession with the person, failing once more properly to address the constitution of meanings by collective social and cultural means. In so methodologically reifying the subject (as argued more generally by Henriques *et al.*, 1984, and more recently by Parker, 1989) and in assuming that researchers are sufficiently immune from the processes about which they are theorizing that they can sit in judgement about the meanings and purposes of others, their formulations are somewhat empirically limited. None the less, their desconstructive flair and innovative ideas will, it is to be hoped, help to shift mainstream psychology in the right direction.

Everyday explanations

Under this broad umbrella are collected a diversity of people who share a desire to treat people's explanations of the world as worthy of exploration in their own right. What they want is to study them in ways that provide opportunities for the expression of ideas, hunches and half-formed theories, in ways that make them visible for observation and analysis, relatively unfettered by methodological or theoretical constraints. Antaki (1988) has collected and described a number of different ways by which this endeavour can be approached, including drawing graphs to illustrate highs and lows in biographical storytelling, writing on and arranging cards, and then drawing arrows between them, and observing defendants argue their case in a courtroom.

The concern, then, is less with drawing up a watertight theory about how explanation comes about, and more with observing and interpreting explanations, in order to gain better understandings of what is going on. This, in psychology, is a version of what is termed in sociology 'grounded theory' (Glaser and Strauss, 1968, is the standard text), where instead of starting with a theory, and seeking to validate it, the approach is to start with some data, and then to try to devise a theory to explain it. Theorization in this area thus lags behind its methodological inventiveness. What it has begun to add is a recognition that explanations are not mere descriptions of assumed cause-and-effect, but also involve moralizing aspects (i.e. about what should happen, as well as what does happen) (Antaki and Fielding, 1981). In general, what seems to be occurring is that attempts are being made to draw upon existing theoretical formulations (such as attribution and Personal Construct theories) as starting points to be modified and extended following the guidance offered by new kind of data collected in novel and more appropriate ways. If you want to explore this area further, a good place to start is the book edited by Charles Antaki (1981) which brings together writings by some of its most influential workers.

OVERVIEW

In this chapter I have reviewed and summarized the main contributions that psychologists have offered to our understanding of the processes underlying explanation, and the methodological approaches they have refined for their study. Overall, I will admit to have painted a rather sorry picture of a discipline so obsessed by scientism that it has generally presented (with a few notable exceptions) an image of people as automata, or – at best – rather boring cognitive 'misers'. I make no apologies for my negativity. It is in any case by no means an unusual view, more broadly in psychology as well as in the specifically social field. Peter Herriot, for example, writing in the mid-1970s about research and theorization concerned with human memory, argued that:

> It has been assumed that the limitations of the [memory] system are more important than its potential. Experimental psychologists have asked why we forget more often than they have asked how we remember. They have made tasks difficult by presenting unrelated meaningless items at a fast rate, instead of giving the subject the

opportunity to use the immense resources at his[sic] disposal in the leisured perusal of the meaningful whole. (1974, p. 4)

Psychology has, I believe, paid a very heavy cost for its obsession with science. Ken Gergen (1986) has summed up one part of the problem neatly: 'experimental social psychology misleadingly suggests that it is portraying nature while systematically obscuring the significance of culture'. In *order* to 'portray nature' (i.e. discover universal laws of action, experience and thought) one has to make theorization and research very simple indeed. Inevitably, then, the *only* image of human thinking and understanding that *can* be derived is one of banal incompetence. If you give the best chef in the world just an onion, a banana, a spoon and a campfire, she or he is never going to create a decent meal, let alone a culinary triumph! Scientific method and philosophy simply do not offer us the right resources to find out how people explain and make sense of their world, for their tenets exclude or destroy the very stuff (i.e. meaning) we need to study. But the crux of the problem lies deeper than this, I believe, within social psychology's failure to bridge the inter/intrapsychic gap (an issue I raised in Chapter 1), and indeed, more broadly, with its inability to escape from the cult of 'individual essence'. As my brief allusions to dialectically-informed approaches at the end of this chapter suggest, I am optimistic that we may be getting close to breaking through. But I suspect we have not got there yet. At least knowing that we need an exit trajectory is a good start.

CHAPTER FOUR

Alternative Empirical Approaches

In the last two chapters we have considered the various theoretical frameworks and ideas that have been used by anthropologists, sociologists and psychologists as they have tried to make sense of the way in which people explain health and illness. In this chapter we move on to examine the different kinds of research studies which they have used to explore this field. I have not attempted to be comprehensive, for this is already a very extensive area of research. For example, I have not included any studies directed to explanations of particular forms of illness (such as Tina Posner's 1977 study of understandings of diabetes, or Waxler's investigation of the social construction of leprosy, 1981). If you do want to know more about this area, the books by Mishler *et al.* (1981) and Caroline Currer and Margaret Stacey (1986) are excellent places to start, particularly Mishler's own chapter 6 on the social construction of illness, and Paul Unschuld's chapter 3 (in Currer and Stacey) on the conceptual determination of individual and collective experiences of illness.

Instead I have concentrated upon research studies that have been conducted to investigate 'lay' explanations for health and illness within contemporary British and North American cultures – that is, the chapter concerns the different aspects of the way in which ordinary people (as opposed to medical professionals) explain, understand and portray health and illness, becoming ill and recovering from illness in general terms. Again, even within this more limited domain, I have been highly selective. Other more comprehensive reviews have already been provided by the Research Unit in Health and Behavioural Change (1989) (Chapter 3 on the 'Social Construction of Health and Illness' is particularly good) Mildred Blaxter (1990), Michael Calnan (1987) and Margaret Stacey (1988). My overall aim is not so much to review this field of research as a whole as to illustrate the main *kinds* of research approach that have been used. I have done this in order to demonstrate how the particular method used in a study both reflects the theoretical base from which the researcher operates, and also constructs the kinds of results that are generated.

Possibly the most significant divide is between research based upon the hypothetico-deductive approach of science, and what sociologists usually term 'grounded theory' (Glaser and Straus, 1968). Hypothetico-deductive research assumes that researchers begin their studies with a clearly articulated theory, and that the study is a quest to prove or disprove that theory. In order to do this, they must make predictions about what will happen (this whole process is covered in more depth in Chapter 5). The study consists of seeing whether their predictions work or not. The vast majority of psychological research is conducted in this way, though it is less common in sociology, and even less so in anthropology. In fact, even by their own lights, most people taking this approach break their own rules. Despite the principle clearly argued by the philosopher Karl Popper (1959) that hypothetico-deductive method can only *dis*prove, it cannot prove anything, the literature in 'health psychology' is awash with studies which purport to demonstrate hypotheses which have been 'proved' (the more cautious merely claim that they are 'supported') and, hence, provide a contribution to progress in our understanding.

Grounded theory, by contrast, is inductive rather than deductive. It sees the research endeavour as one of exploring a field of interest by collecting data, without any prior hypothesis. Rather, theory must be derived *from* the data obtained – it must be data-driven. The task of researchers is to look for systematic patterns in the data which they obtain from their studies, and then devise the most elegant and useful theory that they can to explain it. This kind of approach is also often called 'ethnographic'. (I do not intend to get bogged down here in the complex debates about what constitutes ethnography: there are several alternative formulations.) In this chapter you will find that the majority of studies I have described fall more comfortably into this category. In Chapter 5 I will go on to look more closely at the implications of this approach for the kinds of understandings which it can provide, and the limits upon them.

EARLY WORK ON 'LAY EXPLANATIONS' FOR HEALTH AND ILLNESS

The earliest empirical studies of such 'lay' explanations (usually termed 'lay health beliefs') carried out in the USA (the work of Apple, 1960, is probably the best known) found that biomedical concepts tended to predominate, and doctors were usually seen as the main source of medical consultation and treatment. People also mentioned a range of other sources of medical help and advice, including chiropractors, Christian Science readers and the 'corner druggist', and reported using a wide variety of over-the-counter treatments (e.g. trusses and sun lamps). Consultations with orthodox doctors tended to be restricted to situations where a person's symptoms appeared ambiguous or interfered with work or social obligations. This was found to be particularly the case with poorer people, who were more likely than the better-off to treat themselves, and seek alternative advice. They resorted to medical consultations only in fairly dire emergencies or when they were severely incapacitated. These differences between rich and poor reflected in part problems (in the USA) over paying for treatment, and partly an ethos of robust 'keeping going' in adversity and lower expectations of health typical of working-class culture (Koos, 1954). Early research on the concept of 'health' found that it was usually articulated as a complex of three main constructs: feeling good, absence of symptoms and the ability to perform normal functions (Baumann, 1961), with the working-class people tending to favour the last two categories.

CONTEMPORARY WORK ON 'LAY EXPLANATIONS'

More recent studies in this field have tended to adopt one of three approaches: the 'folklore' approach, arising primarily from anthropology; the 'social determination' approach, arising primarily from sociology; and the 'explanatory plurality' approach, originating from various disciplines, but focusing upon the diversity of alternative accounts of and for health and illness to which people have access. I will deal with each of these in turn.

THE 'FOLKLORE' APPROACH

Anthropological studies of explanatory systems in industrialized countries have tended to concentrate upon examining how the 'lay' beliefs of ordinary people differ from the professional epistemology of biomedicine. In particular they have concentrated upon their links with the indigenous folklore and traditional, commonsense wisdom of the cultural group within which they were expressed. I have selected three studies, one (by Snow) which explored the 'folk' beliefs of poor people living in Tucson, Arizona in the USA; a study by Cecil Helman, a British GP working in Stanmore in the county of Middlesex, of the 'folk' beliefs of his patients; and a third by Jocelyn Cornwell, who explored the 'lay beliefs' of a small group of people living in the 'East End' of London, England. These three illustrations give a good 'flavour' of the way in which anthropologists have approached this field from a 'folklore' perspective.

Snow's study of American 'folk' beliefs

The 'folk beliefs' studies by Snow (1974) derived from a sub-culture within the USA in which it was possible to observe a mixture of European folklore, African cultural roots (particularly concerning genetic illnesses specific to Blacks), the form of voodoo religion that arose from the West Indies (particularly notions of sympathetic magic), and hot–cold theories arising from Spain, via Mexico. These could be seen to have been overlaid by popularized images of biomedicine, particularly those promulgated by the American media (where, for example, far more patent medicines – for instance, for haemorrhoids and diarrhoea – are advertised on television than are seen as acceptable to 'good taste' in Britain). Snow interviewed forty-seven poor, predominantly female and black inhabitants of Tucson, Arizona. She also attended community and religious meetings in order to put the interview data into context. All but one of her respondents had been born in the 'Deep South' and, aged between 35 and 85, most had experienced considerable racial discrimination. Her investigation was very detailed, including at least two lengthy interviews with each person, covering life-history and aspects of work, religious practices and family organization (70 per cent of her sample were single-parent heads of households) in addition to specific questions about beliefs concerning health and illness.

These respondents perceived the world in which they lived as hostile and dangerous, beset by natural agents of disease (e.g. the chill wind and damp, polluted air), supernatural influences (e.g. a punishing God, devils and spirits) and the malevolence of other people (e.g. via hexing, spells and *mal ojo* (evil eye)). Within this worldview, the individual was perceived as powerless, dependent upon the aid of talismans, spiritual healers and religious intervention to cope with illness. Notions of a need for balance were very pervasive, both in terms

74

of the body (to retain its natural equilibrium) and in social life (to avoid God's punishment for being 'uppity', or the subject of envy by others in the community). To stay healthy in this hostile, precarious world it was seen as crucial to eat, drink and live in a temperate, respectable manner. This was regarded as particularly important at times of increased vulnerability – for example, during menstruation and pregnancy, and at particular times (e.g. the waning of the moon) and stages in the life-cycle (e.g. infancy and old age). Within this notion of balance, an important tension was that of hot–cold, which has been traced back from humoral pathology via Spanish folklore and then via Mexican and Puerto-Rican folklore, into American cultural ideas (see, for example, the work of Clark, 1970). Illnesses were thus regarded as either caused by 'too much heat' or 'too much cold', arising, for example, from imbalances in diet, the effects of climate, or exposure to water or wind. By reference to the hot–cold system, complex explanations were built up to account for illness, and to suggest remedies. For example, eating insufficient blood-building, 'hot' food was seen to lead to 'low blood' illnesses like anaemia or tuberculosis.

The ability to heal the sick was seen as a personal gift (usually from God) rather than the product of training. Consequently spiritual, religious or indigenous healers were generally regarded with much more respect and authority than were doctors operating within the conventional US system of health care. These were considered greedy and essentially hostile to the black community and poor whites alike. (This reaction is not at all surprising, given the enormous gulf that existed at that time between poorer North American 'ethnic minorities' and the predominantly white, male, Jewish and Protestant medical establishment.) The worldviews of the two communities operated upon entirely different assumptions, and often came into conflict. For instance, the people using a hot–cold analysis would be perplexed and suspicious when a doctor diagnosed both high blood pressure (hot blood) concurrently with anaemia (cold blood), since, from their analysis, it is impossible to have both at the same time.

Helman's study of the 'folk' beliefs of his patients

In comparison to Snow's work, Helman's (1978) study of the 'folk' beliefs of his patients indicated that within a system of welfare provision of medicine (i.e. the British National Health Service) there are fewer divisions between such beliefs and medical orthodoxy. However, it is important to note that Helman's data were derived mainly from interactions between a general practitioner (himself) and patients, and upon second-hand reports from other health professionals (e.g. via interviews with nurses, other GPs and receptionists). Thus they represent the reports: (a) of people who had taken their medical problems to doctors' surgeries; and (b) that people were prepared to express in the situation of a medical consultation. Helman entitled his paper 'Feed a cold and starve a fever'. His work demonstrated the wide-ranging acceptability of a colds/fevers classificatory system current still in British culture (although he found it tended to be expressed more vigorously and consistently by older patients). Most minor illnesses, according to Helman, tend to be classified (by patients *and* by doctors) according to the way in which they make a person feel ('hot' or 'cold') and the kind of symptoms which they experience ('wet' or 'dry'). This creates a division between 'colds and chills' on the one hand, and 'fevers and infections' on the other. These two different kinds of illness are assumed to have different causes and require, therefore, different kinds of treatment.

Colds and chills are seen as mostly caused as a consequence of exposure to some unfavourable aspect of the environment, in particular, damp, rain, cold winds and draughts (i.e. anything which lowers the body temperature). Exposed skin, particularly on the top of the head, neck and feet (but not face and hands) is seen as particularly vulnerable, if not 'properly wrapped up'. For example, older men said that they thought they were likely to get a 'head cold' after a haircut unless they were careful to wear a hat. Other forms of vulnerability mentioned were *transitions* between hot and cold – sitting in a draught or going out into the cold after a hot bath; seasonal changes in the weather (November and February were both considered dangerous months because of their transitional nature); and shifts from one climate to another (e.g. 'summer colds' attributed to returning from holidays in hot countries to colder Britain).

In order to avoid catching colds, you need to wait a sensible time after a bath before going outside, wrap up warm in winter and change out of damp clothes when you get wet. If you do get one, therefore, you have only yourself to blame. Alternatively, catching a cold is 'the price to be paid' for new-fangled ideas like holidays in Spain, or skimpy fashionable clothes. Strength to fight the cold was seen as built from within, by tonics like Virol, Cod Liver Oil, Haliborange and Sanatogen, and by eating warming food and drinking warming drinks. Indeed, folk beliefs like these have been used in advertising, where processed porridge, for example, is presented in Britain as 'central heating for kids' which will help them to fight off colds. The kinds of treatment that are appropriate also stress the need to warm the body, with hot lemon and honey drinks, hot water bottles, vapour rubs (e.g. Vick's) and ample warming food ('feed a cold').

By contrast, having a fever is seen as characterized by a feeling of 'hotness'. Fevers are considered more severe, longer-lasting and potentially more dangerous than having a 'cold'. A fever is seen as caused by infection from 'bugs', 'germs' or 'viruses' (terms borrowed from biomedicine, but rooted more strongly within folklore than in modern microbiology). Germs are seen as living, invisible, very small malevolent entities that you catch, mostly from other people's sneezes, dirty hands, unsavoury toilet habits or through ill-prepared food. Once inside the body they are assumed to move around and be able to infect almost any part. There are no good 'germs' only bad, harmful ones; viruses and bacteria are seen as equivalent. There is far less blame attached to having a fever. Although always 'caught' from somebody else, this hazard is seen as part and parcel of the risk of normal, everyday social interaction. People with a fever are, however, expected not to spread their germs by going into work with 'flu, or sending a child to school with chicken pox. But in the end, people tend to assume that if there is ' . . . a bug going round' then there is little anybody can do to avoid catching it.

Methods of dealing with germ illnesses fall into three categories: the germs can be ejected – 'washed out' or 'flushed out' by taking fluids, coughed up by taking expectorants, or sweated out (encouraged by hot drinks, warm rooms and extra bedclothes); they can be starved (particularly stomach 'bugs'); and they can be killed, usually by antibiotics. Helman commented upon the considerable pressure generally put upon GPs to supply antibiotics for almost any form of infectious illness, irrespective of their side-effects and inability to treat viral infections. Helman pointed out that the explanatory system used by GPs in their interactions with their patients mirrored these 'folk' beliefs. GPs, he claimed, frequently tell people things like 'you've picked up a germ that's going round' or 'you seem to have a urinary infection'. Despite their vagueness, such statements satisfy patients and reassure them that no further diagnosis is necessary. Seldom does the GP make any attempt to identify the infectious organism, thus promoting the view that all 'bugs' attacking a similar site can be dealt with in a similar manner. Further the willingness of GPs to acquiesce to demands for antibiotics does little to question the efficacy of antibiotics as 'magic bullets' for any kind of infection. Helman suggested that as a result (due largely to the self-limiting nature of the illnesses, and the constraints on the GPs' time and resources) most GPs reassure patients by confirming their expectations about treatment ('go to bed, take plenty of fluids, and keep warm') and offering prescriptions for unneeded, expensive and often positively harmful medications. For instance, at the time of writing the paper, Helman estimated that six million gallons of cough mixtures were prescribed each year on the NHS in Britain, despite the considerable doubts that have been expressed about whether they serve any therapeutic functions other than reassurance.

Cornwell's studies of 'lay beliefs' of Eastenders

Jocelyn Cornwell's early research (1984) investigated the explanations of health and illness given by the twenty-four people whom she interviewed who lived in London's East End (Bethnal Green). She also obtained data about her respondents' housing, work, life-histories and social networks so that she could locate the accounts they gave within the context of their daily lives, family relationships and personal histories, as well as within the broader geographical and historical context of the area. Her analysis led her to construe the beliefs held by her respondents in terms of two distinctly different kinds of account – the public and the private.

Public accounts, usually offered in early interviews and in response to general questions about, say, the causes of illness, she saw as lay interpretation of expert opinion. They were often prefaced by such phrases as 'Well, *they* think that . . . ', reproducing what was interpreted as 'real knowledge' as legitimated by expert medical opinion. These, she argued, were the kinds of account which a researcher should generally expect to be offered in the setting of a formal interview, when interviewees see themselves as somewhat 'putting on a performance'. Such performance variables are well known to psychologists (see for example the work of Rosenwald, 1986). They are one of the ways in which the research process itself tends to reify culturally sedimented discourses as 'what people think' or 'what people believe'. Another way of looking at them is as the products of a particular kind of social contract in which the interviewee offers the interviewer what they (the interviewee) assume the researcher expects to hear.

Private accounts, by contrast, Cornwell argued, arose out of personal experiences, and from the feelings and thoughts that accompany them.

78

They were usually offered in later interviews when Cornwell had become more accepted and trusted, and had managed to reduce the social distance between herself and her interviewees. She did this by spending a lot of time with them, attending social gatherings and showing herself to be separate from 'them', i.e. the medical establishment – for example, by smoking in interviewees' company. But private accounts also arose in response to specific requests for stories about the respondent's own experiences, or those of their family and friends. According to Cornwell's analysis, public accounts tended to be complex, and what Cornwell (personal communication) has termed 'static': 'By static I mean "one thing acts upon the other" and that is it. No movement backwards or forwards.' In other words, public accounts were linear chains of assumed causality, and somewhat abstracted from the context of biography – rather like Young's 'explanatory models' (as described in Chapter 2).

Cornwell saw the public accounts as based upon a three-part classification of illness causation:

• The cause of the illness could be either internal or external.
• The illness could be either avoidable or unavoidable.
• The person was either to blame or not to blame for getting ill.

In fact although logically there were more possible combinations, she observed only the following four combinations in the explanations offered:

1. Internal/avoidable/blame.
2. External/avoidable/blame.
3. Internal/unavoidable/no-blame.
4. External/unavoidable/no-blame.

Within these different combinations, explanations that illness was avoidable and the person to blame were mentioned far less frequently than were explanations that illness was unavoidable and the person not to blame. Blame was also more often attributed to others (e.g. other parents for sending their children to school with infections) than to the person getting ill. Overall personal blame for illness was an unacceptable idea and, in particular, her respondents vociferously denied that people have the capability to alter their lifestyles to promote good health and avoid illness. The only sense of blame that was meaningful concerned the way in which some people were seen as adopting defeatist attitudes or engaging in stupid or careless behaviour. Of Cornwell's twenty-four respondents, only two were prepared to agree with the messages of the 'Look after Yourself' health education campaign current during the period at which she carried out the research (i.e. advice to reduce drinking, stop smoking, eat properly and take exercise).

Cornwell suggested there were many forces militating against people's being willingness to accept advice of this kind. One was the strong moral imperative within the traditional wisdom of working-class culture that morbid thinking about illness must be avoided and instead you should 'get on' with your life. There was also strong resentment about 'being told what to do' by meddling outsiders. It was seen as very difficult for anybody to overcome the influences of their inherited constitution or to be able to cheat fate, and they were able to cite personal experiences (e.g. knowing smokers who had lived to a ripe old age) which ran counter to the advice given. They spoke too about the benefits that possibly 'unhealthy' habits brought – e.g. the relaxation to be obtained from smoking. These kinds of statements are often regarded as excuses or the result of fatalistic thinking, but Cornwell argued that to view them in this way overlooks 'the premium . . . attach[ed] to taking the initiative in relation to health problems . . . making individuals responsible for their diseases . . . conflicts with their most fundamental attitudes and moral beliefs'. Such beliefs about illness causation were, she argued, embedded within a much broader traditional worldview.

She suggested that the more general worldview was primarily a product of the 'hard earned lives' of the East End London working class within ' . . . an unequal, hierarchical, and largely immutable "natural order of things" . . . '. People can respond to exploitation of this kind in one of two ways. They can construe themselves as passive victims, prey to the whims of 'The Bosses', 'The Council' or 'The Welfare'. Or they can, with dignity, see themselves as cheerful, right-minded, robust individuals who have the guts and the determination to survive adversity. Within this perception of themselves, to accept responsibility for illness would be to deny the powerful economic and political constraints acting upon them, and would undermine their sense of themselves as being able to 'win out' over the odds stacked against them. Thus denial of culpability is a logical corollary of maintaining a role as 'survivor' rather than 'victim'. (There are parallels here to the self-presentation of incest 'survivors' who explicitly deny the 'victim' label.)

The private accounts were far less frequent and scattered through the interviews and other conversations, often emerging when other topics were the ostensible focus for discussion. An example is necessary to illustrate the very different flavour of this kind of account. Cornwell wrote extensively about one of her respondents descriptions of her brother Arthur's illnesses and subsequent death. This woman (given the name Mary) saw the sequence beginning when Arthur caught jaundice in the Second World War, introducing a specific 'weakness' in his liver – a condition which many saw as subsequently exacerbated by his drinking, this a result of his 'sociable nature' and its consequences. This led to cancer, but according to Mary it was the surgical intervention for cancer, not cancer itself, that killed him – by 'opening up' his body, and thus allowing the disease to 'get a grip'. Thus in Mary's private account could be discerned a complex network of reasons, linkages and assumed causes and effects, which Mary used to make sense of Arthur's biography and ultimate death.

Cornwell described the reasoning of her respondents within private accounts as not so much a matter of attempting to say who was to 'blame' but rather an attempt to answer questions about 'What if?' What if Arthur had not been sociable? What if he had never joined the Navy? Illness in these accounts was thus often construed as potentially 'avoidable' (i.e. not inevitable). But its complex aetiology, arising – as it was seen to do – from a web of interconnecting elements, meant that it could not be 'blamed' on anybody. Arthur could not be blamed for being called up into the Navy, nor for having a sociable nature.

It is not necessary to engage in intimate conversations to discover aspects of private accounting. For example, work by Morgan and Spanish (1985) using highly public group interview techniques found that in response to requests for 'stories' and 'personal experiences' respondents gave individualized, concrete accounts, whereas in later phases, in response to requests for 'theories', respondents demonstrated categorical, and later abstract, systems of knowledge. Morgan and Spanish suggested that people formulate and use 'health belief schemata' to organize knowledge and thus inform beliefs, a schema being based upon three levels of explanation: abstract understanding, categorical analysis and episodic knowledge. Young (see Chapter 2) has offered a similar framework, though the terms he used were different – explanatory models, 'prototypes' and chain complexes, each representing knowledge in a different form, with different characteristics. More recently (1986), Cornwell herself has argued that the public/private dimension is less important than recognizing the variety of alternative sources of knowledge upon which people based their accounting in different settings and circumstances, and the need to explore these more fully:

> Social and personal experience are more important sources of ideas and theories about the causes of illness, but there are others. There are 'common stocks' of information and ideas in different social milieus; there are information and ideas specific to particular families and informal social networks, and there are 'external' and 'official' sources of information about health matters – medicine and media. The range of elements – symbols and images, factual knowledge and hearsay, folk wisdom and medical certainties – in the common stock of different social milieus remains to be fully documented. (p. 15)

Common themes within studies of 'folk' beliefs

While at first sight it may seem that Helman's patients' and Cornwell's respondents' ideas were closer to those of orthodox biomedicine than those of poor black people in Tucson, if we look closer we can see there are some striking similarities. Helman's data showed that GPs tend to concentrate on providing reassurance and acknowledgement of the individual's symptoms of disease, rather than treatment or accurate diagnosis – not, in practice, all that different from spirit healers promising to remove a 'hex'. Similarly, the three main themes which Snow identified resemble much more closely those of Helman and Cornwell than her descriptions of *mal ojo*, voodoo and a punitive God implied. Her themes were:

> First, that the world is a hostile and dangerous place; second, that the individual is liable to attack from external sources; third, that the individual is helpless and has no internal resources to combat such attack but must depend on outside aid. (Snow, 1974, p. 83)

Helman's patients also saw the world as a hostile place, a source of attack upon the individual – environmentally (in terms of wet, damp and winds) and microbiologically (in terms of 'germs' that can invade the body). They too saw themselves as helpless, assuming that whenever they were ill they needed treatments like cough mixtures and antibiotics rather than accepting that most minor illnesses are self-limiting. That ideas of supernatural causes of illness or personal malevolence did not enter Helman's or Cornwell's analyses may reflect no more than the settings in which their data were collected. The folk studies reviewed here indicate that in Western settings, no less than in the Third World communities that form the basis of most anthropological research, the explanatory systems adopted by ordinary people to explain health and illness, and tackle the problems they raise, can be understood only within the much broader context of indigenous traditional culture and 'folk' wisdom. Folklore and tradition are not just to be found in bygone times or so-called 'primitive' cultures but are alive and active within popular culture in the USA and Britain today. They undoubtedly have historical, indigenous roots, transmitted, for instance, as proverbs and as powerful cultural archetypes, reinforced by socialization, media images and 'professional' endorsement, but, none the less, 'folk wisdom' continues to be deeply woven into the fabric of our everyday understandings of the world.

RESEARCH INTO SOCIAL DETERMINANTS

Over the last twenty or so years an increasing amount of research has been conducted, particularly in Britain, to investigate potential links between the explanatory systems used by certain social groups, and the health inequalities suffered by the worst off. The Black Report (cf. Townsend and Davidson, 1982) established a strong and consistent positive relationship between wealth and health. In study after study, irrespective almost of what kind of illness is involved, the lower a person's socio-economic status, the more likely they are to die young, fall prey to accidents or suffer from chronic and debilitating illness. This finding has been more recently confirmed by the UK Health Education Council's publication *The Health Divide* (1987), which provided evidence that the gap between rich and poor continues, if anything, grows wider as *overall* standards of living rise, despite, in Britain, a system of socialized medical care which includes many initiatives intended to promote health.

Many researchers have wanted to find out why there are such large inequalities between the health of poor and rich people in Britain. Many have argued that the reasons lie predominantly with structural factors such as inadequate, damp and crowded housing conditions, income well below poverty level (making it impossible to afford an adequate diet, and other conditions for healthy living) and unhealthy working conditions (Leslie Doyal's 1979 book is a very readable account of this viewpoint).

However, a number of politicians and indeed a proportion of doctors blame the differences upon the unhealthy behaviour and lifestyle of working-class people, in terms of factors such as their poor diet and their smoking habits. Recently I heard on the radio, for example, a doctor talking about the high incidence of heart disease, who stressed that 'it is the uneducated who come off worst, middle class people, being better educated, are more willing to take their doctor's advice'. Others have blamed the high level of alienation between the medical profession and working class people and structurally and socially induced 'learned helplessness' (as described in Chapter 3). In consequence a number of studies have recently been conducted to investigate the health beliefs of working-class people. Some have focused entirely on particular communities. Others have sought to compare the understandings held by people from working- and middle-class backgrounds. The purposes of this research were to discover to what extent (if any) health inequality is a product of differences in the way in which better-off and poor people think about health and illness, and, in consequence, differences in their propensity to adopt 'healthy' or 'unhealthy' habits and lifestyles.

Lay aetiology and the effects of primary socialization

The best-known British research into lay aetiology is Blaxter and Paterson's (1982) detailed ethnographic study of the beliefs held by working-class mothers and grandmothers living in Aberdeen concerning the causes of disease. This has been followed, more recently, by a large-scale survey of beliefs about health and illness, carried out by Mildred Blaxter and others (Blaxter, 1990).

Mildred Blaxter's early work was based upon content analysis of a series of in-depth structured interviews with each respondent. I will begin by looking at the responses of the forty-six grandmothers (Blaxter, 1983). In their interviews the women discussed a wide variety of reasons for illness. Infection was the most often spoken about, though to a certain extent this merely reflected the commonplace nature of many infectious childhood diseases and the amount of time they spent talking about them. They distinguished between these kinds of mild and untroublesome infections and past memories of serious, life-threatening illnesses like diphtheria. While some reported active steps to eradicate 'germs' (for example, one woman spoke of boiling dishes to get them really clean), generally infection was seen as outside their control — prey to the weather, brought on by damp housing, or 'something in the water'.

84

The next most commonly cited cause was heredity and family susceptibility, including notions about family similarity, and inherited weaknesses. Other ideas concerned the 'natural' ageing process (including the menopause) and the effects of childbearing. All of these explanations also enabled the women to deny any personal responsibility for being ill. They thought that you should expect to suffer the consequences of pregnancy and giving birth, of the menopause and getting old; they are an inevitable part of such processes. The impact of stress, strain and worry, together with reactions of anger, resentment, frustration and despair, was another major category frequently mentioned.

As far as the effects of the environment were concerned, a wide range of different factors were considered capable of increasing an individual's chances of catching an infection, including 'poisons' (e.g. in food or water), bad working conditions and wet and cold climate. The women certainly faced a predominantly hostile environment so far as climate, poor tenement style housing and unpleasant working conditions were concerned. Blaxter argued none the less that to find a cause in the environment was more acceptable than to locate the responsibility in one's own body. When it came to explanations specifically concerned with an individual's own behaviour, the kind of thing suggested was a fondness for sugar, which might lead to diabetes. Blaxter suggested that: self-responsibility was explicitly denied, while the women were prepared to admit it was this behaviour that caused the disease, but in the circumstances, they argued, no one could behave differently.

Although the form of analysis which she used in the study gives the impression that many attributions were singular, Blaxter emphasized that they were generally articulated in the interviews within a complex, biographic storyline. For example, a minor illness, such as 'flu, would be spoken of as leading to bronchitis, which might 'weaken the heart' (i.e. an account similar to Cornwell's 'private accounts'). While a doctor may see a number of incidents of disease as discrete events, to the individual experiencing the sequence they were often interpreted as causally interlinked, and indeed not just linked to each other, but to all manner of life events, circumstances and individual responses.

The overall picture painted of these older women's understanding of health and illness was of low expectations, 'good health' being predominantly portrayed as the capacity to continue to function 'normally' within a stern moral code of 'not complaining', where 'giving in' to illness is a sign of weak character. Within this worldview, the women were able to absolve individuals from any personal blame if they did become ill – their own behaviour may be the reason for illness, but it was not its cause. That cause lay not in themselves, but in the conditions in which they were obliged to live their lives.

When Blaxter and Paterson (1982) compared the accounts of the two generations, the concept of health was similar for both the older women and their daughters of a younger generation. However, their attitudes to doctors and use of medical services were very different. The majority of women from the older generation spoke in trusting, grateful and deferential terms towards doctors, stressing what 'good patients' they were, and disparaging the way in which some people abused the NHS by seeking help for trivial reasons. The attitudes of their daughters were much more varied, and often more critical. Their use of Health Services (both community and hospital emergency services) was far greater than that of their mothers, as were their expectations. Many of these women told stories of arguments with doctors when they failed to give them what they believed was sufficient information, or refused to provide the level of service to which they considered themselves entitled.

Blaxter and Paterson initiated their research to explore the hypothesis that had been publicized by Keith Joseph when he was Minister of Health that deprivation is cyclical – disadvantaged parents transmit the roots of deprivation to their offspring. In particular they wanted to investigate the extent to which the older women had influenced their daughters' views and understandings in childhood, and whether, when the daughters became mothers themselves, they adopted dysfunctional beliefs and hence unhealthy lifestyles. No evidence at all for this analysis was discovered. Blaxter and Paterson argued that whereas there were indeed similarities between the viewpoints of the two generations, it was much more likely that they had a common source (i.e. social disadvantage itself) than that they were a product of familial transmission from mother to daughter. The new generation of mothers saw themselves – and were seen by their mothers – as living in a very different world, in which friends and people like Health Visitors were a much better source of expert and up-to-date advice about health matters than their mothers.

Beliefs about health and lifestyle

Blaxter's later work (Blaxter, 1990) was part of a very large research programme into perceived links between health and lifestyle, which included data from interviews, from questionnaire responses and from measures such as blood pressure from those who participated in the survey. These data were wide-ranging and complex but they included some interesting results on beliefs about health. Content analysis of open-ended replies generated nine definitions of health. These are summarized and illustrated in Figure 4.1.

Definition	*Sample statement*
Not ill	When you don't hurt anywhere and you're not aware of any part of your body.
Despite disease	I am very healthy although I do have diabetes.
A reserve	Both his parents are still alive at 90 so he belongs to healthy stock.
Living a healthy life	I call her healthy because she goes jogging and she doesn't eat fried food. She walks a lot and doesn't drink alcohol.
Physical fitness	There's a tone to my body, I feel fit.
Energy and vitality	Health is having loads of whumph. You feel good you look good, nothing really bothers you, everything in life is wonderful, you seem to feel like doing more.
Social relationships	You feel as though everyone is your friend, I enjoy life more and can work, and help other people.
A means-to-an-end	Health is being able to walk round better, and doing more work in the house when my knees let me.
Wellbeing	Emotionally you are stable, energetic, happier, more contented and things don't bother you.

Figure 4.1   Blaxter's (1990) definitions of health

Although the majority of people expressed multiple concepts of health, the kinds of definitions offered varied primarily by stage in the life-cycle and by gender. Younger men tended to speak of health in terms of physical strength and fitness, whereas younger women spoke more of energy, vitality and being able to cope. In middle age ideas became more complex, with a greater emphasis on total mental and physical wellbeing. Older people, particularly men, focused more on function − being still able to get things done − although ideas of contentment and happiness, often *despite* disease or disability, were also frequently expressed. There were social class differences too, with better off and better-educated women in particular expressing multi-dimensional concepts.

Structural differences showed up strongly in self-assessments of health, with the poorest and most disadvantaged most likely to say that their health was poor, especially in older years. Single parents, those unemployed and those living in areas of high urbanization were all more likely to rate their state of health as low. Measures of health status, made using a complex of self-report questionnaires and physiological measures, showed that although there were the usual social class differences (particularly marked in middle age), these were much more variable than the self-report measures, particularly when various elements (e.g. housing, income and education) were examined separately. Similarly, although the poorest and most disadvantaged were more likely than the better off to report unhealthy habits and lifestyles, the links were by no means straightforward, with complex interactions found between gender, income, age, unemployment and occupation.

Blaxter herself admits that this kind of survey approach is not best suited to canvassing beliefs and attitudes, but none the less, some of her data do raise some interesting questions . Medical advances, better diet, greater prosperity and higher living standards, and health education were the most commonly cited reasons for people being healthier today; poor diet, stress and pace of life and bad habits like smoking and excessive drinking the most commonly attributed reasons for them being less healthy. Generally there was fairly universal agreement that your behaviour and lifestyle affect your health, although Blaxter noted that these were undoubtedly seen as the socially desirable answers to give.

Interestingly, when assumed causes of illness were elicited, it was those who indulged who were *most* likely to see a habit as risking ill-health. While 31 per cent of smokers said that smoking was a cause of heart attack, only 20 per cent of non-smokers did; 35 per cent of overweight people said that it was a cause of heart attack, compared with 21 per cent of those who were not overweight. Heavy drinkers were very much more aware of the risk of liver disease. Similarly, those with 'bad habits' were *more* likely to see themselves as responsible for their own health, although in general terms measures of 'locus of control' were found to have little predictive utility in distinguishing differences in health-related behaviour. Overall, Blaxter concluded that: 'circumstances, including social support, . . . carry more weight for health outcomes than behaviour' (1990, p. 230).

Lay attributions of 'external' and 'internal' control

Pill and Stott (in a number of linked studies from 1981 to 1987) set out to examine beliefs about health and illness of Welsh 'lower working-class' mothers, with a specific focus upon the distinctions construed between inferences of internal causality (i.e. individual responsibility) and of external attributions (fate and the influence of powerful others). They used a combination of in-depth interview techniques (from which they derived indices of health related behaviours and lifestyle) and psychometric instruments, including tests of 'knowledge' and the Health Locus of Control Scale (Wallston and Wallston, 1978). (This construct and research with the scale, including further analysis of Pill and Stott's work, are described in more detail in Chapter 7).

In their 1981 study, Pill and Stott developed a 'Salience of Lifestyle' (SLI) index which they used to distinguish between people whom they termed *lifestylists* and others whom they called *fatalists*. Lifestylists were the women who saw their health as under a level of individual control (although they also saw other factors, like life events and interpersonal relationships, as salient). These women spontaneously reported undertaking health-promoting actions such as taking regular exercise and seeking to reduce stress. Their concepts of health were related to mental and physical wellbeing. They gained higher than average scores on tests for knowledge (i.e. of current orthodox wisdom about the causes of heart attacks and cancer), but they also spoke about the need to evaluate the medical advice offered to them, rather than follow it unquestioningly. Fatalists on the other hand felt they had little control over their health, seldom reported actively trying to improve it, were less knowledgeable, and more likely to rely on the expertise of doctors. To them health was a matter of being able to 'keep going' and fulfil their obligations as wives and mothers. Pill and Stott failed, however, to show any significant differences between the two groups, in terms of their scores on the Health Locus of Control Scale.

In a later study (1985a), using a much larger sample, Pill and Stott further explored the relationship between SLI scores and attributions. Moving away from the simple lifestylist/fatalist dichotomy, they identified three clusters of causal attribution:

- LOW SLI – People who deny any blame or personal responsibility for illness, or say it is to do with being weak.

- MEDIUM SLI – People who think that it is stupid or careless behaviour (like getting cold, or not changing out of wet clothing) which causes illness.
- HIGH SLI – People who believe that good health is a product of a person's lifestyle, their willingness to adopt healthy habits and comply with preventive measures (such as immunization).

Pill and Stott stressed that within their sample 'most of our respondents were probably neither out-and-out fatalists nor did they believe that leading a healthy life would guarantee complete immunity'; indeed 'Most people appear to be quite capable of holding a number of apparently contradictory general theories of causation at the same time. . . . The overlapping nature of the characteristics reveals . . . how those with some degree of belief in the importance of lifestyle decisions develop more complex views which can embrace both fatalistic and lifestyle orientations without cognitive strain.' Pill and Stott looked for links between Health Locus of Control and SLI scores, and other factors such as home ownership, marital and employment status, education and participation in outside organizations (e.g. religious affiliation). But although they did uncover statistically significant links between being higher on the SLI scale and both educational level and amount of religious commitment, with the other variables significant effects emerged only via more complex interactions. For example, house ownership alone did not link significantly to a rejection of 'chance' in illness causation and high SLI scores, but ownership plus more education did.

Overall, Pill and Stott were able to argue against the traditional stereotyping of working-class fecklessness and laissez-faire attitudes, usually contrasted with a greater commitment by middle-class people to healthy lifestyles. Rather they suggested that the poorest off in their studies were in fact being realistic in their attribution of illness to living conditions and the struggle for family survival in an urban environment. Just to give one example, in answer to a question about the main reasons for falling ill, one woman replied:

> Overwork, pace of living – people just not getting the proteins they need and there is just not the money about to give your children what they need . . . I think it boils down to money every time as far as I'm concerned because people like, you know, my husband has to work so many hours to make it worthwhile for your family and your everyday life to go all right – if you know what I mean – as far as food and that goes. There's a lot of worry attached to it – I think it is this that makes

people ill, mainly nerves and, you know, the rush! My husband has to get up at 4.00 a.m. in the morning for the morning shift. I don't think it's right for any man to work like that – if you work the normal hours you haven't got enough. (Pill and Stott, 1985a, p. 989)

Like the women in Blaxter's sample, many of Pill and Stott's respondents had no doubt there *is* a link between behaviour and lifestyle, and health and illness. But the issue of health was not seen as a matter of personal responsibility. If you live in conditions which give you few choices about your actions, they argued, how can (or should) you accept blame? Pill and Stott suggested that: 'What, from one point of view, may be seen as "fatalism" may from another perspective, be interpreted as a realistic appraisal of the complex variables involved in the aetiology of illness' (ibid.). In their more recent paper, Pill and Stott (1987) gave an intricate 'cascade' model which links together socio-demographic factors, understandings and various barriers to action which they see as interweaving in a complex manner to influence lifestyle and behaviour.

Comparing 'middle-class' and 'working-class' accounts

Unlike the previous two research programmes, which focused entirely on the views and understandings of working-class women, Calnan and Johnson (1985, see also Calnan, 1987) specifically attempted to compare the accounts of working-class and middle-class women. Their sample consisted of thirty women from each group who lived in London, all interviewed by a single interviewer. They did find some differences, particularly in the way in which the two groups defined health. The middle-class women offered many more definitions, and there was a tendency to give proportionally more positive descriptions than did the working-class women. This showed up most clearly in the middle-class women's emphasis on health as a feeling of fitness and strength, being active and energetic, compared with a greater emphasis among working-class women on 'getting through the day' and 'never being ill'. There was far less difference in reported feelings of vulnerability, although Calnan and Johnson did observe, as had Blaxter, a tendency for working-class women to see worrying about illness as unhealthy in its own right, as a sign of weakness or hypochondria. For both groups, but particularly for the middle-class women, perceived vulnerability to illness tended to arise out of experience of symptoms (e.g. suspecting a breast lump) rather than a person's own actions (e.g. smoking). Calnan and Johnson suggested that health beliefs of the 'abstract' kind which they examined may be more a matter of rationalizing health decisions than functioning as precursors to action. However, this study is difficult to interpret, Calnan and Johnson themselves noting sampling problems and the fact that some of the effects may have been due to differential responding to the middle-class interviewer. It is also hard to tell to what extent, say, the greater stress laid by working-class women upon not worrying about illness reflected structural differences (e.g. in the resources to allow for 'being ill', or to seek medical advice and treatment) rather than differences in the explanatory system used.

Overall themes in studies of social determination of beliefs and understandings

Within what was defined as 'working-class culture' in these studies, beliefs consistently recur in all three which deny individual responsibility and culpability and demonstrate low expectations and robust stoicism in the face of adversity. At the same time, all the authors say that it is wrong to regard working-class people as *causing* their poor health through their own feckless behaviour. None of the studies really gets to grips with the question of whether working-class values and discourses per se play a role in promoting inequality, although Blaxter's (1990) fine-grained work gets closest to an answer. All authors noted that the structural disadvantages experienced by the worst off are so pervasive and so influential within their daily lives that it was impossible to discern whether their beliefs (e.g. denial of blame) were simply the products of disadvantage, or contributed to it.

Part of the problem arises from the way in which ethnographic method irons out variability in accounting *within* particular groups. Reading these studies, very little impression is given of the diversity of accounts *within* working-class culture – how people who share similar levels of structural disadvantage might have adopted different strategies to cope with it. Even with Pill and Stott's programme of research, where attempts were specifically made to tease out alternative perceptions, the high/medium/low SLI index confounded accounting and socio-economic status. Their data indicated more about the process of upward social mobility than they did about the cycle of deprivation. The more upward social mobility a working-class person achieves, the more they are likely both to have acquired the resources to adopt the behavioural and practical trappings of a good 'lifestylist' and the more likely they are to have internalized middle-class individualistic values.

Thus Pill and Stott's work, as much as the other two studies, leaves us hanging. Do 'lifestylists' acquire their more positive self-perceptions and expectations as a consequence of overcoming or avoiding adversity – or do they overcome or avoid adversity because of the attitudes to life they adopt? Are 'fatalists' fatalistic because life had given them a raw deal, or do they get a raw deal because their fatalism leads them to make no effort to help themselves? These two alternatives are themselves 'explanations of health and illness', as the studies described later in this book will show.

Blaxter's more recent (1990) survey work was able to tease out structural elements in a much more sophisticated manner, but (as she freely admits) large-scale work with fixed interview schedules, in settings likely to engender responses mediated by assumed desirability, is not an ideally suited approach to the fine-grained analysis of the influence of beliefs upon action. Consequently she is able only to reach a tentative conclusion: 'behavioural habits are certainly relevant to health, but perhaps less so than the social environment in which they are imbedded' (p. 202). Her data are none the less intriguing, both those which seem commonsensical (e.g. the gender differences in defining health) and those which are more perplexing (e.g. the way in which smokers are more likely to be aware of its harmfulness than non-smokers). They imply that health and illness are rationalized within the context of broader cultural discourses, themes and messages, which transcend structural classifications. It is to research which explores this avenue that we will now turn.

STUDIES OF EXPLANATORY SYMPATRICITY

The studies which I will describe in this section are ones which have specifically set out to explore *alternative* explanations of health and illness which co-exist and compete within culture. That is, they all assume as a starting point that individuals have access to more than one kind of explanation, varying either in their content, or form, or both. Within anthropological theorization this sympatricity (see Chapter 1 for a definition) is usually referred to as 'medical pluralism' (for instance Kleinman's (1978) division into 'folk', 'popular' and 'professional' systems as described in Chapter 2). Within sociology sympatricity is generally couched within a framework of competing belief systems arising out of sociological divisions (for instance, Friedson's 1970 analysis of the divisions between 'medical' and 'lay' accounting as

93

described in Chapter 2). Within psychology, explanatory sympatricity has been treated theoretically by way of such constructs as 'social representation', 'constructive alternativism' and 'complementarity' (as described in Chapter 3). Thus although their terminology and approaches vary, they all share a common taxonomic thrust, in that they set out to identify and describe alternatives – accounts, images, explanatory-systems or whatever. Similarly they share a perception in which understanding is viewed more as a collective *resource* (upon which individuals can draw) than the property of individuals.

Social representations of health and illness

Claudine Herzlich has, over the last twenty or so years, carried out a large number of interviews in order to explore the alternative ways in which French people make sense of ideas like 'health', 'illness', 'dying' and so on. We will look here first at her early classic work with predominantly middle class Parisians (and a few country dwellers) which focused on health and illness (Herzlich, 1973), and then we will move on to examine the later work which she reported with Janine Pierret (Herzlich and Pierret, 1987).

In her first book, from the lengthy conversations she held with the participants in her studies Herzlich derived sophisticated descriptions of the social representations for health and illness that she saw as being used in the 1960s in French society. Influenced by the work of Foucault (1961) as well as by the work on social representations being undertaken at that time by Serge Moscovici (1961) she regarded these social representations as operating both subjectively and intersubjectively – as explanations that individuals use within their thinking; *and* as discourses operating within the public domain.

Herzlich concluded that different understandings and explanations for health/illness are not polar opposites to each other, but quite discrete conceptions. She demonstrated (in work which pre-dated and undoubtedly influenced that of Blaxter) that individuals have access to multiple conceptions of 'healths', co-existing formulations of different aspects; health-in-a-vacuum; reserve of health; and equilibrium. *Health-in-a-vacuum* was the term which Herzlich used for the notion of health as the absence of illness, of a lack of awareness of the body and/or simply not being bothered by it, essentially a state of 'bodily silence'. *Reserve of Health* she suggested represents health as an asset or investment rather than a state. It has two main aspects: physical robustness or strength; and resistance to attacks, fatigue and illness.

94

Health is something you 'have' that enables you to perform your job, etc., defend yourself against disease, recover from illness. *Equilibrium* was described by Herzlich's respondents as 'real health' or health in its highest sense; it carried the notion of positive wellbeing or 'high level wellness' (cf. Ardell, 1977) in addition to some of the sense of balance and harmony and even some of the attributes that psychologists such as Maslow (1968) have proposed for optimal human functioning, such as 'self-actualization'. Herzlich commented that although her respondents used the term 'equilibrium' with frequency, they found it hard to pin down, and overall it seemed to carry a two-level meaning: a substratum of essential harmony and balance in bodily, psychological and spiritual life – from which a functional sense of self-confidence, alertness, freedom, energy and indefatigableness stem. Thus it had both a psychological reality concerned with self-perception, and a somatic reality connected with physical capability and resilience.

Herzlich's respondents distinguished between four different classes of illness: serious illnesses which may be fatal; chronic conditions; everyday, trivial illnesses like colds and 'flu; and childhood ailments. They also referred frequently to intermediary states between 'real' illness and 'real' health: 'There are the little troubles, the little situations of discomfort which you have more or less all the year round, headaches, the after-effects of alcohol, digestive difficulties, fatigue' (p. 54).

These intermediate states were typified by links to mood (particularly depression and inertia); to their undesirable impact on relationships with others; and their tendency to be long-lasting. However, beyond this, in contrast to the well articulated classification of aspects of health, understandings of illness were more vague, unsystematic and varied. There were attempts to distinguish illness from other states (e.g. accidents and physical disability) and a variety of dimensions were introduced (e.g. severity, painfulness, curability). Despite this lack of clarity, however, Herzlich did identify three 'metaphors' for illness which distinguished between different social representations: illness as 'destroyer'; illness as 'liberator'; and illness as 'occupation'.

Illness as 'destroyer' was an image which tended to be held by people who were or had been particularly active or engaged in society, and for whom any interference with their professional or family role presented a serious problem. Their focus was upon the way in which illness could limit their ability to carry out their responsibilities, and the concomitant loss of social position and subsequent social isolation which they would therefore suffer whenever they were ill. Bound together in this social representation were fundamental assumptions about having responsibilities towards others, and the ability for dependency to make the individual feel 'less of a person'. People who saw illness as 'destroyer' stressed the positive aspects of health. They responded to illness, paradoxically, both by trying to assume control (by denying it, or keeping going as if they were not ill) and by feeling impotent (by 'giving up' when struck). These were the people who avoided doctors at all costs, and would do almost anything rather than accept the label 'ill'.

Illness as 'liberator', in contrast, was a metaphor which stressed the capacity of illness to free the individual from their responsibilities, or the pressures that life places upon them:

> When I'm very tired, I often wish I were ill . . . illness is a kind of rest, when you can be free from your everyday burdens. . . . For me, illness is breaking off from social life, from life outside and social obligations, it's being set free. (p. 114)

The benefits of illness were seen as making possible the kind of intellectual activity that is usually prevented by the pressures of everyday life. The solitude of illness was seen in this context to be enjoyable. And there were privileges to be gained, including the sympathy and care of others. Herzlich argued that within this perception are provided the seeds of the 'invalid' personality, bound up in ideas of the capacity of invalidity to promote self-examination, that experiencing illness can enrich understanding and force upon the sufferer a better and more valid set of values; a belief that experiencing illness is a route through which an individual can attain greater self-knowledge.

Illness as 'occupation' was the notion that when you are ill, you should see illness as a challenge – as something that you must fight with all the powers you have. It stressed that an enormous amount of energy is needed to focus all your strength on getting better. You must not worry about your other responsibilities but concentrate on your recovery. There was also a strong sense of 'mind over matter'.

Although these three descriptions tend to read as though people could be classified according to holding one or other perception, Herzlich was at pains to point out that only some individuals tended to utilize a single representation consistently. Most people drew upon two or all three at different times in their interviews, offering complex understandings and explanations woven out of them all. Herzlich argued that these social representations, singly or in concert, acted as strong determinants, not just of the way in which illness was perceived and responded to, but also of the way in which people saw themselves and made sense of their own identity – not just when they were ill but also when they were well, and particularly when they were in intermediate states between the two.

The disjunction between the different kinds of representations of health and of illness meant that understandings of what makes a person healthy were different from explanations about why people become ill. Predominantly being and becoming healthy was seen as a matter of individual strength and resistance, of a capacity to adjust and find harmony between the self and the environment, in part a kind of 'natural heritage' of bodily strength, in part a product of self-fulfilment. Health was represented as something *inside* the individual. Illness, conversely, was construed as the result of assaults upon health from the *outside*, such as pollution, the wear and tear of modern life, the pressures of confinement. It also included the effects of behaviour (e.g. staying up late, not eating sensibly), but these were usually seen as themselves a product of 'way of life' – dysfunctional responses to the root cause of ill health, the stress, fatigue and pressure of urban living (and less frequently, of country living):

> You could say that now, with the life we lead, certain diseases are increasing because our body no longer reacts because it no longer has enough resistance. . . . Modern life induces a kind of fatigue which makes us ill . . . everything to do with modern work and its conditions makes us more vulnerable to most diseases. (p. 21)

Resistance – the ability to fight off illness – was attributable within this analysis to three main factors:

1. *Inherited bodily predisposition* – people are born physically strong or weak, with high or low or intermediate reserves to fight off onslaughts from way of life.
2. *Temperament* – the ability to fight is in part a product of the kind of person you are.
3. *Specific weaknesses and vulnerabilities* – individuals are seen to vary in the kinds of assault (specific germs) to which they are vulnerable and/or particular parts of the body that are prey to attack, for example 'a weak liver'.

Illness was thus represented as a product of interaction between a person's individual characteristics and their 'way of life'. But it is noticeable that 'way of life' (as described by these middle-class Parisians) was not equivalent to 'lifestyle' (as Pill and Stott would define it) but rather an interpretation in which people are construed as passive objects upon which a particular 'way of life' was imposed. While its illness-invoking qualities were seen as products of the modern 'rat race', the tendency to blame agents in the outside world for illness (directly and vicariously) was very similar indeed to the refutation of personal culpability as seen to be adopted by working-class people in the previous studies.

Later work carried out with Janine Pierret (Herzlich and Pierret, 1987) adopted an historical approach which reviewed writings about health and illness, particularly about major 'scourges', plagues and other epidemics, from ancient times to the present, including diaries and letters as well as books and pamphlets. Their data showed that, irrespective of the time at which people were writing, they always made sense of bodily states of health and illness within much broader explanatory systems. Certainly these incorporated ideas about causation (including causes as diverse as climatic conditions and calamities like earthquakes), but they also addressed beliefs about relations within society to God, to moral codes and, from the time of the Industrial Revolution, to working conditions and the living conditions of the poor.

This later book provides a wealth of historical analysis, exploring changes over time in the way in which illness became individualized and medicalized. For example, while concepts of plague tended to treat this as a *collective* scourge, understandable largely in moral terms, or as the consequence of climatic variation or cosmic events (such as the appearance of comets), diseases such as consumption (tuberculosis) came to be regarded as experienced by and arising from within the individual, with the emergence of the notion of the 'sick person'. For example, despite being more widespread among the poor, it gained romantic connotations as an infliction which beset those of a passionate or artistic temperament.

Further on historically, Herzlich and Pierret traced the unfolding of a 'triumphant discourse' of the 'victories of medicine' (p. 46), due particularly to the introduction of vaccines and antibiotics. This image of an all-conquering medicine, able to cure all ills, was, they noted, still evident in the early stages of their research in the 1960s. But by the 1980s people had become more critical, concerned about illnesses like cancer, which modern medicine seemed much less able to tackle, and, for some people at least, there was a growing feeling that health improvements related less to medical intervention than to improvements in living standards and natural changes in the disease organism (this argument is very clearly described by Thomas McKeown, 1976). Coupled with this view have been growing expectations about the 'right to be sick and receive adequate treatment' (Renaud, 1981) and a growing conviction that 'modern life' is itself a major cause of sickness, both in terms of the pressures it imposes, and environmental factors such as pollution.

'From causes to meaning', Chapter 6 of Herzlich and Pierret's work, offers both an erudite and clearly written review of the aetiology and diversity of explanations for illness, uncovered both by their research and historical analyses. It deals with concepts of biological disorder, upheavals in nature, and of divine punishment; with ideas about contagion; with those relating to way of life, or to the impact of work; and with relationships between the lay representations of ordinary people and those of orthodox medicine. It also explores the ways in which people seek to discover the 'hidden meanings' of their illness, particularly those concerned with the workings of their own minds, and including the notion that people can make themselves ill, or vulnerable; that illness may be seen as a 'price to pay' or a 'ransom' for genius, or for being exceptional.

What Claudine Herzlich and her colleagues have done, therefore, has been to combine two quite different approaches to research within a 'grounded theory' paradigm. They have taken the data obtained in interviews and interpreted them via a cultural analysis heavily informed by their readings of historical texts. They looked both for continuity and for change; at both the historical roots of contemporary images and ideas, and at the way in which events have moulded and reformed them. This approach is generally termed *diachronic*, and is of growing importance among those who regard human thought and conduct as understandable only within the context of their *person*-made properties. Herzlich and Pierret put it this way:

> Everywhere and in all periods, it is the individual who is sick, but he [sic] is sick in the eyes of his society, in relation to it, and in keeping with the modalities fixed by it. The language of the sick thus takes shape within the language expressing the relations between the individual and society. [Personal experiences of sickness are thus] . . . woven into the collective patterns of thought that form the social reality of illness and the sick. (Herzlich and Pierret, 1987, p. xi)

The understandings of older people

Rory Williams has carried out a programme of research to explore and culturally locate the beliefs of older people about health, illness and in particular about ageing and dying, summarized in his recent book (Williams, 1990). He adopted similar methods to Herzlich, focusing his interviews on the people of Aberdeen, Scotland. But his work differed in his use of a system of formal logic to analyse his data to elucidate the 'lay logic' and 'structure of ideologies' that underlie such concepts, particularly in his early studies (1981a and b). And whereas Herzlich had taken specific ideas (such as 'contagion') and traced them over a fairly lengthy historical timescale, Williams adopted a more ecological form of cultural analysis, seeking to contextualize Aberdonian concepts of health and illness, ageing and dying, within their ideas about work, wealth, religion, and what he termed more broadly their 'protestant legacy' of Calvinistic stoicism and fortitude. While this kind of approach retains an element of diachronic analysis (linking back into the past) it also contains elements of a *synchronic* analysis, considering the 'here and now' in terms of the range of contemporary influences upon thought in a particular domain. Williams was particularly interested in the interplay between the influences of material conditions (e.g. those of capitalism, of the introduction of state pension and socialized medical care) on thinking, and the way in which 'ideas themselves generate challenges and counter-challenges, which alter the ensuing pattern of thought' (Williams, 1990, p. 323). An ecological approach was therefore necessary to bring all the required elements into the research frame.

The data which he obtained led Williams to argue that 'old people' cannot be regarded as a single group who see the world in similar fashion. They interpreted the physical manifestations of growing old in a number of distinctly different ways. People who utilized Herzlich's illness as 'destroyer' metaphor tended to see themselves as being 'finished' or 'fading away' as they experienced physical decline in older age. In contrast, people who adopted an illness as 'occupation' metaphor were much more likely to continue to see themselves as basically healthy as they got older, albeit maybe finding themselves slowing down and becoming less active. They saw themselves as 'keeping going' and 'fighting on' despite the inevitable degeneration that old age brought. This helped to explain the apparent paradox which emerged from his interviews (as it had in Blaxter's and Herzlich's), that older people, in particular, often considered themselves 'healthy' even

100

though they reported symptoms of illness. Among Williams' later (1983) sample of older people, over 50 per cent of those experiencing chronic conditions (e.g. arthritis) rated their health as good or excellent.

However, Williams argued that all of his respondents shared a common account of health as strength (a corollary of Herzlich's reserve of health). Within this account, health was seen as something which a person can 'take care of', build up or maintain; or, alternatively, it can be spent or squandered. Williams' respondents talked about how this strength could be compromised in one of at least four ways: (a) by being temporarily depleted, but with full or partial recovery expected; (b) by the effects of localized chronic disease, suggesting a particular weakness of some part; (c) by the development of general weakness which has the effect of overall attenuation; and (d) by the exhaustion of the power of recovery.

Jocelyn Cornwell (1986) has argued that the philosophy which a person adopts in later life is largely a reflection of their life-history and the self-concepts and coping strategies which they have developed along the way. Some of these aspects of biography are common to all members of the same age cohort (e.g. World War II, the introduction of the National Health Service), some are shared by particular groups or collectives (e.g. the poverty and mass unemployment of the Depression in the 1930s that affected working-class people differently from middle-class people), and some are more specific to the individual (e.g. a good or bad marriage).

While Cornwell's work emphasized individual biography as the framework upon which understandings are built in the 'now', Williams' analysis has stressed the role of collective discourse as a basis within which a number of logical premises can be 'made sense of'. For example, he found a common storyline among recently retired Aberdonians that enabled them to reconcile the commonly held view that old age is a set-back by seeing it as a period for repairing defences, arriving at the conclusion that ageing is a resistable process. In their interviews, while putting forward this argument, they constantly referred not just to their own ideas, but to what they thought 'other people would think' and to moral and ethical standards set both by individuals for themselves and by the community at large. Williams described three main 'schemes of ageing': as a resurgence; as a siege and as a delayed capitulation: 'each internally coherent, which at once supply and limit the stock of ideas on which Aberdonians draw. It is between these possibilities that those who search for coherence have to choose' (Williams, 1986b, pp. 15–16).

Thus while Cornwell's analysis of the explanations which people gave about their state of health in old age was predominantly one of making sense of *individual* biographies, Williams was much more concerned with the *collectively* held and used discourses that are available to the individual. For Williams it is this stock of knowledge that people draw upon in their attempts to make sense of their own feelings and ideas, which they frequently recognized as being paradoxical and conflicting. He regarded these discourses as reference resources which an individual can use to impose structure upon their personal understanding. They are not just specific to the topic in question, but encompass more commonly shared values: 'this generation had the basis for a unified consciousness of certain distinctive values – respect for neighbourliness, for authority, for perseverance and thrift' (Williams, 1986b, p. 19).

Thus Williams saw the process as a product of a personal dialectic, with the individual explanation arising both by way of reality-constructs-person and person-constructs-reality processes. Overall, however, he concluded that it was the consensual, unitary cultural pattern of ideas which held most sway, with disagreements tending, in their expression, none the less to reaffirm central themes. People tend to argue much more about their interpretation than outrightly to deny their validity or salience. Alternative systems of beliefs were not self-contained or isolated from one another, but dialectical variations on the same themes in dynamic interplay with each other:

> In all these different aspects of Aberdonian culture, therefore, there is historical debate and competition between patterns of thought which are both related and opposed, and which stem from religious and economic divisions which have been evolving for a long time. (Williams, 1990, pp. 321–2)

Studies of 'control' and 'release'

This concept of competition between conflicting ideas has been studied specifically by the sociologist Robert Crawford, working among the wealthier members of 'middle America'. Crawford (1980) pointed out that for this group 'healthism' has become a dominant cultural image:

> A new popular health consciousness pervades our culture. The concern with personal health has become a national preoccupation. Ever increasing personal effort, political attention, and consumer dollars are being expended in the name of health. The past few years have

witnessed an exercise and running explosion, the emergence of a vocal and often aggressive anti-smoking ethic, the proliferation of popular health magazines, and the appearance with amazing frequency of health themes in newspapers, magazines and advertisements for even the most remotely related products. . . . On numerous social occasions, and in spite of much professed rejection of concern or derisive amusement, personal health has become a favourite topic of conversation. (p. 365)

People in the affluent West, he said, have become increasingly health conscious. They are continually bombarded with advice about diet, about exercise, about their sex lives and their leisure pursuits, not only by their doctors and by health educators, but by the magazines and newspapers they read and the television shows and advertisements which they watch. Crawford documents the emergence of a new healthist industry, which markets designer jogging suits, nautilus machines, 'healthy' food and exercise tapes. The hash-brownies of the 'laid back' 1970s have been replaced by the wholemeal-added-fibre-low-saturated-fat brownies of the 1990s. Today, in the West, he argued, health has not just been individualized (i.e. promoted as a private possession, to be invested in and protected) but commodified. A concern for health is no longer the prerogative of cranks – today it is an essential part of being a successful and desirable person.

Crawford backed up his arguments by research (1984), again using extended open-ended interviewing techniques coupled with cultural analysis. As well as evidence for the 'healthist' image, his data also identified a second, contrasting one, in which health is perceived in terms of a 'release' from pressure. This image of health is about giving in to temptation and luxuriating in the sensual pleasures of eating, drinking, recreational drugs, sex, etc. Crawford argued that this 'release' motif is more than just a way of denying the dominant cultural theme of 'responsibility' and the protestant work ethic, and more than individualistic hedonism or antagonism to authority – 'health-as-release' is a competing cultural theme in itself. It is moulded by the social pressures of consumer society to see oneself as entitled to life's pleasures – the 'good life' that is marketed by the food, tobacco, confectionery and alcohol producers, among others:

Consumption itself must be understood as a moral demand system, with its own controls, internalizations, and modal personalities. Our notions of self, fulfilment, and even health are substantised through the 'gorgeous variety of satisfactions' that the new system both offers and demands. (Crawford 1984, p. 91)

Crawford therefore portrayed contemporary 'middle Americans' as the objects and subjects of two opposing mandates: one to adopt self-discipline (both in the search for health itself, and as the diligent and reliable workers which a consumer society needs to produce its goods); and the other to indulge in gratification (as the consumers essential to the sale of those goods). This tension is epitomized in paradoxical messages to diet *and* to eat delicious food. Such 'double bind' messages create their own forms of illness, such as bulimia and other eating disorders. They reach their extreme within the elixir of pleasure and pain offered by health clubs: 'We'll work you out and then pamper you' as advertised by a Chicago health studio.

Support for the universality of Crawford's findings in Europe as well as the USA has been provided by work by Alphonse d'Houtaud (e.g. d'Houtaud, 1976 and 1981; d'Houtaud and Field, 1986), which identified four main concepts of health: health as a hedonistic way of life (showing parallels with Crawford's 'release' image); health as equilibrium, as an absence of dis-ease, and as vitality. By further analysis he reduced these to two main categories (in some ways similar to Crawford's), which, however, d'Houtaud attributed differently to people from different social classes. Manual workers — the 'working class' — he said, tend to adopt images of health connected with its functional attributes to enable them to work, to fulfil their duties in both personal and collective terms. Those from managerial and professional classes tend more to stress enjoyment, self-fulfilment and personal satisfaction. There are obvious parallels here with the work of Blaxter and Calnan and Johnson already described.

Crawford, like Herzlich and Williams, noted that although some people tended to focus on one or other of the cultural mandates he identified, most people he interviewed drew upon both. Within 'middle America's' market dominated economy, he suggested, health has become incorporated into a variety of culturally sedimented representations. These are further constructed and at the same time purveyed by the mass media, to serve commercial ends. Both of the themes he identified stressed self-esteem and fulfilment, but offer contrasting routes by which they are to be gained. People, then, do not rely on a single understanding; rather they draw upon several, their understanding continually shifting between contradictory alternatives.

Alternative images of health care

In the 1960s Will Stephenson, the originator of Q methodology, carried out a series of studies to investigate alternative 'images' of health care that were current in the culture of the North American Midwest at the time (1962, 1963); these studies were concerned with the organization and funding of the medical systems and what people could expect from them. Using a combination of intensive open-ended interviews and Q methodology (which will be described in more detail in the next chapter) he identified three alternative accounts.

The first was an account which was predominantly expressed by poorer people. It construed existing medical care and treatment at the time as effective and benign, but the practice of medicine as based too much upon profit, as too specialized and as over-professionalized. It favoured a shift to an insurance based system for paying for medical treatment, which was seen as able to maintain people's independence, choice and self-sufficiency while avoiding the crippling costs of the existing fee-for-service system. The second account, expressed more by the wealthy (including many people who were themselves medical professionals) was satisfied both with the current practice of medicine and with its ability to cure illness and maintain health. This account endorsed the prevailing fee-for-service means of payment, wary of any move to an insurance based scheme, which was seen as a threat to the independence of medical practitioners. The third account, expressed by a single individual, a person who was a liberal and a Democrat, focused on wellbeing rather than mere health. While broadly favourable towards current medical care, it saw health as just one among many important human values. This account favoured a socialized system of funding that would determine provision of health care in response to need (e.g. in old age) rather than ability to pay.

These accounts were identified by factor analysis of a Q-sort (based upon the writings of a contemporary opinion leader) and elaborated by data from detailed interviews. For the second study (Stephenson, 1963) a new Q sample of 56 statements was constructed containing a few of the items from the previous sample, but mostly new ones derived from statements people had made in the interviews. For example:

- Welfare takes away individual responsibility – you have somebody else to look after you.
- I think everybody should have medical care who really needs it, and should pay for it in proportion to his [sic] income.
- The statement of a goal in life is paramount for people looking for direction for themselves – we all need a sense of 'living'.

- The unknown should be left alone; much of what the scientists are discovering can only lead to harm.

This study is of particular interest because the accounts were gained from people who were disabled or chronically ill, and their carers. The disabled/ill people ranged from a 94-year-old widow who, Stephenson described, was 'suffering from nothing more than hurt pride and old age' (p. 58) to a 23-year-old college sophomore, paralysed from polio in both arms and legs, who manipulated pages of books (and, when he came to do it, the Q-sort cards) with a stick held in his mouth. The group included six people with polio, two people confined to wheelchairs following accidents, three people suffering from coronary disease, a quadruple paraplegic, somebody with congenital syphilis, several with cancer and seven older people (aged between seventy and ninety-four) who were experiencing multiple physical symptoms of chronic illness. All participants in the study were intensively interviewed first, using pictures to get conversation going, then this was followed by more specific questioning about health and finally a focus on chronic illness. After the interview the respondents carried out a Q-sort using the new sample of statements that had been derived from the interview protocols of the respondents in the previous study.

Three factors were identified. The first (Factor I) Stephenson labelled the independent viewpoint; the second (Factor II) the interdependent; and the third (Factor III) the dependent. These can be briefly summarized as follows:

Factor I: Independent

The main theme of this account was very strong approval of medical professionals, seeing doctors and nurses as well qualified and competent professionals who know their job, valuing personal qualities as well as technical skill, and seeing existing medical treatment as highly effective against both physical and mental illness and in preventing illness and promoting healthy old age. The account was highly antagonistic to any form of socialized medicine, denying any need to offer free services to those who could not afford them or to put more public money into medical aid. The interviews with the people whose Q-sorts loaded strongly onto this factor all emphasized a powerful commitment to independence. This focused on the need to struggle to achieve, to manage on one's own and pay one's own way. This was expressed with a certain harshness and an emphatic moral

106

undertone that it is wrong to be dependent, and sinful to be weak – and also morally wrong to disrespect rightful authorities such as doctors, or find any fault with so dedicated and selfless a profession as medicine. Most of the people who expressed this account, despite their disabilities, were managing to hold down jobs or lived in families sufficiently well off to care for them without need for welfare or external support.

Factor II: Interdependent

This account saw people as having the right to medical care as a product of need, not ability to pay, and stressed the humanitarian obligation of society to help the chronically ill; also it endorsed broader social values (e.g. provision of foreign aid). The interviews of those who expressed this account clearly impressed Will Stephenson. He wrote of 'the liveliness of mind, alertness, charm and wonderful adjustment' of all the individuals whose Q-sorts identified this factor and noted that 'they accept no easy solutions, no hard-and-fast stereotypes . . . they are flexible and autonomous . . . they are realistic and essentially libertarian . . . they idealise no one, and yet can be grateful'. Some of these people commented that they had accepted financial support (e.g. from the Polio Foundation) and it had saved them from financial ruin. They saw society as needing to operate in a way in which people could retain their dignity and self-esteem, and yet be interdependent – giving and accepting help from each other.

Factor III: Dependent

The main theme running through this account was that those who are chronically sick or disabled need the support of others, and medical care should be available to all who require it, irrespective of ability to pay for it (and indeed, that this should have priority, say, over the provision of foreign aid, which would be better spent on federal medical programmes for poor Americans). Perhaps not surprisingly the people whose Q-sorts identified this factor were the poorest in the sample, usually lacking in education and most of them living in the poorest slums in the area. Their interviews described an overall picture of gross deprivation – with chronic illness and disability meaning that they could not work, with the welfare payments which they received being inadequate for well people, let alone sufficient to provide for the needs of the sick, and with their disabilities being exacerbated by the physical constraints of their poor living conditions, inadequate diets and inability to afford the medical treatment they needed – and the psychological impact of 'existing' rather than living.

Accounts may have different aetiologies

Stephenson noted that there were no obvious demographic differences between those who expressed either the accounts linked with Factor I or Factor II. Both sets of people were relatively well off and able to cope with their disabilities, but had constructed different images of themselves and of how society should operate. The people who expressed Factor I were also those for whom personal independence was as a deeply held value, whereas those who expressed Factor II placed more value on equality. The psychologist Rokeach (1968) has suggested that of all his 'terminal values', 'freedom' and 'equality' are the most distinctly political. For example, participants in and sympathizers with civil rights demonstrations are much more likely to stress 'equality' as their most important value, whereas those who are positively unsympathetic to such views are more likely to place 'freedom' as most important. The people who expressed the Factor III account were so structurally constrained by their material disadvantages, socially low status and lack of power in addition to their physical handicaps or chronic illnesses, that they seem to have had little opportunity to construe their illness in terms of alternative values. It was just another factor in their overall state of dependency and powerlessness.

This study suggests that different accounts are likely to have different aetiologies; people arrive at the explanations they use by different means. What might be important for one kind of explanation may be unimportant for another. For some people, social or structural or cultural forces may be the major determinant. But for others, different factors entirely (e.g. identification with particular social groups or ideologies) may be the key to understanding why they make sense of the world in the way they do.

'New Age' explanatory systems

Levin and Coreil (1986) also used a Q analysis to identify different accounts for health and illness, though their focus was upon what they termed 'New Age Healing' in the culture of North America. Their data were not derived via Q methodological study of people's sorting of statements to portray their opinions (the method used by Stephenson), but from Q analysis of the authors' own interpretations of variables relating to aetiology, origins of founder, orientation of teachings, source of healing, means and styles of treatment. These were based upon written descriptions of eighty-one examples of 'New Age Healing'. Five independent factors were identified, and with further interpretation of these data, they arrived at a typology of three main alternative accounts.

Health through doing

Here the major emphasis was upon ways of attaining bodily and psychological health or wellbeing, usually by new means rather than rediscovering ancient teachings. Its philosophy was secular, Western and not supernaturally orientated. Examples were Biogenics, Eidetics and a variety of ideologies upon which had been built therapeutic communities such as the 'Cornucopia Living Love Center', Kerista Village and 'Wellness Associates'. While the groups concerned varied widely in their conceptualizations of health and healing, all shared a holistic approach in which body, mind and soul being seen as equally important, and stressed the role of individual action and 'doing'.

Health through knowing

The focus here was upon esoteric teachings as the route to health, drawing upon some ancient corpus of 'truth'. The groups adopting this account professed belief in supernatural healing and sources of illness, and many defined themselves as explicit churches or religious sects, including the Theosophical Society in America, the Universal Church of Scientific Truth, and the Ojai Foundation. These groups perceived the oneness of all humans as critical, placing strong emphasis upon learning from 'teachings' and intellectual engagement as means of enlightenment, and thus health, and stressing the role of 'knowledge'.

Health through spiritual transcendance

This account was characterized by ideas (predominantly adopted from Eastern philosophy and religion) that view spiritual life as the basic means of attaining good health. Routes to health were mainly through forms of contemplation and meditation. Examples included Swami Rama's Himalayan International Institute of Yoga Science and

Philosophy, Chowado Henjo Kyo, the Inner Light Foundation and the Inter Cosmic Spiritual Association. While the other two accounts often included meditation or contemplation within their practices and treatments, within this account such practices are central, stressing the role of 'inner experiencing'.

'Alternative medicine' as a challenge to orthodoxy

These three different descriptions remind us that new ideologies (e.g. existentialist and humanistic accounts, as described in Chapter 1) and the worldviews of other cultures, particularly from the East, are having an increasing impact upon popular accounting, observable in the emerging public and 'professional' acceptability of and more frequent resource to 'alternative' medicine (see for example the work of Aakster, 1986). In Britain 'alternative medicine' has gained the added endorsement of royalty, rendering homoeopathy in particular less 'cranky' in popular discourse in Britain than in, say, North America. The 'New Age Healing' accounts also suggest that in contemporary Western culture as well as in the East religion may not only provide a background framework of values (as Williams has argued for the Calvinistic tradition in Scotland) but in some accounts be much more directly linked with explanations for health and illness (e.g. as in Christian Science and Spiritualism as well as religions such as Buddhism and Hinduism).

Overall themes in studies of cultural sympatricity

These studies portray the way in which people explain health and illness as much more complex than either the 'folk' or 'social determinants' approaches. In this view people seldom, if ever, rely on a single explanatory system, but rather draw upon many. This is true in at least three senses. First, as particularly illustrated by the work of Herzlich and Williams, people frequently give explanations for health which are quite different from the ones they adopt for illness, and indeed, often there are further sub-divisions, including alternative explanations for processes like recovery from illness and ageing, and for capacities like 'resistance'. Second, as evident from the work of Cornwell and Morgan and Spanish, the kinds of 'knowledge' from which accounts are constructed vary. In some cases it is abstract and semantic, in the form of an explanatory model; in others more personal or episodic. Finally, explanatory accounts are indeed culturally sympatric. They co-exist and compete, both as alternative 'ways of making sense of the world' available within the cultural marketplace of ideas, and within individual thinking itself, as contradictory representations; a repository of stories to be drawn upon at different times and in different circumstances.

In this chapter I have only been able to describe selectively and review some of the studies available in the contemporary literature which describes empirical studies of 'lay' accounting for health and illness in British, French and North American culture. A number of themes emerged, but two are particularly strong and consistent. The first of these is that although biomedicine is the orthodox 'professional' explanatory system in the West, 'lay' explanations are not the mere watered-down versions of biomedicine that many physicians assume (cf., for example, Stoeckle and Barsky, 1980). Whereas the scientific basis of biomedicine expressly decontextualizes its explanatory capacity with regard to causes of health and illness, 'lay' explanation for health and illness is deeply and intimately bound within a broader framework of making sense of the world in which 'folk wisdom', the ideologies and values of particular cultures and social groups, personal experiences, religion and ethics all play a part.

In ordinary everyday life people seldom 'make sense' of such questions as 'Why me?' and 'Why now?' by turning (literally or metaphorically) to the appropriate medical text. They do so within a much broader set of 'plausibility structures' (cf. Berger and Luckmann, 1966). They work out where they stand and what options they have, not within some narrow aetiological cause and effect theory, but in terms of what they see as the social, circumstantial and environmental forces acting upon them, and the way in which they see themselves. Consequently, the perceived extent of an individual's personal control over and responsibility for health and illness cannot be decided by reference to an explanatory model restricted to health and illness alone. Whenever anybody tries to make sense of these topics, they do so within a much broader and richer tapestry of ideas and perceptions of their world, and their own place 'in the order of things'.

It is this which provides the second major theme of studies of 'lay' explanation − investigations of perceived control and culpability. The explanations divided between those which asserted that health is very much a matter of individual striving and personal control (notably the 'healthist' image described by Crawford, and the 'New Age Healing' systems described by Levin and Coreil; also some of the views expressed in Herzlich's and Williams' studies) and those which denied personal responsibility, notably the views described by Blaxter and Patterson, Pill and Stott, and Cornwell. In these accounts, people did not deny that certain actions ran the risk of causing or increasing the likelihood of illness, or that certain 'ways of life' were bad for health, but to agree with such notions is *not* to imply that individuals have much control over whether they stay healthy or become ill.

These two themes provided the impetus for my own research, which I will go on to describe in Chapters 6 and 7. But before I describe my own work, it is important to consider the issues surrounding the relationship between the methods of research you use and what you discover. This I will attempt in the next chapter.

CHAPTER FIVE

In Search of Social Constructionist Research Methods

The studies described in the previous chapter used a variety of different research methods. The ones chosen partly reflected the discipline-base of the researchers who conducted them, and partly what they wanted to achieve – what questions they were seeking to answer. We can divide the methods they used into six main categories:

1. Experiments.
2. Psychometric methods.
3. Interviews.
4. Observation.
5. Cultural analysis.
6. Q methodology.

In this chapter I will briefly describe and illustrate each kind of method, and then comment upon its usefulness (or lack of it) for pursuing a social constructionist approach. Once more, I have written for a wide audience, and I assume that you will skip over whatever is familiar to you. My aim is to clarify some of the issues which arise when we seek to report and interpret data, consider how methods relate to theory, and to what extent the methods used constrain and construct the results obtained.

EXPERIMENTS

The first experiment I ever did was at the age of thirteen in a biology class. We took two geranium plants which had been kept in the dark to stop them making starch by photosynthesis and put them both under identical glass bell jars, firmly stuck to a glass plate with grease. In one jar we included an inert chemical. In the other we included a chemical that removed carbon dioxide from the air. After two days on a sunny window-sill, we took the plants out of the jars and tested their leaves for starch (the product of photosynthesis). The plant kept without carbon dioxide had made no starch, whereas the one with the carbon dioxide left in had. I remember to this day what we were told to write in our exercise books: 'since the only difference between the two plants was the presence or absence of carbon dioxide, and the plant without carbon dioxide did not produce starch whereas the one with carbon dioxide did, we may conclude that carbon dioxide is essential for photosynthesis to take place'.

A conversation ensued between my teacher and myself, in a mood of rebellion (this was, after all, the 1960s), when I argued that we had proved nothing of the kind. He asked me to explain. 'Well', I said, 'how do we know that is the *only* explanation. There could be others.' 'What others?' he asked. 'Um, for instance', I said 'we could, unbeknown to us, have been invaded by aliens from outer space, who had disguised themselves as geranium plants, and rigged experiments to fool us.' 'Aha', he said, and then introduced me to a cunning device called 'Occam's razor' – when in doubt the simplest explanation is probably the right one. But I discovered later in my scientific career that the philosopher Popper had cautioned scientists to recognize that experiments can never prove anything. All they can do is disprove. These days I am prepared to bet that carbon dioxide *is* necessary for photosynthesis. But I recognize that we can never know for certain – until the day some geranium reveals itself as a visitor from Alpha Centauri!

So even conventional experiments in the natural sciences can never provide definitive facts about cause and effect. They can offer only supporting evidence for the hypothesis under scrutiny, and this will usually be a lot less clear-cut than my sortie with the geraniums. However, once experiments are used to study human behaviour, life gets a great deal more complicated, and a great deal more equivocal. Experimental method depends upon keeping absolutely everything equal apart from the variable you want to study, which is impossible where people are concerned. And so in psychology, particularly social psychology, true experimental method has had to be watered down. Instead of looking for definitive effects observable in single cases, researchers must do their best to standardize conditions as far as possible between different experimental trials, and then look for systematic differences between them, using repeated experimental trials and/or lots of people. The basic idea is that if enough trials are run and enough people take part in the experiment, the random and inevitable variations in behaviour will be so swamped by the effect of the experimental manipulation that a significant difference can be observed and measured.

As good an example from social psychology is the study in which Jones, Davis and Gergen (1961) investigated the hypothesis about correspondent inference, i.e. that people will tend to explain the behaviour of others according to whether they construe it as appropriate or inappropriate for their role. The researchers speculated that behaviour which is role-consistent would be seen as mainly influenced by the situation, but behaviour which is role-inconsistent would be mainly attributed to the person. The experiment consisted of getting people to listen to tape recordings, which they were told were of job interviews. They were asked to say to what extent the 'interviewees' were responding to the interview situation, or were acting 'in character' with their personalities. Their hypothesis was that an interviewee who was courteous, showed interest in the company, and was keen to work for them would be regarded as acting according to the demands of the *interview situation*. One who was rude, disinterested and uncommitted to the job would be seen as a rude, distinterested and uncommitted *kind of person*.

The point about this kind of experiment is that the researchers knew that there would be a lot of variability in the experimental setting. The people who took part were bound to differ in the way in which they saw the world, so too would aspects like their mood at that time, and many other factors. Similarly, however cleverly 'set up' to vary *simply* in respect of being expected or counter-expectational job-interview behaviour, the tape recordings would be bound to differ in lots of other ways too, and so the experiment could not mimic my geranium experiment and consist of asking a single person to listen to two different tape recordings and make a judgement. The researchers had to get lots of people to listen, and use several versions of each kind of interview. They needed to include in the experiment enough people, in enough trials, that the variability caused by random factors would be low, relative to the effects of the experimental manipulation. The desired outcome would be that the level of situational attribution of role-consistent behaviour would be high and the personal attribution would be low, in contrast to high personal and low situational attribution of role-inconsistent behaviour. Thus what they were hoping for (and indeed achieved) was a difference in scores for the two conditions which was statistically significant. The term 'statistically significant' has a precise mathematical meaning in this context, to do with the probability of a result occurring by chance. In other words, the probability of such a result happening by chance, as a consequence of the background variability and not the experimental manipulation, needed to be something like odds of 20 to 1 against (this is about the lowest considered respectable – 100 to 1 is preferable).

A major problem with experiments of this kind is that in order to create conditions amenable to being sufficiently controlled to get statistically significant results, the experimental set-up has to be made very artificial. The question then arises, is it so artificial that behaviour is quite unlike that of real life? As I described in Chapter 1, the demands of experimental method were seen by interpretational social psychologists to be so distorting that they produced an image of the person as an unthinking automaton and results which were so trivial that they taught us little of interest about what is salient to *human* social behaviour.

One response was to attempt 'natural experiments' outside a laboratory. A good example is the study conducted by Wallston and Wallston (described in their 1981 review) at a health fair. They observed the number of health promotion leaflets that people took, and then asked people to complete the HLC scale. Their hypothesis was that the more 'internal' scorers would take more leaflets, on the assumption that 'internals' would be more likely than 'externals' to look for ways of promoting their own health. As will be described in Chapter 7, their results were inconclusive, although they were able to show that overall people who attended the fair had higher average 'internal' scores than people recruited at an airport. Was the lack of a positive result because the HLC scale was a poor instrument – or a 'ceiling effect' (given that people who attend a health fair are likely to be much more motivated than the norm to take action to adopt more healthy habits and lifestyles). As soon as you try to set up experiments in real life, it becomes much more difficult to control the conditions or have a high degree of confidence about interpretation.

From a social constructionist stance, however, the flaw of experimental method is more fundamental. From this perspective, the reason why researchers can gain confirmatory evidence for their hypotheses is not because they are testing universal laws of human behaviour, but because both the researcher and the subjects taking part in the experiment share common understandings about the world. For example, a Western worldview weaves a story about the way that people behave in which role-consistency across situations is seen as a normal and ordinary and expected quality. In other cultures, role-consistency is less important. All the expectational rules about being a job interviewee might be quite different.

PSYCHOMETRIC METHODS

Psychometric methods share with experimental method a commitment to the hypothetico-deductive approach. Where they differ, in the main, is that instead of manipulating variables in short-term, set-up situations, researchers explore patterns of responses to questionnaires or scales of some kind. They make hypotheses about systematic variability in scale responses according to different conditions. In social psychology typical studies like this generally concern what are assumed to be enduring traits or characteristics such as opinions, attitudes or beliefs, and how these may relate to behaviour or prior experience. A good example is Wallston and Wallston's (1978) investigations using the Health Locus of Control construct. Rotter's (1966) original Locus of Control hypothesis was that, due to social learning (as described in Chapter 3), people differ systematically, according to whether they construe themselves as in control of what happens to them (internal control) or see control over events as located in chance, luck and fate (external control). Wallston and Wallston applied a similar hypothesis to people's understandings of health and illness. They designed a questionnaire containing a series of statements, to which people were asked to respond by stating agreement or disagreement. The kinds of statements they used were:

- If I get ill, it is my own behaviour which determines how soon I get well again.
- Luck plays a big part in determining how soon I will recover from illness.

A new scale has to be tested on a sample of people who accurately reflect the characteristics of the population as a whole. Features like sex, age and social class are taken into account. The scale is tested for 'reliability' (that consistent results are obtained whenever it is used) and 'construct validity' (that it is about what the researcher says it is about). Correlations between items are examined to test for 'consistency' (that the scale 'hangs together' as an entity) or more sophisticated factor analytic tests are carried out to discern whether the scale is tapping a more complex mix of constructs. Wallston and Wallston refined their original scale, for example, to include a third dimension untapped by the first, an attribution of control to 'powerful others' (how and why they did this is described in more detail in Chapter 7). They included extra items, and at the same time made responses more fine-tuned by asking for agreement/disagreement along a seven point scale (this is usually termed a Likert format). They re-named their scale the Multidimensional Health Locus of Control (MHLC) Scale. The kinds of items they added were:

- Following doctor's orders to the letter is the best way for me to stay healthy.
- The type of care I receive from other people is what is responsible for how well I recover from an illness.

Scales of this kind can be used in one of two ways, either as a measure of the *dependent* or of the *independent* variable in a study. The independent variable is whatever the researcher sets up as a 'cause' of the effect she or he is intending to produce. In my school experiment, the independent variable was the presence or absence of carbon dioxide. It was this which was expected to *produce* the different result in the two plants. The dependent variable is whatever the researcher expects to be the 'effect' of manipulating the independent variable. With my geraniums, the dependent variable was the presence or absence of starch. This result depended upon whether I allowed carbon dioxide to remain, or I removed it from the bell jar. The same principle applies in the social psychology experiment described above. The independent variable was in the in-role or out-role interview behaviours on the tape recordings. The dependent variable was the attribution of its origins to the situation or to the person.

An example of the MHLC Scale used as an independent variable is a study by Olbrisch (1975) in which she hypothesized that among people who are treated for gonorrhoea, those who had more 'internal' attributions would be more likely to plan to take preventive measures to stop them catching it again. Those with 'external' attributions, viewing illness as a matter of bad luck, would be less likely to have such preventive plans. As you will discover when you read Chapter 7, this study, as with many like it, failed to confirm its hypothesis. No significant differences were found between those who had high 'internal' and those with high 'external' scores on the MHLC Scale.

In terms of using the scale as a measure of the dependent variable, Tolor's (1978) study is a good example. The hypothesis here was that people who had suffered more illnesses in childhood would be significantly more likely to adopt an 'external' MHLC attribution in adulthood, compared with people who had fewer childhood illnesses. Tolor confirmed this hypothesis for women, but not for men. The scores of women who had experienced many childhood illnesses were higher than those who had experienced few, by an amount that had only about a 1 in 20 likelihood of being due to chance.

Social constructionists see a number of problems with psychometric methodology, some of which were raised in Chapter 1. Firstly, by pre-determining the categories available for response, the approach imposes researchers' view of 'how the world works' and hence studies can never do more than confirm or not confirm their pre-conceptions. Harré (1979) expressed this point cogently:

> The use of questionnaires with limited range questions . . . which effectively preclude elaborations and reinterpretations . . . means that the concepts deployed . . . are predetermined. The effect of this is to produce not a representation of the social world being studied, but the representation of the shadow cast upon the social world by the prior conceptual apparatus deployed by the person who constructed the questionnaire. (p. 115)

Applied to the Wallston and Wallston study and their MHLC Scale, for example, the criticism is that the scale not only imposes a particular attributional framework of external/internal/powerful others, it also imposes a pre-defined meaning upon each one. 'Powerful Others', for instance, is taken to mean the benign influence of medical professionals and caring relatives. There simply is no opportunity for, say, a Marxist to attribute ill health to capitalism, inequality and oppression. The scale suppresses this viewpoint entirely.

This leads to a second criticism, which is of the assumption that the researcher can 'operationally define' what statements *actually* mean. Such definitions, Brown (1980) argued not only 'replac[e] the subject's meaning with the investigator's' but treat their own understandings as barometers for the understandings of others. Where there is disagreement, this is because others are deluding themselves, seeing the world awry, or whatever. 'Everybody is out of step but me!'

A third objection is that psychometric method constrains variability.

As Potter and Wetherell (1987) argue, 'the possibility of a respondent giving *contrasting* views on a topic is . . . precluded; ambivalence, the expression of flexible opinions tailored to context and inconsistent responses are ruled out by the response format' (p. 40, emphasis in the original). The MHLC Scale assumes that people's attributions are constant for all situations and cannot, for example, accommodate the view that falling ill is mostly a matter of bad luck, but getting better is mostly about proper treatment and looking after yourself. Such 'inconsistent' responses (however plausible and commonsense) simply cannot be dealt with by the scale. Furthermore, no psychometric scale allows people to respond 'well it depends' or 'I'm in two minds – I both agree *and* disagree'.

These restrictions do not stop the people who take part in studies from trying to express themselves outside of the strait-jacket imposed upon them. People frequently do contradict themselves in scale responses (see, for example, Turner and Krauss, 1978). Quite subtle changes in wording often lead to large differences in response (Marsh, 1982), suggesting that respondents often see things in the scale which were not envisaged by its originator. None the less, response variability is generally treated as something that needs to be ironed out of the study by using more people, more trials or more careful instructions; or as an indicator that the scale is faulty. It is seldom regarded as an expression of true inconsistency, itself worthy of study. Brown (1980) writes of the 'behavioural alchemy' by which social scientists transform the things people say and do into something quite different.

Finally, probably the most destructive criticism of all is that psychometric scales are incapable of measuring anything 'real' at all. At the very best, they can show where there is consistency between one 'story of reality' and another, but nothing more. This last point has been well articulated by Brown (1980):

> the correlation and factor analysis of scale responses leads not to a taxonomy of behaviour, as is commonly thought, but to a taxonomy of tests. . . . This misconception might be compared to that of a physicist who, if upon discovering a high correlation between the measurements of his[sic] watch and his wall clock, assumes he has measured time. All that he has really shown is that his two measuring devices are related, which says nothing about time. There is no underlying dimension, such as time, which is causing the two time pieces to correlate or to load highly on the same factor; it is simply that their mechanisms have been constructed in virtually identical ways. (p. 5)

INTERVIEWS

Given that both experimentation and psychometrics tend overly to constrain the task of gaining information about the way people construe the world, the obvious question is to ask why we cannot simply ask people what they think – in other words, interview them. This is indeed a very common approach, used in many of the studies described in the previous chapter, either alone (as in, for example, Snow's, Herzlich's, Blaxter's and Williams' studies) or in conjunction with psychometric scales (as in, for example, Pill and Stott's work).

Any one of these could provide us with an example here. Each one of these researchers set out to gain insight about the way in which people construe the world by conducting interviews in which questions were asked which required answers intended to illuminate respondents' understandings and attempts to 'make sense' of health and illness. However, there are also a number of problems with interviewing for a social constructionist approach. First, there is the nature of the research interview itself, and the difficulties it poses for mutual understandings. Harré (1979), for example, has commented:

> The interview itself is a social event, heavy with ambiguity, and shot through with efforts at self-presentation by both the interviewer and the interviewee, so it is doubtful whether, in many cases, the interviewer understands the answers of the interviewee or the interviewee understands the questions of the interviewer. Each, apparently, reconstrues the speech of the other in accordance with their own conceptual framework. (p. 115)

Such problems are not entirely insurmountable. Jocelyn Cornwell (1984), for instance, made use of the social nature of interviewing to increase both her ability to gain information, and to 'get underneath' the social veneer of people talking as strangers. She repeatedly interviewed the same person, and members of the same households, not just formally, but by being around during the day and attending social events. This both affected the way people spoke to her, and what they were prepared to discuss, and, presumably, gave her more opportunity to see things through their perspective. In consequence she obtained what she defined as two kinds of data – 'public' accounts and 'private' accounts, which differed in systematic ways (although similar distinctions were also obtained in other studies by asking different kinds of questions).

The problem which remained, however, is the inability to know to what extent she and her respondents understood what was being said in similar ways, and how much they were (albeit without being aware of doing so) using the same words, but interpreting them differently. This problem is well known to anthropologists and classical scholars. Indeed a whole area of study – *hermeneutics* – has been developed to look for ways to understand the writings, sayings and actions of others (separated by historical time or cultural distance). This problem becomes particularly acute at the stage at which the interviews are subjected to analysis. Traditionally in social psychology some form of 'content analysis' has been used, although other approaches are possible, such as Williams' (1981a,b) logical analysis. Researchers begin by listening to the interviews and drawing upon prior work or theory in order to devise a system of response classification which they can impose on the interview transcript. Unfortunately, how the classification is reached usually remains shrouded in mystery. Seldom, if ever, do researchers give unequivocal accounts of how they arrived at the one they used. For example, while acknowledging the inherent problems in the endeavour, Crawford (1984) described his analysis thus:

> The study of meaning is riddled with problems of shared and opposed assumptions and categories as well as dangers of unconscious, personal projections. Several 'readings' are possible. The identification of themes is derived from a systematic analysis of transcripts and tapes. Categories of interpretation involve an interplay of theory and data: listening to and reading the interviews, categorizing the topics along several dimensions, searching for integrating concepts, and listening and reading once again. (p. 64)

Basically all that Crawford is saying is that he used his own skills and expertise as a cultural analyst to impose a system of classification which meshed, reasonably well, with the accounts he obtained. His emergent themes of 'release' and 'control' were not the constructions of the people he interviewed, however much informed he was by them. They were the products of *Crawford's* construction as he conducted his analysis. Whereas experiments and psychometrics constrain what *can be* obtained by imposing a classification before the collection of data, interview methods constrain what *is* reported, by imposing a classification after the data is collected. Interviews are much more sensitive to people's own views of the world, but interview studies are never simple accounts *of* their views of the world. As Potter and Wetherell (1987) argue, this kind of selective reading required for analysis takes place:

when the analyst handling interviews or texts select out those which *appear* to be significant when listening to the tape or reading the document. The great danger here is that the researcher making selections will simply mirror his or her prior expectation. In this situation data can be used to simply buttress the favoured analytic story, rather than being used to critically evaluate it. (p. 42)

This leads on to a second problem, raised, for example, by the anthropologist Boyer (1987), of the impossibility of knowing to what extent the content of an interview reflects an individual's idiosyncratic version of reality, and to what extent its themes are ones shared within their culture. The task of the researcher is to disentangle the two, which must always depend upon their ability to identify common threads that run through different interviews, even though they may be expressed quite differently. Potter and Wetherell's argument that this 'can easily obscure theoretically interesting differences in discourse' (p. 41) means that the researcher cannot win. It is necessary to sift out the idiosyncratic. Yet is also important not to iron out the inconsistent or the unusual, thereby denying recognition of themes, images or stories which may be muted in general discourse. The question is, how do you decide which is which?

OBSERVATION

Observational methods are of three kinds. First there is participant observation, used mainly by anthropologists and sociologists, who spend time being with (or even living with) the objects of study, participating as far as possible as members of the group and hence gaining knowledge and insight about their social and cultural life. Ethologists use similar methods, although the aim is to interfere as little as possible by using techniques which enable researchers to remain themselves unobserved. Psychologists who study animals in their natural habitats follow this approach. Both of these involve long-term observation over considerable periods of time. Finally, observation may be along a much shorter time-scale, where, for example, behaviour is observed behind a one-way mirror, or using video cameras. Sometimes observation may form part of an experiment, where frequency of specified actions (e.g. picking up leaflets, time spent using a keyboard) are used as dependent measures in the study.

Directed towards finding out about understandings, the most usual is for researchers to observe people in situations where they express their beliefs, views or whatever. In the studies described in Chapter 4, for instance, Snow (1974) used observation during religious meetings, and Helman (1978) during surgery visits, to provide additional information for their analysis. Morgan and Spanish (1985) used observational techniques in conjunction with group interviews, noting not just what people said, but how they argued with each other.

These observation methods suffer similar problems to those of interviews, in that the outcome of the research is reliant upon the skills of the researcher to identify the salient without denying aspects which may be uncommon, but none the less important. Researchers are generally highly skilled at weaving a coherent story of events which comes across as a plausible and convincing account of what happened. Given that social constructionism is based upon the assertion that people are 'competent negotiators of reality', what else would you expect?

CULTURAL ANALYSIS

Cultural analysis includes a range of approaches which share in common an explicit attempt by researchers to examine texts and images of various kinds, and seek to make conceptual links between the versions of reality expressed, and the cultural motifs or images or themes or stories which inform them. Texts may be of any form of cultural product – transcripts from interviews and from plays, movies and television programmes, books and other documents (e.g. legal statutes) and so on. Images may be paintings, photographs, advertisements or movies. This method has more in common, in many ways, with the study of literature and art than with conventional social science. A good example is the work conducted by Herzlich and Pierret on 'scourges' and 'epidemics' (see, for example, the first three chapters of their 1987 book). We can also see evidence of it in Crawford's study. He began his report with the statement: 'The body is a cultural object. As our most immediate natural symbol it provides us with a powerful medium through which we interpret and give expression to our individual and social experience' (Crawford, 1984, p. 60).

Within his paper he drew upon the results of his interviews as starting points for analysis, but then moved into a cultural arena to speculate about how the different motifs he had identified could be linked with historically developed ideas, such as that of self-control, linking back to the work of Weber (1930) on the protestant work ethic, and Foucault's (1977) suggestion that discipline is a regimen imposed within the power relations between dominant and submissive groups in society. Young's (1980) cultural analysis of the 'discourse on stress' used similar techniques, as did Taussig's (1980) work on how patients see themselves as patients. I would also include discourse analysis under this heading, although variants of the approach differ in the extent to which they are directed to small-scale intensive work on the discursive functions of specific segments of text, or towards broader explorations of cultural themes as articulated within the text.

Explicitly, researchers using these forms of analyses do not expect to find single coherent stories being told, but rather a weave of contradictory ideas and images intermingled. It is the researcher's job to disentangle them (while still acknowledging their polysemic properties), locate them in their cultural and historical contexts, and explore how they were constituted, how they interface with one another and how they are moulded and changed over time and across cultural space. Gleeson (1991) has, for example, speculated about how discourses may become *archived* – no longer used in a particular culture, but still available as myths or historical stories (e.g. the way in the West explanations of madness as 'spirit possession' are no longer used, although we still know about them from reading the Bible). Rex Stainton Rogers has adopted the term *cultural tectonics* to describe ways in which sympatric discourses oppose and compete with one another for dominance. The methods used for these kinds of endeavour consist of looking for evidence of the articulation of a discourse, by a process not dissimilar from the way in which themes in interviews are recognized and classified. The differences are in the source texts used, which often include those presented by the mass media, in historical documents, in political propaganda, and so on, as well as in the things people say and do in research settings.

With these similarities to interviews and observation, cultural analysis suffers from much the same problems. One is the covert nature of the analysis itself, where little is (or maybe even can be) reported about how the links are made or insights are arrived at. Researchers must draw upon their own stock of collective cultural knowledge, in order to recognize its manifestations, and in doing so they cannot claim to be using objective, external sources of reference. We (for I place myself firmly in this camp) would argue that we are not in fact doing anything different from the scientists who use experimental and psychometric methods. The difference is that whereas they deny that they are constructing a particular version of reality, we explicitly admit to doing so. We expressly regard our conclusions as 'cultural products, the contingent outcome of interpretative social acts' (Mulkay, 1991, p. 91), which is all very laudable, but leaves the people who read our work able to wonder why they should take any notice of what we say. If we are claiming to do no more than 'tell a convincing story', what do we really have to offer?

This problem is usually referred to as that of 'relativism'. If researchers refuse to claim any epistemological superiority for their version of reality, then, the argument goes, any version is as good as any other; none has greater validity. The resolution, Mulkay argues (1991) is to abandon certain notions, particularly those of validity and causality. By abandoning the idea that a version of reality is determined in some way (by social learning, immutable laws of human action or whatever), it becomes possible to stop being concerned about validity, and think of knowledge-use and knowledge-production quite differently. In a cultural analysis approach, other features, such as function and morality, are what matter. It is more meaningful to ask 'what can be it be used to achieve?' or 'What are its ideological implications' than to wonder 'Is it valid?' I will take up these ideas in Chapter 8, when I have described some of my own research, and we can explore these questions in relation to some of the alternative accounts of and for health and illness that I have identified.

None the less, the problem with cultural analysis remains that the versions of reality, accounts, stories – call them what you will – that are identified and described are dependent upon the researcher's knowledge and skill. There remains the ever present probability that many versions will remain unidentified or muted by gaps in our knowledge, or by our failure to look in the right places or recognize them when we do see them. Cultural analysis is, after all, a form of analysis, not a method for the production of accounts. Therefore, I would maintain, it needs to be coupled with some other method which will enable alternative accounts to be produced. Some researchers use observation and interviews to generate sources for analysis. Together with others, I have added another method to my armoury, which I believe has something unique to offer. This is what I will go on to describe now.

Q METHODOLOGY

In 1935, William Stephenson, working as Spearman's research

assistant during the time when he was formulating and refining factor analysis, made what was at the time a highly radical suggestion. Stephenson's idea was twofold: to consider data in terms of what he called 'self-reference' (as opposed to seeking objective definitions or tests), and to treat this data in terms of each individual's whole patterns of response (rather than looking for patterns item-by-item or test-by-test *among* people). For example, he showed people a set of pictures of vases, and asked them to order them along a dimension from 'ones I think are most aesthetically pleasing' to 'ones I think are most unaesthetic'. In this way, the data reflected the individual's views, irrespective of any judgement of external reference. With data from a number of people he performed a factor analysis, but instead of correlating data sets by-item in the usual way, he correlated the data by-person. Basically what this did was to yield factors which identified different, independent patterns of response. For instance, one pattern might be that round vases were seen as aesthetic and slim vases as unaesthetic; another pattern might be regular vases seen as aesthetic and irregular ones unaesthetic. What was salient for one might well not be salient for another. Beauty, in this approach, was very much in the eye of the beholder.

I do not intend here to go into great detail about the history and methodological niceties of Q methodology, since these have been more than adequately covered elsewhere (Brown, 1980, is the standard text; Kitzinger, 1987, and Stainton Rogers, W., 1987, offer other accounts; William Stephenson's own account is in his 1935 original paper and his 1953 book). All I will do is provide a sufficient description to enable readers to make sense of the studies I conducted using Q methodology.

Q method, as it is conventionally used for the purposes for which it was designed, does not set out to 'measure' anything objectively. It is intended to offer participants in a study opportunities to express their viewpoints or beliefs or 'versions of reality' by the way in which they sort a number of items – usually, although not always, statements (cartoons, photographs and posters have also been used). The task of the researcher is to supply them with a *Q-set* of items (sometimes called a Q-sample) which, as far as possible, reflects the broad range of ideas, statements and arguments about the topic in question. Will Stephenson (1986a) has given the term *concourse* to this population of ideas from which the Q-set must be sampled. The Q-sets used in the two studies I have reported in this book are listed in Appendices 1 and 2, if you would like to look to see what they are like.

Participants take the items, presented on separate cards or small sheets of paper, and usually begin by sorting them into three piles: agrees, disagrees and 'don't knows' (other dimensions are used, but this is the most common form). Next, they continue sorting, using a grid provided which specifies sub-categories of agreement and disagreement, and how many items should be placed in each. Usually this is like the one shown in Figure 5.1.

STRONGEST ◄ — — — — — — — — — — — — — ► STRONGEST
DISAGREEMENT   AGREEMENT

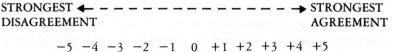

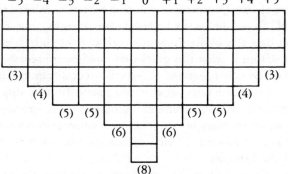

Figure 5.1   Sample grid used in a Q-study

So, for example, with the grid in this Figure, the participant must select, from the statements provided, which three he or she agrees with most, and place these in the +5 position. Next, four must be chosen for the +4 position, and so on. Similarly, at the other end, the participant must choose three statements to place in the −5 position, four for the −4 position, and so on.

Data from these responses are coded numerically (e.g. −5 statements are scored 1, −4 statements scored 2, up to +5 statements scored 11) and entered into a factor analysis program (although Will Stephenson did all his by hand!) with each participant's data down along a column, their responses to individual items across rows (i.e. the opposite to the usual manner of setting out data for a factor analysis). In this way, when the factor analysis is performed, what are identified are alternative patterns of response. (Again I will not go into detail here of the statistical features of factor analysis. Brown, 1980, provides a very thorough explanation in his Chapter 4, for those who want to know more of the technicalities.) Usually the data are then subjected to a technique called *rotation* which optimalizes the separation between factors. This can be 'done by hand' (these days using a computer program) or by a standard technique, such as varimax.

Thus, once the analysis is performed, the researcher is provided with a list of factors identified. Each factor represents a pattern of response which conforms to certain mathematical criteria for being independent from all the other factors. Each factor will have been estimated from all of the data from all of the participants (i.e. it is based on calculations to do with the overall variability in the scores in the study). But for somewhere typically between three and eight factors in a study, one or more participant's Q-sorting pattern will be very similar to the pattern identified. This is indicated by them gaining a high loading on the factor concerned (typically these will be from 0.9 to 0.6). Their Q-sorts are usually termed *exemplificatory Q-sorts*, and the people who provided them *exemplars*. Where several Q-sorts exemplify a factor, a 'best estimate' of the pattern is obtained by calculations of weighting and averaging. In this way, a number of alternative, independent sorting patterns will be identified. The researcher's task at this point is to go back to the items themselves, and begin to interpret the factor according to the juxtaposition of the statements. For example, consider a situation where the following three items have been chosen for the + 5 allocation:

- When I'm ill enough to consult my doctor, my recovery will be faster if I comply properly with the treatment I get.
- If I were ever seriously ill, I would have a lot of faith in the ability of doctors to find a cure.
- When I'm ill, my recovery depends a lot on the quality of medical treatment I get.

Their combination, and the fact that these were given the greatest prominence at the 'agree' end of the sorting pattern, begin to paint a picture of an account in which modern medicine is highly regarded, where recovery from illness is seen as very salient, and where compliance with medical treatment is seen as very important. Other patterns will tell other stories. Used in this way, Q method provides source data, from which cultural analyses can be conducted. Steven Brown (1980) summarizes it like this, stressing the likelihood that a Q study will usually lead to unexpected results:

Q samples provide the launch pad for an investigation, an entrée into a phenomenon, the scientist's best initial guess as to how a particular administrative situation, social consciousness, or whatever operates. The data gathered with the Q sample may lead in quite different directions. . . . There is never any guarantee, in other words, that splash-down will occur in the same area as the point of departure. (p. 39)

Those of us who use Q method in our research do so because it is the only technique that we have found which places the *participants in the study* in control of the classification process. A factor cannot emerge unless participants sort items in ways that enable it to do so. Of course, participants can work with only the raw materials that researchers give them – the statements we select for the Q-set. Sometimes participants complain that we have not provided the right statements to give adequate opportunities for them to express their opinions. This means that we have to take a lot of care in the construction of the sets, in negotiating our interpretations afterwards, and in being prepared to re-do the study, taking their suggestions on board. Constructing a Q-set thus consists of gaining a 'best estimate' of the concourse from as many diverse sources as possible, recognizing that this is inevitably an intuitive process, and then subsequently selecting the statements to be used in the study, again intuitively, from the 'concourse-estimate'. We do this by conducting interviews and performing various kinds of observation and cultural analysis, by pilot testing, and by seeking advice from participants.

To make a Q-sort reasonably easy to complete, the statements need some sort of balance, otherwise people find it difficult to follow the grid provided. Whereas Stephenson (1953) argued that the researcher must select balancing items (but not opposites), those of us who work within a social constructionist approach do not believe that we can do so, given that the same statement can mean very different things to different people. We therefore also use pilot testing to get a rough balance from different viewpoints, to clarify wording and to avoid repetition. Similarly, it is important to try to include statements in the Q-set which are, more or less, 'about' the same topic. Again, given that people construe the world in different ways, this is not at all straightforward, but once more we use pilot testing and our own stock of cultural knowledge to do the best that we can.

It is also necessary to be careful in our interpretation. There are a number of ways in which we try to ensure that our reports of the viewpoints or accounts expressed are reasonably accurate articulations of what participants intended to express in their Q-sorting. One is to observe while sorting takes place. Although this can be extremely time consuming, it is usually highly informative. Another approach is to provide participants with lists of the items in the Q-set, and to ask them to write open ended comments beside them. A third alternative is to conduct interviews with participants who exemplify factors, to negotiate and flesh out summaries with them.

The final outcome of the Q study itself is a series of factor interpretations. These summarize the account or viewpoint expressed, woven out of the item placements and written or spoken comments. In the next two chapters you will find these kinds of summaries, derived from the two Q studies I conducted. However, for those of us working with Q method from a social constructionist perspective, we see the factor interpretations as only a stage in the process of cultural themes and images, as described above. In Chapter 8 you will find the results of the cultural analysis which I conducted on eight of the accounts which I identified in the studies.

In the previous chapter, I included Stephenson's own Q studies of images of health and illness (1962, 1963), which provide a good illustration of the approach. In his second study he identified three factors, which, when interpreted, identified three alternative accounts: independent, interdependent and dependent. Each one portrays a quite different understanding about how the practice of medicine should be organized: as a 'fee for service' system in which individuals must take responsibility for themselves; as a system of mutual support, in which rights to treatment are matched with responsibilities; and as a welfare system, where those in need of treatment are entitled to support, irrespective of their inability to reciprocate.

At first sight, Q methodology appears to have more in common with psychometrics than it does with cultural analysis. It constrains participants both in the items provided, and in the limits placed on their responses, and it uses numerical measures, statistical analysis and mathematic criteria. This has led to a number of problems. First, it has in its history been misused by researchers unwilling to accept its principle of self-reference. This has led to a situation where, for example, Q-sorts were used to measure mental health (e.g. Rogers and Dymond, 1954) by comparing the Q-sorts of mental patients describing themselves against a template Q pattern of the 'ideally healthy person'. Indeed, the Q theorization and research conducted by Block (see, for example, Block, 1961) is in fact better known than Stephenson's own.

Not surprisingly, given that it is commonly viewed as a psychometric test (because it is in this form that it is best known), Q method has been criticized for failing to meet the standards set for psychometric testing. Q studies, for example, have been accused of being 'unreliable' because they do not produce the same responses when repeated. From a social constructionist viewpoint, this is no problem, since there is no expectation that an individual will express the same views on two separate occasions. In a Q study the focus is not on individual response, in any case, but upon the accounts identified. However, the most common criticism is that the factors are not the products of participant's sorting, but of the researcher's selection of the statements. This is true in the same way that artists are constrained by the kinds and colours of paints they can use. Certainly researchers can (and do) limit the accounts that can be expressed (I take up this point in the next chapter), but they cannot *make* accounts appear. Only the participants in the study can do that.

It is this which makes Q method highly suitable for social constructionist research. It allows the process of cultural analysis to be *shared* between the researcher and the people who participate in the research. As used by those of us who have adopted it as a social constructionist method, we begin – and end – with cultural analysis of various forms. But sandwiched in between we take our 'best estimates' of the ideas, statements and arguments we think are significant to a topic or area of debate, and offer them to other people, so that they can respond to them. In fact, it is this element which makes Q research very hard work – for the researcher persuading people to take part; and for participants actually carrying out the sorting task. It is not unusual for people to spend more than two hours on a sort. Participants tell us that it makes them think very deeply, and face up to the contradictions and complexities in their ideas. What is happening is that *they* are being asked to do what the researcher usually does during analysis and interpretation of data – decipher and decide what to do about its ambiguity, lack of clarity and muddled ideas and themes. Participants must choose what is most salient, and how the different statements compare and contrast with each other. The sorting task puts the participant in charge of at least that stage of the study.

There is another reason why Q method has something unique to offer social constructionists, and that is the particular form of factor analysis used which compares each individual's whole pattern of response with each other person's whole pattern of response. Factors thus emerge out of systematic similarities between different people. Although in some cases a factor will have only one exemplar, factors cannot emerge out of the random or utterly bizarre sorting of an individual. To achieve the mathematical criteria to be identified as a factor, it must be based upon a substantial proportion of the variability in the data, which can arise only when the response pattern is more widely dispersed, even if in attenuated or partial form, in the responses of others. In this way the analysis acts as a mechanism for identifying *collective* understanding, albeit articulated by individuals.

MODERNIST AND POSTMODERNIST METHODS

In this chapter I have described six forms of methodology. The first two – experimentation and psychometrics – are based firmly upon a hypothetico-deductive philosophy of science, and essentialism. These principles were adopted within a modernist worldview, as a defence against irrationality. They stress normative principles of impartiality, emotional and subjective neutrality, and universalism (Mulkay, 1979). The aim of research within this approach is to generate reports about 'real things' expressed in an 'unitary, autonomous, socially removed authorial voice' (Mulkay, 1991) – a single, coherent story 'telling it like it is'.

The remaining methods – interviews, observation, cultural analysis and Q methodology – can be used (even though they not always *are* used) within a postmodernist approach, which acknowledges that the social world is always construed in a multiplicity of different, sympatric, often contradictory ways. From this perspective, research is intended to uncover the alternative versions of reality experienced and expressed by people, in a way that makes no claim to objectivity or unique authority. Its aim is also to locate its products within culture and society. At the same time the research endeavour itself, as much as the subject matter under research, is viewed as a social and cultural product, in no way immune to distortion or different from any other social endeavour.

DIALECTIC RESEARCH

I would argue that this exploration of diversity involves two somewhat different processes. The first is basically taxonomic, which is to explore the social world and identify some – amid the cacophony – of the versions of reality expressed. The success (or otherwise) of this venture cannot be judged in terms of validity — of finding (or not finding) things which are (or are not) 'really there', since reality has no meaning here (other than as a product of social construction). Rather, the aim is utility — are the versions identified useful in aiding our understanding? We can call this process *dis*-location, since its purpose is to extract out of chaos some kind of systematic conjunction of ideas which conceptually 'hang together'. Having identified these alternative versions of reality — accounts, images, metaphors, call them what you will — the second process is to *re*-locate them back into their cultural and social contexts, rather like a hologram which, while separate from the whole, none the less implicates the whole. This second stage is a necessary component in any methodological approach which seeks to be dialectic.

In other words, I would argue that no single method can be truly dialectic. Both *dis*-location and *re*-location are necessary for that to be achieved. Consequently, I believe that a social constructionist method must be one in which a number of different methods, each capable of achieving something that the others cannot, are used in conjunction with each other. This is the approach I have used in the studies which I describe in the next two chapters.

CHAPTER SIX

Studies of Explanatory Diversity

Explanations of health and illness (including those used by professional healers) are almost always articulated within broader discourses (such as religious belief or folk wisdom). They are often as much to do with a person's definition of themselves (e.g. as 'winner against the odds' rather than 'victim') as they are with giving reasons for why things happen, and they frequently include ideas about (and denials of) blame and responsibility. In this chapter I describe the first of two studies I carried out in order to identify and describe some of these explanations.

DERIVATION OF THE Q-SET

I began my research by talking to people, both in formal interviews and in informal conversations — at conferences, around the dinner table, on the bus and at the hairdresser's. As well as helping me to draw up a list of statements from which to select the Q sample for my first study, talking to people in this way allowed me to gain entry into a new field of investigation. It exposed me to a diverse range of different viewpoints and ideas and allowed me to develop a better understanding of the kinds of debates and issues involved. In this spirit, I did not select people to interview formally according to principles of representativeness or sampling. Rather I did my best to find people who were likely to draw upon diverse ideas, understanding and indeed whole worldviews, as different from each other (and my own) as possible. There were six women and seven men. Their ages ranged from sixteen to seventy-two.

Two interviewees described themselves as 'health theorists'. The first was a sociologist, like me investigating health beliefs, who talked both about her own views and those of the people she had been studying in her research. The second was the director of an organization concerned with health promotion, who spoke at length about links between lifestyle and illness. Two more identified themselves as 'working class', a pensioner who had been a housewife all her adult life, widowed and living on her own in an 'inner city' area, and a farmworker, an active trades unionist, living in a rural setting. A computer technician was chosen as a representative of the 'new right'. He lived in the north of England. A woman who ran 'Keep Fit' classes at the local Sports Centre was selected for her particular interest in 'health-as-beauty' and as someone who was upwardly socially mobile – she grew up in a very poor, working-class family but spoke of her desire to 'better herself'. The grocer (his name for himself) was the proprietor of an 'upmarket' food shop, chosen as a 'traditional conservative' and as a 'foodie'. The school student, also from the north, was included as a younger person and somebody holding 'left-wing' views. A range of different health professionals included a retired pharmacy technician who had worked in large hospitals throughout her working life, a Health Visitor, a medical student (a member of an ethnic minority, from a Muslim background), an occupational physician working for a large food company, two GPs (one fairly traditional, and the other a trained homoeopathist) and a dentist. As well as sampling different professional interests, these people also reflected different class, political, religious and cultural backgrounds.

The interviews were semi-structured, in that I set an agenda of issues and topics to be covered and specific questions to be asked, but were largely open ended. Given the diversity of the interviewee sample, different people naturally focused on different aspects of 'health and illness'. For example, the occupational physician employed by the food company had a lot to say about the relationship between 'big business', government policy, diet and health. At the time of interview he had just returned from a visit to the USA, and provided a great deal of information (and expressed firm views) about the comparison between attitudes to health here and in North America. Each interview lasted beween one and three hours, although in several cases I telephoned the interviewees to clarify particular points and in two cases I conducted a second interview, to enlarge on topics raised. From the interviews I generated 327 statements, as close as possible to the words actually used, as a basis for the 'concourse estimate' I needed for my study.

In the period of four months during which the interviews were taking place, I kept a research notebook, into which I recorded statements about health and illness from a variety of sources: from my reading of the academic literature, discussions (e.g. at academic conferences) with other colleagues working in this area, conversations in informal social settings, media sources including television, radio, newspapers and magazines, and by reading or re-reading novels (e.g. Butler's *Erewhon*, 1872, and Axel Munthe's *The Story of San Michele*, 1929) and 'popular' magazines and texts with a medical or health theme, including old books (e.g. *The Practical Doctor* by a Harley Street Specialist, undated). As with the interviews, the intention was both generally to 'immerse' myself in as many different pertinent discourses as possible, and specifically to look for items with which to build up the 'concourse estimate'. I took the notebook with me wherever I went, and actively sought to read as many different magazines, newspapers and books; to watch as much television and listen to as much radio; and to enter into as many informal conversations about 'health and illness' as I could. From this notebook, 179 statements were selected to add to the pool.

Unfortunately, I did not obtain a copy of Stephenson's unpublished Q studies of 'images of public health' (described in Chapter 4) until some time later, and was therefore unaware of the Q samples which he had used, which would have been valuable in setting up my own.

At the end of this phase of data collection I had gathered over 650 statements about health and illness. Of these about 150 concerned with social policy issues and/or matters of funding were excluded, as I had by then decided to focus specifically on *explanations* of health and illness (albeit often linked to other issues and concerns like politics and morality). I thus arrived at 506 statements, derived from the interviews and other sources, which formed my first 'best guess' at the concourse. These were reduced by selection to provide a broadly representative sample of the different ideas and views being expressed.

An initial pilot Q study was conducted with a Q-set of 54 items sorted by 30 participants, and the feedback used further to refine the Q-set and improve administration. I retained 39 of the pilot set items, although some were rewritten following feedback. Further items were added from suggestions made by participants, from pilot study negotiations and further interviews, and from the updated research notebook. A pool of 196 items was then assessed by seven associates for comprehensibility, salience, repetitiveness and balance. As a result of this procedure, some statements were rewritten, some replaced, some recouched in terms of their converse form and some rejected, to generate a final set of 80 items. These are listed in Appendix 1.

PARTICIPANTS

The study was based upon the data provided by 70 participants, 26 of whom were men, 42 women, the remainder not providing information about gender. Their ages ranged from between 14 and 63 (the majority being in their 30s and 40s) and all were unpaid volunteers. About half of the participant sample were chosen to represent particular kinds of professional expertise and experience, religious affiliation and political views. About half were recruited to ensure a broad spread of 'ordinary' viewpoints. Occupations included students (recruited from three colleges), teachers, lecturers and researchers, administrators, an architect, a social worker, a factory worker, a cellarman, a fireman, a police officer and a retired army major. Twenty-four were health professionals, including nurses, GPs, hospital doctors, physiotherapists and a dietician.

MATERIALS

The Q-sort was provided in loose leaf form to be cut up by participants, together with markers. Written instructions, response forms and two additional comments booklets were included. The first comments booklet was to be filled in before and the other after the Q-sort itself was completed. Generally I gave the materials to participants, or asked somebody else to do this for me (e.g. college teachers), and these were returned by mail.

RESULTS

The 70 completed Q-sort response grids were subjected to a by-person factor analysis with varimax rotation. I selected seven of the factors identified for detailed interpretation, description and analysis. Having carried out an initial interpretation, I negotiated these with participants who had provided an exemplificatory Q-sort for each factor, and used their comments to flesh out the reformulated interpretations. In the following interpretations, comments and quotes are always from people whose Q-sort exemplified the factor in question.

Account 1: the 'cultural critique'

Seven participants' Q-sorts acted as exemplars for this factor, including three students, a hospital doctor, a researcher, a teacher and myself. Its emergence as a first factor suggests that my own interests led to an over-representation of people sharing similar views in the participant sample. As I indicated in Chapter 5, in a taxonomic approach, this does not matter so long as when you read study interpretations you remember that the order in which factors appear does not imply anything about the frequency or importance of accounts within the general arena of thinking and debate.

This account explained health in terms of power, status and wealth. Poor health is the product of inequality, exploitation and disadvantage. The worst off and marginalized in our society were seen as having very little choice about the unhealthy lives they lead. For example, the doctor wrote: 'I worry about the people who live in dreadful housing, who work long hours and who cannot afford to feed themselves or their children properly. They don't stand a chance. They simply do not have the chance to be healthy.' And a similar comment was made by the teacher:

> Health is much more to do with social and economic conditions than doctors and kidney machines. People who live in dreadful housing, without transport or the money to buy decent food cannot help but have worse health. Once you know the data, just how much worse is really shocking.

Concern was expressed that items about exploitation of Third World countries had not been included. This additional item was suggested by one of the students: 'you need to include something on the cost of developing Western medicine in terms of suffering and death of Third World peoples (e.g. dumping of contraceptives, baby milk powder).'

An explicitly social constructionist analysis was indicated in this account in its perception that labelling people as mentally ill is used as a form of social control, that being ill is something we learn to do, and that diseases are invented by doctors rather than merely discovered by them. The teacher suggested: 'yea, like pre-menstrual tension, post-natal depression . . . post-natal *oppression*, more like!' The researcher wrote: 'things like anorexia, alcoholism and drug addiction are all inventions . . . there's nothing *real* about them.'

Issues of ideology were given prominence, both in the Q-sort allocations and in comments. Capitalism was seen as inherently anti-health, and drug companies more concerned with profits than making people well. Comments included:

> Doctors are bribed to prescribe more brand named drugs by companies offering incentives – e.g. holidays, etc.

> they [Government departments] are lobbied by those with the money to bribe the politicians.

> health care is increasingly becoming dominated by the firms who market the equipment and drugs . . . the NHS is increasingly squeezed for funds by their greed.

There was strong cynicism about the supposed benefits of modern medicine. Modern therapeutic achievements and modern drugs were seen to make limited contributions to good health. Many forms of treatment were seen to do more harm than good. There was little faith in the ability of medical science to eradicate disease: 'Half the time it makes people worse – overprescribing of tranquillisers, unnecessary operations.' Doctors were viewed as treating symptoms, not the underlying causes of illness and recommending surgery when it is not really necessary. The profession of medicine was portrayed as: 'an "old boys club" serving its own interests rather than those of the patients, and keeping promotion for members of the medical mafia'.

Going to the doctor was not seen as making you feel better, indeed one participant crossed out the word 'better' and substituted 'worse'! Doctors should not play God by expecting unthinking compliance, or threatening disease as retribution for not doing what they tell you. They have no right to decide whether, and under what conditions, people should be given information. A good health service is one which respects people's autonomy even if that puts people at risk.

In the comments, particularly, it was clear that the account was not just about the way in which doctors exploit and misuse their professional power; it was couched in the context of a much more general theory of the relationship between the relatively powerless individual and powerful hegemonies of many kinds. For example, the researcher made a general point in response to an item about health being to do with state of mind: 'Feel uncomfortable with all these "mental" items. Resent anyone daring to interfere with or make assumptions about my state of mind. Doctors already claim the right to administer judgements about my body. That's enough. Keep them off my mind.'

Overall this was an articulation of the 'cultural critique' proposed by Ehrenreich (1978), as described in Chapter 2, p. 20. However, in my interviews with the people who had exemplified this factor, there was a noticeable split between two alternative articulations of the account.

The researcher, for example, insisted that my interpretation was incorrect because, for her, it is specifically 'ruling *men*' who 'create a stressful, polluted and noxious environment for me, and then try to sell me the notion (as well as the equipment) that I can counteract it if I do press-ups and eat brown rice'. My attempts to negotiate an account summary with her based on the 'cultural critique' was met with strong and repeated rejection. For her, only an explicitly feminist analysis provided an authentic account of her views. But one student (also a woman) denied the feminist analysis just as vociferously. For her the blame could equally well be placed upon women as men:

> That women have played only a small part in the oppression of the working class reflects, true, that women have been pretty powerless throughout most of history . . . but living within a Thatcherite economy, with that bloody woman the prime architect of the most strident and vicious form of capitalism we have ever seen, don't talk to me of *man*-made misery.

This split indicated that my selection of items for the Q-sort have been insufficiently inclusive of specifically feminist items to provide an adequate platform for a feminist critique to be articulated. This was not in fact an 'oversight', but the result of a decision I made following the pilot testing of the items. There I also found similar tensions within the factor, divided between a Marxist and feminist critique. The feminist critique is predicated upon the assumption that: 'the taken-for-granted understandings of the world, particularly insofar as they relate to gender and sexuality, rely on a construction of reality which oppresses women' (Kitzinger, 1984, p. 40).

Marxist analyses, in contrast, focus upon the impact of capitalism. McKinlay (1984), for instance, couched his critique in terms of a perception of capitalism as a 'predatory' force within Western society:

> the rapinous activities of large-scale capitalist institutions (mainly banks, insurance companies and industrial corporations): the act of invading, exploiting and ultimately despoiling a field of endeavour – with no necessary commitment to it – in order to seize and carry away an acceptable level of profit. (p. 2)

He argued that within such a system the business of medicine has been rendered a highly desirable source of profit, and in consequence, particularly in North America, predatory organizations have invaded and now dominate 'health care'.

141

At the pilot testing stage I therefore faced a difficult decision. The demands of Q-sorting limit the number of statements you can include in any study. To include sufficient items for both accounts to be articulated would have restricted my ability to pursue others. For several reasons I decided in my main study against an approach like that taken by Peritore's investigation of the 'New Left' in Brazil (1986), which would focus specifically on the ideological and political aspects of 'health and illness'. I wanted to develop a broad account taxonomy, and did not want to become side-tracked into consideration of just one set of issues or forms of understanding. My interest was as much in the general processes and psychological functions of explanation itself, as in the content of the accounts. Such a diversion would have limited my ability to explore accounting across a range of viewpoints, social and cultural situations, etc. Secondly, I felt that the discriminations between the variants of the 'cultural critique' were already well documented in the literature and, as a growing field of academic interest, this area was likely to be covered extensively elsewhere.

Most importantly, however, although Q methodology is not intended to provided information about the segmentation of opinion within any population as a whole, I did want the research to offer a basis for a better understanding of *popular* accounting. While the 'cultural critique' is of great interest within an academic discourse, it is not generally salient within the accounting of 'ordinary people'. Academics do not lack opportunities to express their views, and I did not want to be persuaded to develop the 'cultural critique' at the cost of denying a voice to others less privileged.

I have devoted space to explaining what is often 'hidden' within research reports (cf. Reason and Rowan, 1981) – the thinking behind decisions made about what to *exclude* from study – because it is a crucial issue for Q as an emancipatory methodology. Like any other technique, it is not neutral, nor can it be utilized outside the power relations of researcher and researched. In choosing to study one thing, inevitably the researcher chooses not to study others. Q has its methodological constraints that demand selection of research questions (based upon judgements like the ones I have described above). The researcher decides what opportunities will be provided within the Q sample, and what people to invite to participate. These inevitably control the accounts that will be published as the 'results' of the study. The results are not mere products of the data obtained, but are products of these decisions. My desire to pursue a broadly based exploration of

142

explanatory diversity meant, therefore, that I chose to develop a Q sample for my main study that tried to extend opportunities for other kinds of account. Most of all, I wanted to take an abductory (Stephenson, 1953) approach which sought to discover the unexpected and unpredictable rather than merely further refining the divisions within a particular account.

I have therefore included discussion of the feminist version of the critique, since it was expressed so strongly in the interviews and comments of two of the participants whose Q-sorts exemplified this factor, but I freely admit that my Q-set did not offer opportunities for it to be expressed in the Q-sort data. This, I believe, is part of the benefits of methodological diversity (as described in Chapter 5). It means that an account which may be suppressed by one methodological component can none the less be acknowledged.

Account 2: willpower

This account was exemplified by the Q-sorts of a secretary and a student. A similar account had emerged in the pilot study, that time exemplified by the Q-sort of a retired GP. I have included some of his comments, at appropriate points (where items were common to the two studies).

Whereas the 'cultural critique' account was articulated almost entirely within the socio-political explanatory arena, this account sited explanation almost entirely within the province of the individual. It saw the body's functioning as a resource, biological (in terms of its self healing properties) and psychological (in terms of state of mind aiding recovery) upon which the individual can draw to promote health and fight off disease. Comments from participants illustrate these two interwoven themes. The student wrote about the item which suggested that illness is a punishment for misdeeds: 'No, never, but if someone believes this, they may inflict it upon themselves subconsciously.' The secretary commented about disease and decay being inevitable: 'Of course they are eventually, but this question implies a somewhat surrendering attitude.'

This idea of positive thinking linked with a view of the individual as able to control, and as responsible for, their health. For example, the item stating that the worst off in our society have very little choice about the unhealthy lives they lead was disagreed with, and drew the following comments:

143

Even the poorest people have a lot they can do for themselves.

False, almost everyone can be clean.

There was a positive view of medicine. Modern drugs were seen to make a major contribution to health and medical progress of genuine benefit. Alternative forms of medicine were also seen to offer important resources for healing.

The account emphasized, however, that health and illness are products of bodily and mental functioning, and that state of mind can aid recovery. There was strong agreement with seeing illness as a 'challenge' and for researchers needing to look for the underlying causes of so-called spontaneous recovery. Negative effects of 'state of mind' were also regarded as important; illness can become a 'way of life' and it is quite possible for people to die of a 'broken heart'. Thus whereas the 'cultural critique' account specifically denied many of these ideas because they 'pass the buck' to individual responsibility, this account accepted them because they do hold the individual responsible.

This account accepted stress and pollution as causes of ill health, but with most emphasis upon stress:

> Yes, the stress of modern life has a lot to answer for, where many people let themselves get run down in the constant hurry and seeking after consumer goodies

> True – particularly stress.

The image portrayed of doctors was that it is their caring and concern that is as important as their technological expertise. This was most explicitly articulated by the GP in the pilot study:

> Often what people need is just a little reassurance that their symptoms are nothing to worry about. Once they stop worrying, the symptoms often clear up.

> People need a doctor they can trust . . . the relationship between the doctor and patient is crucial to healing and care.

But the role of medicine itself was played down, other than as a means to bolster and encourage the individual to strive for their own recovery. The secretary commented: 'Someone may be better off being told of their serious illness so they can "switch on" the will to live.' Again and again 'positive state of mind' and 'willpower' were stressed as what really mattered:

It's up to you to think positively, to refuse to give in.

You've got to be prepared to fight it off. If you don't you just get worse.

Illness is not a natural state, and therefore health has to do with positive thinking.

That this construal is pre-eminently one of health and illness under the control of the *individual* is further evidenced in two ways. First, there were similar comments from the secretary and the student about an item stating that other people being unpleasant can 'make me ill':

I can see it might affect someone's state of mind, but they don't have to give in to emotional blackmail.

Indirectly yes – but only if one lets it get one down mentally. You don't have to give in.

From this viewpoint, it is not the unpleasantness of other people, per se, that causes illness, but the effect that this can have upon individuals if they *allow* themselves to be affected.

The second indication that health and illness were considered matters of individual, not social, forces was the emphatic refutal of any political or ideological dimension to health. For example, the item about the label of 'mentally ill' being used for social control was strongly denied and stimulated the following written comments:

Not in this country!

Russia Only!

The item stating that we will only improve the overall health of people in the world when we have found ways to overcome the fundamental injustices between rich and poor was also strongly rebutted and the following comments were written:

I find this term 'injustice' makes this a nonsense. Poverty is not an injustice.

I totally disagree, this is complete rubbish.

Political rubbish. Must have come out of a communist manifesto.

The strongest rejection, however, was reserved for the most overtly political items, such as the suggestion that, as doctors are committed to preserve life, they have a moral duty to support nuclear disarmament (given the strongest disagree allocation). The written comments were:

> No, as some would say that through disarmament more may die through conventional warfare.

> Rubbish. Politics has nothing to do with it. Doctors have personal lives and ideals – are not doctors all the time.

Indeed, so incensed was one participant in the study (not one who acted as an exemplar, but a doctor whose Q-sort loaded strongly on this factor) at the very inclusion of such an item in the Q-sort that he wrote me a letter telling me to remove it from the questionnaire (sic) since 'reproducing this kind of politically biased clap-trap in the name of research does you no service as a scholar'.

Account 3: health promotion

Although the factor gained strong loadings from several participants' Q-sorts, it was exemplified only by the Q-sort of one woman, a nurse teaching in a school of nursing. She told me she was teaching a course on health promotion, and her very articulate expression of this account no doubt reflected her special interest.

The account itself focused very specifically on health rather than illness, and was predicated on a view of health as a fundamental human right, a positive state of wellbeing and 'one of the most important things in life'. Within this account good health is never a matter of luck. Disease and bodily decay can usually be avoided or delayed. Health can be promoted by changes in lifestyle, improved living conditions and gaining greater spiritual and psychological equilibrium. What is more, not only is this better for you, it is more satisfying. The item stating that life is 'too short and too sweet' to spend too much time worrying about health was strongly rejected:

> This is rubbish. It implies that living healthily is boring and miserable, when the opposite is true. Eating well and taking exercise are not just good for you, they are enjoyable – and feeling fit (which you can only do if you live a healthy lifestyle) is to be able to enjoy life to the full.

However, there was some concern expressed about the way in which these ideas have become commercialized. The nurse commented about the item that suggested striving to be healthy is 'just another fashion': 'This is a dangerous statement, which devalues the notion of seeking after health by one's own actions whilst a little of me agrees – I'm unhappy that people are being led to feel you need expensive clothes to take exercise.'

While this account stressed the need for individuals to adopt healthy habits and lifestyles, however, it is not 'individualistic'. The nurse made the point specifically, explaining that she had placed the item about taking responsibility for health in the mildly disagree catagory: 'because health education is crucial, and not everybody is well enough informed'.

The account acknowledged inequalities in health between rich and poor, and the poorest having little choice about their health. Indeed the nurse several times directly referred to the impact of social disadvantage, although she was generally more concerned with educational disadvantage rather than structural inequality:

> The inequalities in health between those in Social Classes I and II and those in . . . Classes IV and V are scandalous. Health . . . is strongly linked to education – the more years of schooling a mother has had, the healthier her children are likely to be.

This account, as expressed by the nurse teacher, was informed by the messages of the (now defunct) Health Education Council. For instance, commenting on her endorsement of the item that the Government cares more for tobacco tax revenues than health, she said: 'The HEC has almost no funds for anti-smoking advertising compared with the tobacco companies.' And in response to the item saying the Government has suppressed information about food she commented: 'Yes, the reports produced by the HEC are being put under pressure by lobbying from the Food Industry.'

The account contained clear concern about environmental causes of illness, although the item about the effects of stress and pollution was only mildly agreed with because: 'It's too easy just to blame stress and the environment, when there is a lot you can do – excuses don't help people to strive for themselves.'

There was guarded approval of modern medicine, including its therapeutic advances and the benefits of modern drugs. That individual health-promoting behaviour was seen to need the support of proper medical services was shown by the rejection of sports facilities as more useful than hospitals, 'this being a cop-out for providing good health care'.

Overall, then, this was an account sited squarely within the 'health promotion' discourse, stressing the benefits of health education and individual action and lifestyle while concerned about inequality in a world in which health is as a fundamental right denied to many by their own ignorance, the constraints imposed by the lives they led and cuts in medical services. It was critical of Government, seeing it as swayed by the powerful interests of 'Big Business' and the Govenment's shift to monetarism resulting in reduced medical care, but it was very much less concerned with oppression and exploitation than the 'cultural critique' account, less concerned with medical hegemony and more willing to accept the benefits of orthodox medical care.

Account 4: the 'body as machine'

Once again, there was only one participant's Q-sort which exemplified this factor, although there were once again many more loading fairly strongly on it. She was a dietician, working at a large teaching hospital.

This account strongly and consistently supported biomedicine, perceiving modern therapeutic achievements as having made major contributions to health care, and the progress made in pharmaceuticals as critical in fighting disease. It saw us as fortunate to live in a world of medical excellence, denying that doctors just treat symptoms, or that medical treatments do more harm than good, against which item the dietician wrote: 'No, proper medicine is still the best if you have something seriously wrong with you.'

Of all the accounts it is the one which regarded medicine most as a science, stressing the efficacy of doctors' technological expertise as more important than 'bedside manner'. The image of the body is of a machine that can either run smoothly (if properly fed, serviced and maintained) or badly (if neglected, or if there is a breakdown). In response to the item about technical expertise being more important in a doctor than personal qualities, she wrote: 'When there is disease or decay, what matters is his [sic] skills to put right what went wrong, or at least patch it together to regain the capacity to function once more.'

This account also strongly advocated taking personal responsibility, seeing health in adulthood as depending upon building up a robust constitution when young, and taking proper care in adulthood as able to prevent many of the illnesses of old age. Her own area of interest showed in the dietician's comments: 'A proper, wholesome diet in childhood is essential to health in later life. Mothers who have had poor diets all their lives have far more troubles in pregnancy, and have smaller babies.'

Many people were seen to suffer from illnesses caused by their own bad habits. The worst off in our society were seen to have real choices about the unhealthy lives they lead. Her comments were:

> But we have the responsibility to maintain our own health. Some people feel it up to others to make them healthy.

> Education helps but people have a choice, they may not use the knowledge to their advantage.

The following additional item was suggested: 'Some people don't want to participate in their treatment, they should be educated to the contrary.'

Taking personal responsibility meant, in this view, also making your own decisions. When it comes to medical treatment, patients should not be expected to follow their doctor's orders. The comment added here was: 'Patients should decide if the advice is in their best interests.'

Overall the account protrayed being healthy or ill as largely products of mechanistic, biological processes. The practice of medicine was construed as a technical 'fix' for mending dysfunctional bodies and clearing up disease. As it is a purely technological endeavour, people are entitled to be told what alternatives there are for treatment, and weigh up the benefits and risks involved in each one. People can do a lot and should act as necessary to keep their body in good running order, and hence avoid its breakdown. That they failed to do so was sometimes a matter of ignorance, sometimes laziness, and sometimes just pure cussedness.

Account 5: 'inequality of access'

Two participants' Q-sorts exemplified this factor, a social worker and a physiotherapist. Both described their political views as 'left-wing' and both mentioned that they had been active members of trades unions.

Within the account ill health was seen here as a product of the injustices between rich and poor, and the impact of capitalism. The poor and exploited in society were assumed to have little choice about the unhealthy lives they lead. The Government was seen as more concerned with tobacco revenues than people's health, and information about improving diet was viewed as having been suppressed because of lobbying by the food industry. Health foods and jogging suits were portrayed as just more ways to persuade people to spend money. Although in these respects it paralleled the 'cultural critique' account, it was overall much closer to the viewpoint Ehrenreich (1978) labelled the 'politico-economic'. It construed health as a fundamental human right and agreed that doctors have a moral duty to support nuclear disarmament, statements regarded as naive within the 'cultural critique'. However, it is when responses to modern medicine are compared that its contrast with the 'cultural critique' is most apparent.

	cultural critique	inequality of access
Modern therapeutic achievements (like heart transplants) are important contributions to progress in health care.	−6	+3
Fringe medicine is a dangerous intrusion on proper health care.	−3	+2
Many forms of medical treatment today seem to do more harm than good.	+3	−4
Treating people as 'mentally ill' is often a means by which society controls those who don't conform.	+5	0
Modern drugs have made a major contribution to fighting disease.	−3	+3
Adequate food, better housing and proper drains have done more to improve our health than all the medical discoveries of the last 100 years.	+6	−3
We are fortunate to live in a world of medical excellence – skilled surgery, highly trained professional care etc.	−2	+2

While the 'cultural critique' account denounced modern medicine as an institution of hegemonic power, frequently incapable of providing cure or care, this account accepted it as an effective means to tackle ill health and disease. It distinguished between, on the one hand, the power hierarchy and self-servingness of the State within a capitalist system; and on the other, the orthodox practice of healing as an inequitably allocated but essentially benign resource.

I think it's scandalous that the NHS is always totally strapped for the funds to offer the kind of service people deserve. People are dying and waiting in pain for totally unacceptable periods because of this Government's determination to push private health care.

Fundamentally, the concern here was with inequality of access. The poor, the inarticulate and the marginalized get a much smaller slice of the cake than the rich, the vocal and socially skilled, and those in positions of authority and power in society. 'No, it's not just money. Middle class people know how to argue to get what they want, and they keep arguing until they get it.'

However, this account also introduced a more 'personal' element into the 'political' discourse described by Ehrenreich. Several of the stronger 'disagree' allocations in the Q-sort were used to deny personal blame for ill health, that illness is a form of weakness, or that illness can be a response to people being unpleasant, as one participant made clear when responding to the item 'If people are unpleasant to me, it can have the effect of making me ill.' She said:

> This is all 'blame the victim' stuff, when the real culprit is the bastards in the Government who — yes, certainly their bloody 'unpleasantness' if you want to call it that. I'd call it downright vicious disregard for the plight of others.

In combination, then, this account operated within the domains of the social and the individual, expressing a politico-economic analysis of ill health as the product of social disadvantage and the inequitable distribution of the benefits of modern medicine. Its perception of illness was of something 'real' rather than socially constructed. It denied that the individual should ever be seen to blame for any ill health they suffer.

Account 6: a 'body under siege'

This account was exemplified by the Q-sort of a woman lecturer in a polytechnic. While it regarded biological aspects of illness — particularly viruses and other germs — as important, it portrayed psychological forces as crucial, with strong assertions that emotion can lead to physical illness. For example, in response to the item about other people's actions being able to make you ill, the lecturer wrote: 'Oh yes, makes me physically sick. Literally, I frequently puke up when somebody upsets me or something distresses me.'

The notion of illness being something that is learned was strongly rejected (comment: 'no, crap idea'). The combination of emotional but unlearned causes of physical illness implies that this account adopted a somewhat psychodynamic model of aetiology, and certainly the idea of stress was seen as central. It was, however, very different from the 'willpower account' which, while adopting some psychodynamic terminology, stressed the ability of the individual to use their resources of 'mind' purposively. While therapies like relaxation and the 'will to live' were seen as able to aid recovery from illness, this account denied there was any benefit in treating illness as a 'challenge'.

An extremely intriguing grouping of allocations for this account are those which have to do with personal responsibility. Unlike the others, this account consistently gave positive allocations to these items:

	body under siege	the remainder
If people are unpleasant to me it can have the effect of making me ill.	+6	+1 to −6
I can't help seeing illness as a 'weakness' in myself and in others.	+4	−1 to −5
When I'm ill I feel as though in some way I'm to blame.	+4	0 to −6
When I'm ill I don't just feel pain and discomfort, I feel less of a person.	+2	0 to −6

I will come on to consider these responses in more detail later in this chapter. Together with these feelings of guilt and being unable to control unconscious forces or the negative emotional effects of mistreatment by others, there is a sense of biological threat too. She explained this in some detail in her interview:

I was absolutely staggered once when I went to the doctor with something recurrent like cystitis and he said it will go away by itself. I never thought of it as going away by itself, though I suppose it does sometimes . . . but I'm very frightened of illness, and not very happy to assume the body will heal itself. I would worry myself sick just to leave it, in case it turned into something worse, or got really dangerous.

The overall image is of a helpless individual trying to cope in a hostile and dangerous world, constantly liable to attack and having to rely on outside aid. This theme is familiar from the work of Helman and Snow, as described in Chapter 4. Here it has been woven from a more modern fabric of psychodynamic ideas, but its portrayal of the individual as 'under siege' is strikingly similar to the one we have seen before.

Account 7: 'robust individualism'

This account was exemplified by the Q-sorts of a GP and a personnel officer in a large food company. Within this account health was itself highly valued and illness was seen as largely the result of the stress and pollution of 'modern life'. It asserted that people should take personal responsibility for their health, about which the GP wrote: 'Which includes private health care and insurance. If people had to pay for their treatment, they would look after themselves a lot better.'

The account's central theme was the importance it accorded to individual freedom. This was illustrated in a number of ways. First in connection with its strong denial that doctors have any moral duty to support disarmament, as shown in the comment for the personnel officer: 'No – personal freedom must be regarded as paramount to life, difficult as this choice may be.'

Another instance was the GP's response to the item stating that people should be allowed to 'die with dignity'. Explaining his placement for this item in the Q sort, he wrote: 'Agree, but the decision must always be the individual's right, not society's.'

In the interview the GP had more opportunity to make his sense of robust individualism evident:

> What I'm saying I suppose is that for me personally, I value my own freedom more than anything else. I do see the person as, in the long run, their own judge and jury . . . it's not for me to tell another what to do, and it's not for anybody else to interfere with my God-given right to make my own mistakes and take my own risks.

Thus although the Q sample provided few opportunities to express this view, the account appears far less concerned with explaining health and illness than about ideas of individual freedom, although this did not extend to the freedom to have your follies paid for by others. The personnel officer wrote: 'Only if they feel free to pay the costs too! It's my taxes that pay for their treatment, and I object.'

In this vein the comments portrayed health very much as an 'investment' which can (and should) be insured, and health care little more than a business in which medical professionals are engaged. Patients are consumers, as indicated by the comment that the personnel officer made about patients following doctor's orders:

> Having consulted an expert, of course it makes sense to follow his [sic] advice. That's what he's paid for. But second opinions should be sought in cases of uncertainty. It's the patient who takes the risk, and he must make the choice, based on the best information possible.

This combination is thus one of robust individualism and of health as an 'investment' – a commodity that can be bought, sold, insured and squandered. In using a monetarist metaphor for health, it constructs a perception of individuals as free, within the market, to do exactly as they like, so long as they are prepared to accept the consequences if anything goes wrong.

ACCOUNT DIVERSITY

Whereas the other studies I described in Chapter 4 seldom identified more than two or three alternative themes or images or viewpoints, in this study I was able to identify at least seven. Not only did they differ widely according to their agreement or disagreement with statements, but also in what they treated as important. Using a combination of methods in concert, in ways that offered people opportunities to choose what they wanted to concentrate upon, the outcome was a rich and varied mosaic of accounts.

This is both the appeal and the drawback of using Q methodology. Q-sort data certainly give access to a level of diversity that is informative and fascinating. At the same time, it places heavy cognitive loads on the researcher and the reader. Reports of studies like those described in Chapter 4 are made easier to write and to read because they limit account descriptions to just two or three. With seven accounts identified, it is much more difficult to 'get a handle on' the data. As outlined in Chapter 1, such problems are endemic when scholars from any discipline seek to be true to the 'proliferation of accounts' which arise when seeking to cope with the 'radical interpretative diversity of the social world' (Mulkay, 1991). The discussions and analyses that follow are my attempt to make this task easier, while not unduly simplifying or distorting the accounts themselves by imposing too much further analysis and classification. Within Q methodology it is the analyses and classification that the people participating in the study impose upon a particular concourse of propositions that are the focus for study, and it is the job of the researcher not to re-analyse these further, but rather to seek to understand them better.

Alternative explanations for health and illness

All of the accounts contain within them explanations for health and illness – explanations of why people are healthy or well, what makes them ill and, when they are ill, what makes them recover. This is, however, nowhere as simple as some theorists have assumed it to be. The consensual rejection of the item which stated that illness can be a punishment for misdeeds places all seven of the accounts outside of a 'personalistic' framework (see Chapter 2). However, even within each account there was no straightforward distinction between, say, endogenous and exogenous ascriptions of cause. Probably the best known and most frequently used classification is the version of this proposed by Wallston and Wallston (1981), who, working from the notion of general locus of control developed by Rotter (1966), argued that people differ in their attributions of the site of control over health and illness, dividing between those who see the site as one of 'internal control' (primarily an individual's own actions) and those for whom control is sited externally (i.e. determined by the effects of chance or fate), more recently extended to include a second form of 'external control', that of 'powerful others'.

Figure 6.1 shows a general analysis of the reasons ascribed for health, illness and recovery for each of the seven accounts, derived from Q-sort placements, comments and interview data. For not one single one of these could an internal/external health locus of control classification be applied – all combine both aspects. However, more detailed analysis does show that some accounts at least, for some aspect of health/illness/recovery, tend to favour one or the other.

Beginning with an analysis of the ascribed reasons for health, it can be seen that explanations vary widely. Some, like behaviour, mind, heredity and the body's own defences, are from within the individual. Others, like chance, social policy and medical advances, operate from outside of the individual. The 'cultural critique' account focused on reasons *outside* of the individual – external control, with the major emphasis placed upon social forces that exploit and oppress the weak, the poor and marginal or minority groups. Thus although there was recognition, within this account, that health is affected, for example, by an individual's lifestyle, this 'internal' element was seen as largely

155

determined by social forces which enable some the freedom to adopt a healthy lifestyle, but deny this option to many. In contrast, the 'willpower' account focused upon influences arising from *within* the individual – internal control. Here the emphasis was upon an individual's own behaviour (looking after themselves), but particularly upon the exercise of will. While external influences like good living conditions were seen to be salient, the stress was firmly laid upon internal control – health comes primarily from within.

However, not all of the accounts by any means ascribed influences primarily in one domain or the other. Explanations for why people become ill were particularly widely spread. Those arising from within the individual included behaviour (e.g. bad habits, not following courses of treatment properly), mind (e.g. negative attitudes, worry and stress) and heredity. Those arising from outside included luck and chance, other people, disease organisms, products of social forces (e.g. pollution from industrial waste, the aggressive marketing of tobacco and alcohol) and medical intervention (e.g. iatrogenic illness).

As an example of how both external and internal influences were seen to play important roles, the 'health promotion' account obviously combined the two. It identified behaviour as crucial. Illness was seen to be a product of such things as smoking, a poor diet, drinking alcohol to excess, taking insufficient exercise, etc. However, it also identified social, political and economic forces as encouraging these bad habits, such as the aggressive marketing of tobacco, a lack of health education, and Government policies. Added to all of these was the impact of pollution as seen to have a direct role in making people ill.

Explanations of recovery ranged over a wide number of factors, both arising from within the individual (such as the body's own mechanisms of defence), and those operating from outside (such as medical treatments). Some accounts stressed this aspect more than another. For instance, the 'body as machine' account was much concerned with agents of recovery, with the role of technological medicine placed as paramount. Similar understandings regarding recovery were articulated in the 'inequality of access' and the 'robust individualism' accounts, although recovery was, in itself, of less overall salience to the latter. The 'cultural critique' (including its feminist variant) and the 'health promotion' accounts were generally unconcerned with recovery, for different reasons: the 'cultural critique' and 'feminist critique' accounts because of their focus on reasons for ill health, the 'health promotion' because of its accent on prevention.

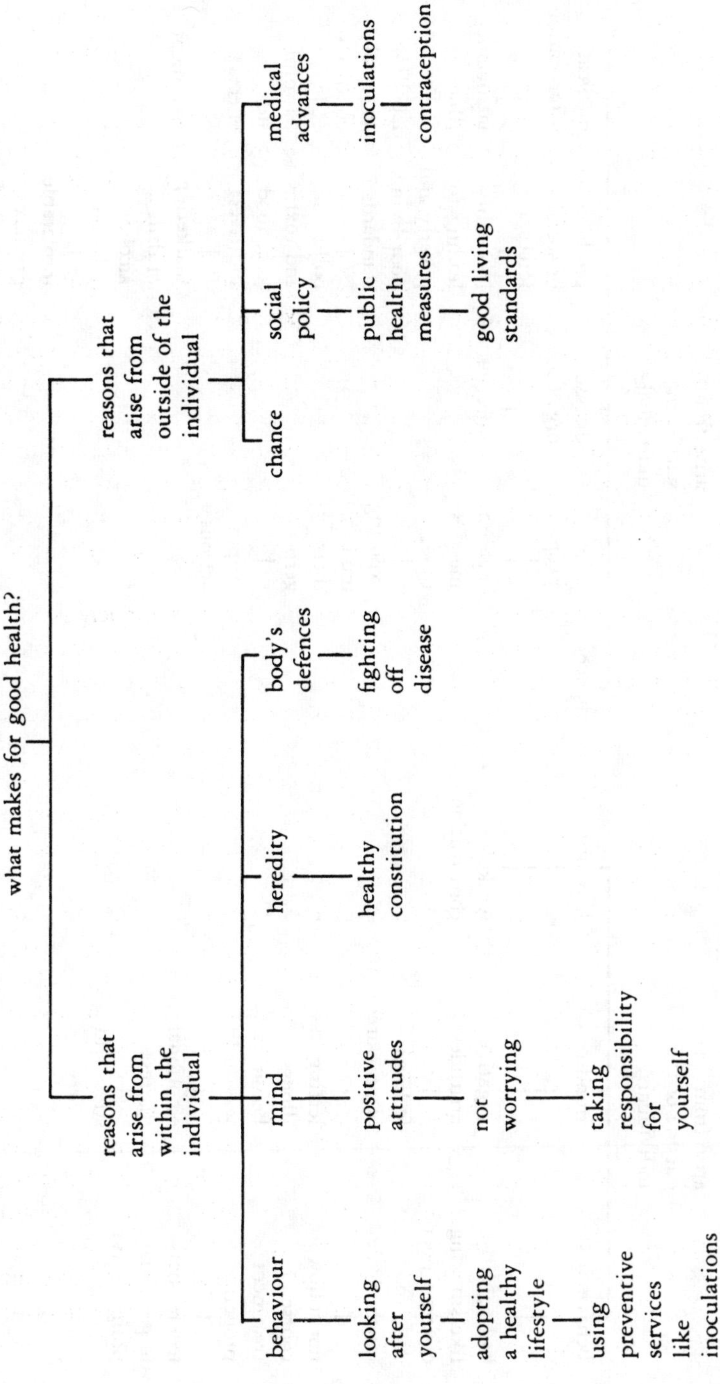

Figure 6.1(a) Explanations of what promotes good health

what makes people ill?

reasons that arise from outside of the individual

reasons that arise from within the individual

behaviour
- bad habits like smoking, eating a poor diet, too much alcohol
- not following course of treatment properly
- fecklessness (e.g. sexual promiscuity)

mind
- negative attitudes
- feelings of pressure
- letting illness become a way of life
- emotional distress
- stress and worry

heredity
- weak constitution

chance

other people
- making me upset
- exposing me to their germs
- stupid actions

disease organisms
- infection

products of social forces
- inequality leading to poverty and poor living standards
- pollution and toxins (e.g. food additives)
- marketing of drugs, alcohol, tobacco
- intolerable pressures (e.g. caused by unemployment)

medical intervention
- iatrogenic illness
- labelling as social control
- harmful side-effects of treatment

Figure 6.1(b)   Explanations of what causes illness

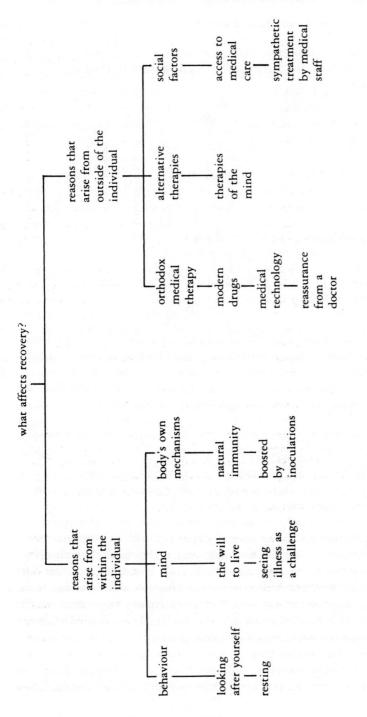

Figure 6.1(c)   Explanations of what affects recovery

Alternative models of society

Several of the accounts adopted strikingly contrasted stances about the position of the individual in society, as illustrated by their responses to these items:

	cultural critique	inequality of access	willpower	'robust individualism'
We will only improve health overall when we have overcome injustices between rich and poor.	+6	+5	−5	−3
The worst off have little choice about the unhealthy lives they lead.	+5	+5	−2	−5

The 'cultural critique', 'inequality of access', 'willpower' and 'robust individualism' accounts all assumed that lifestyle and social circumstances are crucial determinants of health status, and hence all couched their explanations within the interplay between the individual and society. They were, however, informed by opposing models of society. The 'willpower' and 'robust individualism' accounts took a 'structural functionalist' or 'pluralistic' view of society. They assumed that various social or cultural groups (i.e. different social classes, different genders, different ethnic groups) co-exist in a functional manner and that individuals have a choice about their lifestyles and living conditions. Consequently health status in this view is a product of individual decision making and circumstances. By contrast, the 'cultural critique' and 'inequality of access' accounts operated within a 'dominance' or 'conflict' worldview, in which individuals' choices and life chances — and consequently health status — are largely constrained and defined by their social position. Indeed, individual freedom to choose was at the very heart of the 'robust individualism' account's view of the world, whereas the lack of choice for the most vulnerable and oppressed groups was focal for the 'inequality of access' account.

Alternative portrayals of the role of medicine

There was a divergence in the way in which each of these four analyses portrayed the role of medicine. Between the 'willpower' and the 'robust individualism' accounts the distinction lay predominantly in perceptions of the medical profession. Within the 'robust individualism' account, medical professionls were pictured as traders and entrepreneurs whose services are paid for by the consumer, and whose job it is to perform particular tasks of monitoring, maintenance and repair. Health care, in this analysis, is a commodity to be bought and sold, and health an investment to be protected by sensible after-care and insurance (see Busfield, 1990, for a more detailed articulation of this viewpoint). The limits to personal freedom are only those that impose damage or unfair costs on others – where *their* investment may be threatened. Within the 'willpower' account, in contrast, the task of health care was depicted as a traditional 'profession', with its code of practice, obligations of service, and gentlemanly disdain of profit – the image of 'Dr Cameron' who knows each patient as an individual, and has the wisdom to respond to each of their individual needs. The contrast resonates with that between the 'New Right' and traditional conservative views on professionalism more generally.

Similarly, within the overall 'dominance' analysis there were two contrasting critiques, differing in their assumptions about the status and efficacy of orthodox medicine as viewed from either an 'essentialist' or 'social constructionist' worldview. For the essentialist 'inequality of access' account, the 'science' of medicine, like all science, is ultimately a neutral analysis of a naturally occurring reality, within which the practice of medicine is essentially a neutral response. Diseases are things-out-there that can be observed, diagnosed and treated. Within such an analysis, whatever may be superimposed by, for example, the impact of professional paternalism, the actual techniques of medical practice and treatment were seen themselves to be functional. Their purposes are, as they purport to be, to cure disease, save lives, reduce distress, ameliorate human anguish. The problem is not in the techniques themselves, or even mainly in the way in which medicine is practised, but in the way that resources are allocated. Against a principle that medical care should be available as a product of need, it was seen by this account to be inequitably distributed, with those who have money, influence or social skills able to grab a larger slice of the cake.

Within the social constructionist 'cultural critique' account, the so-called science of medicine is a chimera, a cleverly constructed mask of benign neutrality drawn over the face of medicine as a social institution, whether that of the medicine-for-profit of the 'New Right', or the patronizing humbug of the traditionally conservative 'profession' of medicine. Diseases are reifications of the doctor's 'medical gaze' and deeply socially sedimented ascriptions of 'disorder'. The problem from this standpoint is not one of the 'haves' snatching all the goodies, leaving the pickings to the 'have-nots', but the questionable nature of the 'goodies' themselves – good for whom?

Alternative assumptions about responsibility and blame

The tendency to attribute blame to others rather than to events is a major theme in attribution theory (as described in Chapter 3). We can see this theme most clearly woven within the 'inequality of access' account, which in particular used extreme allocations in the Q-sort to stress their lack of personal culpability for illness, and by contrast in the 'body under siege' account where self-blame was highly salient:

	inequality of access	body under siege
I can't help seeing illness as a 'weakness' in myself and in others.	−5	+4
When I'm ill I feel as though in some way I'm to blame.	−6	+4
When I'm ill I don't just feel pain and discomfort, I feel less of a person.	−3	+2

The 'inequality of access' account rejected blame in a personal context. One of the people who provided the exemplificatory Q-sorts in her interview summed up her reasoning succinctly:

> I don't get ill very much, only the usual things nobody can avoid like the odd cold. And I don't feel to blame for that sort of thing, that would be stupid. It just happens to everybody . . . so when I put those ones there [i.e. placed the items in the −4 positions] I think the reason why was that I was objecting to the whole idea of illness being something

that people should feel guilty about. I think I was reacting against that kind of claptrap about people 'wanting' to be ill. It makes me sick! It's an insult. . . . It's just used as another way of knocking people and making them out to be spineless.

Ideas of blame must be denied, because they are unfair, and they imply that a person is weak, defenceless and lacking in 'grit'. Yet this kind of weakness and vulnerability is precisely what was at the core of the 'body under siege' account. It is not surprising, perhaps, that this is the only account where self-blame is so consistently accepted. The woman whose Q-sort exemplified this account gave a noticeably psychodynamic explanation. She spoke at some length about the way, in which illness was paradoxically treated in her childhood, particularly by her mother:

illness in our family was a sign of weakness . . . an excuse for not pulling your weight. . . . Mother got very cross with us when we were ill, but that was the paradox, and it might explain a lot, if she really thought you were ill, then of course she waited upon you and you got all her attention.

But at the base of her 'guilt' she suggested was the instillation, in her childhood, of the principle of service – that the way you show that you love and care for somebody is to do things for them:

I'm fairly sure it's from my childhood. It was very strongly instilled that one has a strong responsibility, also a religious thing. It goes back to my mother instilling in me at a very early age the principle of service. I did a lot of little services for her as a demonstration of love and it is the single most dangerous thing in my life that I still see services – cooking, caring for clothes, buying little presents – I see that as my strongest expression of love and it leaves me with the most awful problems in my own life and it means I spend all my time trying to do everything for my family and friends and even complete strangers. . . . I feel guilty if I don't match up, because if I'm not fit and well, then I need other people to look after me and I'm not able to look after them . . . and so I get frightened.

If love equals service, then not performing service equals a denial or retraction of love. Within this, in classical Parsonian terms, illness offers the one legitimate reason for withholding service while not being seen to withhold love. But within a psychodynamic framework, which directs that we must seek out the 'real' motives for our actions, it can also imbue illness with guilt: 'I do ask myself "What are you trying to

163

avoid with this headache?" and wonder just how much I am unconsciously providing myself with a convenient way out of an embarrassing situation, or something I don't want to do.'

Also drawing upon psychodynamic notions, however, illness can be 'my real and more selfish me, standing up for myself and saying "no"'. This account, fleshed out around a self-concept as 'under siege' is thus able to make sense of feelings of 'blame' for illness. By seeing yourself as having insight into your deeper motives and able to admit that illness may be serving an emotional function allows for a different interpretation of the 'victim' label. Yes, I feel powerless and prey to threats and forces I cannot control. But no, I am not just a weak and defenceless person. I am a self-aware person, with the courage and honesty to admit my human frailty.

In popular discourse, however, psychodynamic concepts offer something more. The key may lie in this woman's use of the term 'my *real . . .* me'. When she spoke of her 'real me' saying 'no' she linked this to an account of her changing role as a woman:

> Like most women of my age, I was brought up to believe that my role as a wife and mother is to look after others, and to put my needs and wishes in the background . . . but more and more I am beginning to . . . believe that I have needs and wants too that I have a right to look after.

Within this context, an episode of minor illness (like a headache) can *both* be interpreted as a 'healthy' and desirable unconscious signal which legitimizes the indulgence of a day in bed reading ('my body is telling me what I really want and need') and yet as something which raises guilt ('my body is telling me I don't really love my children').

This distinctly different response to notions of guilt and blame is, I suspect, a reflection of different discourses operating within different sub-cultures. It is risky to speculate about class-based cultural difference, given the potential to oversimplify and to offend. I think that such speculations are worth pursuing here, though, as they may offer an important insight. Stern stoicism and a determination not to be seen as spineless is a strong theme in working-class culture and, as several researchers such as Jocelyn Cornwell and Mildred Blaxter have noted, is often expressed by working-class people in relation to illness, together with vehement denial of blame. In contrast, 'guilt' is a popular and acceptable motif among middle-class women, especially in relation to their responsibilities to their children.

I would suggest that what matters is not the acceptance or denial of blame in itself, but that discourses in the different sub-cultures draw upon different images of authentic personhood. In middle-class culture, being self-aware and able openly to acknowledge conflicts between meeting one's own needs and those of others are pertinent and highly valued qualities. In this context, to admit to feeling guilty is normal and ordinary. But within working-class culture such admissions would be seen as self-indulgent and pretentious. At the same time the qualities of 'not giving in' and refusing to accept blame that makes you a self-respecting person in working-class culture would be seen as naive, defensive and foolhardy in middle-class culture. For some accounts, at least, the particular understanding of health and illness drawn upon appears to have a lot to do with the way your available discourse portrays the person you should aspire to being.

CONCLUSIONS

In this chapter I have identified and described some of the accounts that operate in our society concerning health and illness. They are diverse and wide-ranging, differing in what they assume to be salient, both in terms of content and in the kinds of explanation they offer. What may be an appropriate domain to understand one account may be quite irrelevant for another. Some were amenable to psychological interpretation – they offered opportunities to examine accounts as forms of self-presentation; others were much more amenable to sociological interpretation, providing models of how society operates, or how the role of medicine should be understood.

However, this level of diversity poses problems if you want to concentrate on explanations. Having established to my own satisfaction that accounts about health and illness differ in the extent to which they *are* explanatory, I decided in my second study to focus in upon explanation by finding out how people explain health and illness in four situations: what makes them healthy; what enables them to improve their health in the future; what makes them ill; and, when they become ill, what enables them to recover. At the same time, I decided to focus in on ideas about blame and responsibility. These seemed the keys to making sense of explanation, and in any case I had my own axe to grind. I was thoroughly unhappy about the ways in which psychologists studied these topics, and I wanted to see if I could do better.

CHAPTER SEVEN

Explanations of Responsibility and Blame

This chapter concerns the way in which people explain responsibility or blame for health and illness. It begins with a look at what psychological theory has to tell us about these concepts, especially the way in which they are used to explain misfortunes. Of particular importance here is the notion of *locus of control*, extensively used (in the form of the Health Locus of Control – HLC – Scale) for investigating people's attributions of responsibility for health and illness. We will look first at some of the problems associated with this scale, its use and the assumptions on which it is based before we go on to examine a study I conducted in order to challenge the HLC scale, and to argue for a different approach.

ACCOUNTING FOR MISFORTUNES

Psychologists working from a psychodynamic perspective generally assume that when people explain why misfortunes happen, they look for ways that let them feel safer, less threatened or less at fault. Freud himself suggested that people adopt a 'psycho-logic' using a variety of self-justifications (it wasn't my fault, I couldn't help it) or threat-reducers (I would never do anything that stupid, so a calamity like that couldn't possibly happen to me). In psychodynamic terms these kinds of explanation are 'ego-defensive'. They allow individuals to retain an image of themselves as competent and immune to moral rebuke or sanction. But it is not just psychodynamic theorists who view people this way. Within a more functionalist approach, Smith, Bruner and White (1956), for instance, have suggested that one of the major reasons why

166

people hold and express particular opinions is their adjustive functions for the person's self-perception.

The self-justificatory tendency to attribute blame to others rather than to events is also a central tenet of attribution theory (as described in Chapter 3). This kind of self-defensive response to calamities has been specifically investigated by Walster (1966) and Shaver (1970). Being faced by a tragic event that happened to somebody else, they argue, engenders a need to believe that it could have been averted, and therefore would not happen to them. And so the victim is blamed for their misfortune. Indeed, the more serious the tragedy, the more uncomfortable it is to acknowledge the risk of something similar happening to oneself. Thus the worse the calamity, the greater the tendency to see the victim as culpable. These kinds of attribution theories assume that the explanations people adopt are a product of a need to feel in control of the environment.

However, the acceptance of *self*-blame is a much more complex area. A willingness by people to blame themselves for misfortunes (e.g. following accidents, serious illness or the birth of a sickly or 'handicapped' baby) has been observed in a number of studies (Tennen, Affleck and Gershman, 1986, provide an extensive review). The explanation usually offered is that blaming yourself allows people to confort themselves with the belief that similar misfortunes can be avoided in the future. However, this works for blame only in respect of something you did, because there is the chance, by changing your behaviour, of averting a similar misfortune in the future. People are unwilling to accept that something in their character is to blame. As you cannot change your character, that would mean continuing to be 'at risk' from the same tragedy happening again. Tennen and his colleagues found, however, that people differed in their willingness to blame themselves for illness. Blame was understood differently by different people. It also varied in its salience, being of central importance for some, and unimportant for others.

We have already examined the main social learning theory approaches in this area in Chapter 3, including Rotter's internal/external control formulations. Although the external/internal dimension has also been considered more broadly within attribution theory (see Kruglanski, 1975, for a review), it is Rotter's locus of control construct which is the best known and most extensively used formulation for examining people's understandings of responsibility in relation to health and illness. I will now trace the history of this work, since it provided the starting point for my second study.

WORK WITH THE ORIGINAL 'LOCUS OF CONTROL SCALE'

Rotter and his associates conducted a substantial programme of psychometric research, based upon a locus of control scale, which was used to distinguish between 'externals' (E) and 'internals' (I), and often therefore abbreviated to the 'E/I scale' (Lefcourt, 1981, 1982, 1983 and 1984 offers extensive reviews of this work). However, it was not long before the simple bipolarity of the E/I construct was questioned. For example, Hersch and Scheibe (1967) noted that whereas scores on the Rotter E/I scale were relatively homogeneous for 'internals', those who scored as 'externals' displayed far more variability. This suggested that different meanings were being attributed to the 'external control' construct. A number of other traditional factor analytic studies also indicated that the E/I concept operates as a multidimensional construct. Collins (1974), for example, identified independent factors which suggested that the E/I scale breaks down into four components: belief in a difficult world, a just world, a predictable world and a politically responsive world.

The most influential proponent for expanding upon the E/I bipolarity, however, has been Levenson. She has extended the original scale to include 'Powerful Others' (PO) as a third site for perceived control (her chapter in Lefcourt, 1981, provides a summary and review of her work and the reasons for it). Her decision to expand the scale arose as a consequence of her own experiences of frustration when she was forced to extend her studies by an administrative ruling: 'Lack of my personal control did not result in my becoming a frustrated fatalist. Instead I believed that events were predictable, and that there were powerful others who were in control of these events' (Levenson, 1981, p. 16).

Part of Levenson's argument was based upon her rejection of what she saw as an implicit value judgement in the E/I dichotomy – that 'internality' is assumed to be in some way morally superior to 'externality'. Levenson did not want to accept the 'fatalistic' label of externality since she felt that her frustrations were justified. They were not the product of her own weakness, but of the oppression of others.

Multidimensionality increasingly becomes important in the consideration of links between perception of control and social-political action (see Klandermans, 1983, for a review). This was because early work with the E/I scale tended to favour 'internality' as the more socially desirable worldview within North American culture, with its stress on the individual's commitment to self-determination, carrying with it the implication of personal rather than collective responsibility. Lefcourt (1981) commented, for example: 'An internal locus of control may be one prerequisite for competent behaviour and an external control orientation seems common for many people who do not function in a competently healthy manner' (p. 191).

Further, the assumed bipolarity of the construct was undoubtedly a product of its development with exclusively middle-class (and predominantly student) samples. People from different social class and/or ethnic backgrounds make sense of their worlds in ways that do not fit within this framework. McClelland (1971), for example, described the pervasive valuation of personal control in North American white, male, middle-class culture as 'need-power' and argued that far from being functional and desirable, it is divisive and can be positively fatal (he suggested that it may lead to suicide, when people fail because of what they see are their own inadequacies). To be fair, Rotter himself specifically recognized the cultural limitations of the E/I construct:

> Theoretically, one would expect some relationship between internality and good adjustment *in our culture* . . . . In regard to the other end of the distribution . . . very high scores toward the external end may suggest, *at least in our culture*, a defensiveness related to significant maladjustment. (Rotter, 1966, p. 16, my emphases)

By compounding within its concept of externality fate *and* the actions of others, the unidimensional E/I scale denies expression to worldviews which stress, for example, the importance of power relations. Whereas Rotter and his associates assumed (and had provided data to support the contention, e.g. Gore and Rotter, 1963) that it would be 'internals' who would participate more readily in socio-political action, a number of other studies specifically concerned with radical political activism found the opposite. Individuals who scored highest as 'externals' were those *most* likely to actively participate in civil rights, women's rights and other protest activities. A series of studies by Levenson and Miller (1976) showed that, given the opportunity, the more that individuals with radical or left-wing views were politically active, the more likely they were to attribute control to 'powerful others'.

These expressions of 'externality', while they do indeed deny personal control, have nothing to do with fatalism. Rather they construe the individual's role in society, the events that occur in their lives, and especially any disadvantage that they have experienced as the consequence of oppression and exploitation by those with more power. For example when Levenson and Miller studied attributions of control within members of the feminist movement, they found that separatist lesbian feminists were more likely to endorse control by 'powerful others' than other feminists, and more likely to see themselves as lacking internal control. It makes much more sense to interpret this in terms of the explicit ideology of lesbian feminism (that women are exploited and oppressed by the patriarchy) than to argue that lesbian feminists were more 'fatalistic' than other feminists.

THE DEVELOPMENT OF A 'HEALTH LOCUS OF CONTROL SCALE'

Wallston, Wallston, Kaplan and Maides (1976) sought to develop a version of the locus of control scale specifically concerned with attributions for states of health and illness. As first formulated it took the same form as the original Rotter E/I scale, dividing people into those who attribute their state of health or illness to their own behaviour and lifestyle (internal control) and those who attribute their health and illness to chance (external control). This original version of the Health Locus of Control (HLC) Scale was used extensively in a large number of studies, but proved disappointing, yielding inconclusive and contradictory results. Consequently, Wallston and Wallston decided to extend their scale to include a 'powerful others' (PO) dimension, just like Levenson. (And also like Levenson, they adopted a Likert format.) This they termed the Multidimensional Health Locus of Control – MHLC – Scale.

What is surprising is that despite the political context for Levenson's introduction of 'powerful others' as an additional dimension on her scale, when the Wallstons redesigned their Health Locus of Control Scale (Wallston, Wallston and De Vellis, 1978), in their formulation of 'powerful others' items they focused exclusively upon the *benign* influence of orthodox medicine and family and friends. This can be observed by examination of some of the items they introduced:

- If I see an excellent doctor regularly, I am less likely to have health problems.
- Health professionals control my health.
- Whenever I don't feel well, I should consult a medically trained professional.

- When I recover from an illness, it's usually because other people (for example doctors, nurses, family, friends) have been taking good care of me.

Thus the operational definition of 'powerful others' built into the MHLC Scale was totally at odds with the rationale from which this dimension was introduced. It is true that it included items which can be interpreted *either* as an endorsement of the idea that doctors, nurses and the like provide effective services to improve health and offer treatments against disease, *or* as supporting the notion that they may act in ways detrimental to health and which deny services to the disadvantaged. But this ambiguity seems not to have occurred to them (evident from their data interpretation). Wallston and Wallston appear to have had an image of 'powerful others' so blinkered by their own liberal-humanistic vision of the world that they did not even try to introduce a PO construct analogous to that devised by Levenson. It seems not to have occurred to them that medical care might be anything other than benign. Another source of potential distortion is that their scale overall makes the assumption that people are consistent in their attributions of control across situations. It assumes that, for example, somebody who sees doctors as crucial for curing illness will also regard doctors as crucial to preventing illness. These considerations apart, Wallston and Wallston's new scale undoubtedly did represent an improvement over their earlier unidimensional version.

None the less the Wallstons' initial high hopes for their new scale were rapidly dashed, as they themselves admitted rather forlornly when reporting data from a study about willingness to pick up health education literature at a health fair:

> Now with three scales rather than one we felt we could not miss . . . .
> We wish we could report the unqualified success of this strategy . . .
> but we could find no combination of health-value and . . . beliefs that
> explained the variance in number of hypertension-related pamphlets
> chosen. (Wallston and Wallston, 1978, p. 116)

Equally discouraging results were obtained by the large number of other people who attempted to find links between the MHLC Scale as an independent variable, and measures of health preventive or treatment compliance behaviours. Olbrisch (1975) found no differences between the plans for future prevention of gonorrhoea patients between 'internals' and 'externals'. McCusker and Morrow (1979) found no links between MHLC scores and cancer-preventive actions. And even with very large samples (participants in the 'Weight Watchers' programme) Stuart (1979) found no significant links at all between MHLC measures and a wide variety of health behaviours. Carnahan (1979) found no links with dental behaviour. Wallston and McLeod (1979) and Lewis, Morisky and Flynn (1978) found none with compliance with a hypertension reduction regime. Baughman (1978) studied female clerical and secretarial employees with results that even Wallston and Wallston describe as 'mixed but generally unimpressive'. Better results were obtained by Wildman *et al.* (1979) for links between internality and smoking reduction, but in another study, by Kaplan and Cowles (1978), the better compliance of 'internals' was found to be short-lived. The only area where the MHLC scale did seem to offer some predictive validity was in the case of renal dialysis patients, with Sproles (1977), Binik and Devins (1979) and Levin and Schulz (1980) all finding significant links between either internality or externality and compliance with dietary regimes.

Wallston and Wallston seem to have been undaunted by this catalogue of failure, and argued that, anyway, the scale is more appropriate as a dependent variable measure. Yet even in this situation, they were able to cite only 'modest support' for their scale in explaining antecedents of health beliefs. This included a study of their own (DeVellis, DeVellis, Wallston and Wallston, 1980) which showed that for patients who had experiences of epileptic seizures, externality was more salient than the norm; another by Nicholson (1980), who showed that after hospitalization on the birth of their first child, mothers gained higher external and lower internal scores than the norm; and another by Tolor (1978), which linked frequency of childhood illness to scores on externality, a result found only with women and not with men. As a dependent variable to provide evidence about changes in health beliefs following some form of intervention, they cited four studies, all of which also offered very disappointing results.

In fact the only research where the MHLC Scale gave encouraging results on its own was in relation to differences between groups of people that you would expect to have differing viewpoints, not so much about health, but about life in general. For example, Sproles (1977) found that Blacks expressed more external views than Whites, Harkey and King (in Wallston and Wallston, 1981) that contraceptive users and women who had had an abortion were more internal than unmarried mothers, both finding greater externality with persons having lower levels of education, and of lower socio-economic class. Wallston and Wallston's own study (Wallston *et al.* 1976) demonstrated that people who attended a health fair scored higher on internality and lower on externality than a general sample recruited at a local airport. Saltzer (1979) demonstrated higher internality scores for patients attending a weight reduction programme than those being treated for cancer by chemotherapy. With regard to the 'powerful others' attribution, women having just given birth to their first baby scored lowest (Lowenstein, 1979), and diabetics scored the highest (Nagy, 1979). The big problem is that for all of these, the data can just as easily be seen as showing that people who score low on 'internality' and high on 'externality' or 'powerful others' are people who have very contingent reason to believe that they truly do not have much control over their lives!

Wallston and Wallston were faced therefore with a whole series of results so disappointing that one wonders why they bothered to report them (and the fact that they were published at all speaks volumes about the whole endeavour of academic publication). However, on top of this they were in a situation where the positive results that they were able to obtain were paradoxical. While in a few studies internality did give some positive indications of 'healthy' actions, externality was (albeit still infrequently) a *better* predictor. The problem about that was that quite often it was *externality* which proved to be linked to 'healthy' behaviour (e.g. compliance with drug regimes). In other words, at least as often as not, it was the self-motivated 'internals' who were *least* likely, and the 'fatalistic' externals who were *most* likely to do what health professionals wanted them to do! Internality proved not to be the desirable trait that had been supposed, at least as far as many forms of health-related behaviours were concerned. Wallston and Wallston's general reaction to the sorry history of their scale, smacks of the same self-justificatory interpretational gymnastics that other theorists have been only too willing to accord to the victims of 'psycho-logic'! They conclude their review of studies using the MHLC Scale by saying: 'health locus of control research is still in its adolescence, full of pimples and promises, quivering on the brink of adulthood' (1981, p. 235).

STUDIES USING HEALTH LOCUS OF CONTROL WITH BRITISH SAMPLES

The studies reviewed by Wallston and Wallston were all conducted with North American samples. The best known and most extensive work with the MHLC Scale and British samples is that of Pill and Stott (1981, 1982, 1985a, 1985b, 1987 (some aspects of their work have already been described in Chapter 4)). In a series of investigations with Welsh working-class mothers, they set out to look for links between MHLC scores and health-related actions, knowledge and aspects of lifestyle, and a range of demographic variables. In their initial pilot study (1981), Pill and Stott found the scale as disappointing as had the American researchers. They obtained no significant correlations between a salience of lifestyle index (SLI), developed by them to tap a mixture of attitudes to health, knowledge about such things as a 'healthy diet' and reports of health preventive actions, and MHLC scores, other than a small but significant negative relationship between 'powerful others' and SLI scores. They commented in relation to the internality dimension:

> The scale does not distinguish between a locus of control for health maintenance and a locus of control for illness behaviour. Moreover, it allows those who place emphasis on modification of personal behaviour for prevention and self-treatment of illness to score as highly as those who stress the use of screening procedures and professionals for both prevention and illness. This must account for some of the contradictory findings and the sometimes disappointing predictive value of the tool. (p. 98)

And with regard to the 'powerful others':

> There is, of course, no logical reason why an orientation to prevention that recognises the importance of day-to-day decisions in personal behaviour could not coexist with frequent recourse to the physician. The relationship between physician and patient could be very different, with the professionals being used as sources of advice to be evaluated and queried at the consultation. (p. 98)

Later work bore out this supposition. A subsequent, more comprehensive study with a much larger sample (Pill and Stott, 1985a) indicated that while 'powerful others' scores overall did not correlate with SLI, two items from this part of the scale did show significant negative correlations with it: 'Whenever I don't feel well, I should consult a doctor' and 'Regarding my health, I can do only what my doctor tells me to do'. In other words, these data suggest that women who saw themselves as responsible for maintaining their own health were less likely to agree that 'doctor knows best'. Pill and Stott also commented that a high 'chance' score need not indicate 'fatalism', but

174

may be simply 'a realistic appraisal of the complex variables involved in the aetiology of illness. . . . The forces of the market place are very powerful influences which are essentially external and beyond the individual's control.' As they also argued in their later paper that year (Pill and Stott, 1985b), attributed locus of control is just one among a large number of variables which determine overall worldview and action.

ATTEMPTS TO REFORMULATE THE SCALE

Nash (1987) has also severely criticized the HMLC Scale, and consequently devised a new version of her own (although careful examination of her scale items suggest that her thinking was no more politically aware than Wallston and Wallston's. There is no indication that she even bothered to go back to the original Levenson work.) Using her modified MHLC Scale, Nash found similar paradoxical results to those obtained using the original. Nash's highest 'internal' scorers turned out to be those who, when interviewed, described themselves as having what she saw as 'unhealthy habits' (i.e. smoking taking little exercise and eating 'junk food'). Nash saw the MHLC as unsuited to British samples. However, rather than wondering what was wrong with the constructs themselves, she attempted to explain her data by reference to a number of formulations, derived from people like Janoff-Bulman and Brickman (1980). They have suggested that extreme scores on the Rotter 'Locus of Control Scale' demonstrate dysfunction, showing different patterns of 'pathological' thinking. Very high 'chance' attribution, in this view, results in a 'pathology of low expectation' (i.e. being too easily discouraged). Very high 'internality' on the other hand results in a 'pathology of high expectation' (i.e. stubbornly persisting with insoluble tasks). The healthy, adjusted way to be, in this analysis, is neither strongly 'external' or 'internal'. Wong and Sproule (1982) coined the term 'bi-locals' for people like this, individuals Nash described as 'sensible people who operate within their external constraints to achieve realistic goals'.

Nash argued, therefore, that part of the reason why the MHLC Scale had proved so ineffective at predicting health-related actions is that, contrary to Wallston and Wallston's expectations, high 'internal control' attributions are not necessarily functional, nor linked to the kind of 'sensible' explanatory system likely to be expressed by the kinds of people who do sensible things like seek out health education information and preventive services, and who have adopted healthy lifestyles. However, Nash's attempts to reformulate the MHLC Scale were not very successful. Indeed, her typology appears to be even more conceptually biased than the original. Her scale yielded 'chance' and 'powerful others' factors (this last was, however, related only to compliance with medical care and advice). But her 'internal' factor seems to have more in common with Pill and Stott's image of 'taking care of yourself' than the original concept of 'internality'. Her factor derived from responses to just these two items:

- Good health depends largely on my taking good care of myself.
- If I was unwell it would probably be because I hadn't been looking after myself properly.

Her data also indicated two additional factors, which she labelled 'realism' and 'idealism', though it is hard to follow her logic for so naming them, given the items which loaded onto and defined them. 'Realism' in fact looks much more like conventional 'internality', with these items providing definitive loadings:

- Good teeth are mostly a matter of sensible eating and brushing.
- If I were financially successful, it would probably be because I proved I was capable.
- Good teeth are mostly a matter of regular dental checkups.
- If I had a lot of friends it would be because I do things for other people.

'Idealism' was defined by items about the ease with which money can be made, the desirability of having friends because 'it's easy to be popular', and 'In life you can have anything if you want it enough'. When Nash describes this as 'unrealistic over-optimism' it is all too easy to see where her own values lie. Like Wallston and Wallston before her, Nash has fallen into the trap of believing that she could objectively define the explanatory systems of others, when in truth all she was doing was imposing her own upon them.

DECONSTRUCTING THE HEALTH LOCUS OF CONTROL SCALE

The catalogue of failure for the Health Locus of Control Scale, and the

176

various attempts to modify and improve it, are not because the scale is pimply, badly designed, or insufficiently sensitive, although it is indeed all these things; it confounds a number of potentially contradictory concepts. For instance, although self-blame and self-determination are both subsumed within the 'internal' dimension, they are not necessarily concomitant. The scale assumes that people adopt a single explanatory system, whereas different aspects may well be understood in different ways – illness prevention and recovery from illness may well have differently attributed causes. It imposes ideologically biased and naive interpretations, such as treating perfectly plausible appraisals of such things as poverty and poor working conditions as mere 'fatalism'. But these faults are not, in my view, its downfall. The scale fails to work because it is methodologically incapable of yielding the knowledge which it is intended to uncover. As I discussed in Chapter 5, you cannot discover how people make sense of the world in this way. My next study set out to lend empirical support to my assertion.

THE STUDY

I wanted to deconstruct the MHLC Scale, and offer something better in its place. I wanted to explore, from what people themselves said and did, the different ways in which people attribute control over and responsibility for health and illness. My research consisted of asking people to tell me (in a number of different ways) what they thought were the reasons for and influences upon the following:

1. Their current state of health.
2. Their ability to achieve better health in the future.
3. Whether or not they become ill.
4. When they are ill, the speed and likelihood of their recovery.

At the same time I also wanted to pull to pieces (quite literally) the constructs of the MHLC Scale, and make its inadequacies evident. To achieve these two goals I asked the participants in my study to make responses to three instruments. The first was the MHLC Scale, modified only by replacing the word 'sick' and 'sickness' by 'ill' and 'illness' (because of the different meaning that 'sick/sickness' has in Britain compared with North America). The second was a health-control Q-sort, structured in part by way of an analysis of potential influences suggested by the previous study and devised in part via piloting of items. The third instrument was a lengthy Likert scale, divided up into the four situations listed above, which systematically covered the different kinds of influences identified in devising the concourse for the Q-sort which I have called the Influences on Health and Illness (IHI) Scale, for convenience. This was intended to provide a link between the MHLC Scale and the Q-sort, in that its format was similar to the MHLC Scale but its analysis (factor analysis by persons) more equivalent to the Q-sort. It also offered an opportunity to explore the potential for Q analysis of Likert style data. Details of the instruments devised for the study are provided in Appendix 2.

Participants

In order to increase my chances of uncovering a range of explanations I recruited participants from a diversity of sources including colleges in the north and south of the UK, the Samaritans, secretarial, broadcasting and other staff at my work-place (who also recruited family members and friends), a Spiritualist Church, and members of various orthodox and 'alternative' medicine organizations, clinics, hospitals and practices. I made strenuous attempts to include more 'working-class' people than I had in the previous study, for example by seeking contacts via a local pub, a housing scheme for retired people, and in local shops. I also recruited a Hindu student, a woman with spina bifida, a psychotherapist, a woman who had had a mastectomy and another who had been operated upon for a pituitary tumour. A total of 100 sets of materials were given or sent out, 83 of which were returned in a usable form in time to be included in the analysis. Participants were given a book or record token as an incentive, except for the Samaritans, who received a contribution to the organization's funds.

Procedure

The three scales were given or mailed out to participants who were provided with a stamped addressed envelope for the return of completed scales and response forms. Most participants worked from written instructions. As in the previous study I asked people to write open ended comments as well as complete the scales themselves. In this study I did not, however, interview the participants as well.

Results

When all the materials were returned, the Q-sort responses were coded in the usual way. The Q sort and the IHI data were subjected to by-person factor analysis, factors extracted by varimax rotation. The Health Locus of Control data were partitioned in the orthodox manner to give separate internal, chance and powerful other scores for each participant, but were also by-person factor analysed for exploration of the factors which would emerge.

MULTIDIMENSIONAL HEALTH LOCUS OF CONTROL (MHLC) DATA

The scores obtained in this study for 'internality' averaged 22.76, somewhat lower than is typical for other studies using the scale, but the means for 'chance' (17.54) and 'powerful others' (15.11) are within their usual ranges. However, for all three sub-scales, my data contained much more variance than is usual, with the standard deviations approximately double those typically found. This is not surprising given that many of the participants were deliberately selected for diversity, and provided some reassurance that I had indeed achieved it.

However, where the data became more interesting is when a by-person factor analysis was carried out. Sixteen independent factors with eigenvalues greater than one were derived, though here I will describe only the seven which were most easily interpretable. These are summarized in Table 7.1.

Table 7.1   Factors extracted from by-person factor analysis of MHLC data

Factor	N	Average factor loading	Average MHLC scores		
			I internal	C chance	PO powerful others
1	22	.82	27.8	11.6	12.5
2	6	.79	15.4	28.3	12.3
3	1	.82	12.5	22	18
4	1	.75	21	24.5	28.5
5	1	.81	12.5	14.5	13.5
6	1	.86	29.5	22	20.5
7	1	.81	21.5	15.5	16.0
X̄			22.8	17.5	15.1

MHLC Factor 1, derived from the scores of 22 participants, clustered together response patterns in which the 'internal' scores were relatively much higher than 'chance' or 'powerful others'. MHLC Factor 2, derived from the scores of six participants, clustered together response patterns in which 'chance' scores were relatively much higher than either 'internal' or 'powerful others'. About half of the variance in the data overall was thus attributable to these two factors – 'internal' and 'chance'. The original internal/chance distinction emerges from by-person factor analysis of MHLC Scale responses as it does from the more traditional analysis.

However, for the remaining five factors, the simple internal/chance/powerful others division of the MHLC construct does not emerge as clearly. Even with the limited data obtained from responses to this scale, carrying out *by-person* factor analysis begins to deconstruct these constructs in some interesting ways. All of the remaining factors, while being constituted from the data of all the participants, were exemplified by just one individual's response pattern.

The participant exemplifying MHLC Factor 3 gained raw scores which were not very informative. Although her 'internality' score was lower and her 'chance' and 'powerful others' scores were higher than the relevant overall means, none was clearly dominant. Hence this was neither a clear 'chance' or 'powerful others' viewpoint, but something more complex and more interesting, which can be discovered by the pattern of her responses to different items. She strongly endorsed two 'powerful others' items:

- The type of care I receive from other people is what is responsible for how I recover from illness.
- Health professionals help keep me healthy.

However, she disagreed strongly with others:

- I can only maintain my health by consulting health professionals.
- Health professionals control my health.
- Regarding my health, I can only do what my doctor tells me to do.

The viewpoint expressed looks very much like the one which Pill and Stott (1981) found among those of their Welsh working-class mothers who had a high 'healthy lifestyle' index score. They rejected powerful others as *controlling* their health, but none the less recognized that health professionals can play a role in health promotion and maintenance. However, unlike Pill and Stott's high scorers, this woman had a below average score on the 'internal' sub-scale. Even though she endorsed items that assert control (e.g. I am in control of my health) her 'internality' score is depressed by rejection of items which imply culpability (e.g. Whatever goes wrong with my health is my fault). Like Cornwell's respondents, she was willing to accept responsibility, but not blame.

MHLC Factor 4 had a high 'powerful others' score in relation to the 'internal' and 'chance' scores, and provided the clearest identification of the 'powerful others' viewpoint (although 'chance' was also quite strongly attributed). The separate responses indicated that getting ill and being well are both seen as matters of 'what will be will be', but both family and friends and medical professionals were seen to have a lot of influence, particularly over recovery from illness. While overall the 'internality' score was low, it was the strong rejection of self-blame items, and of items which suggest the individual can *prevent* illness, which depress it. But recovery *was* seen as something that can be worked for.

MHLC Factor 5 was notable because of its low scores in all the three categories – all are below the overall means, suggesting a viewpoint in which nothing is seen to make a lot of difference, identifying what may be a genuinely 'fatalistic' viewpoint. MHLC Factor 6 was in contrast one where all scores were higher than the overall means, indicating a viewpoint which regards health and illness as multiply determined, affected by all three kinds of influence – 'internal', 'chance' and 'powerful others'. Some insight into this pattern is provided by a letter sent to me by the woman whose responses exemplified this factor, who was born with spina bifida, who had always walked with crutches and had experienced surgery many times in childhood. She clearly had good reason to endorse all three. She wrote:

> having filled in all the questionnaires, I realised that I was taking a different attitude to different ones . . . my spina bifida was just bad luck, I can't really blame anyone or anything . . . but that does not mean I can ignore advice about diet, or the need to keep active even within the limits of my handicap if I want to be healthy. I *have* to keep my weight down and do my exercises regularly if I'm to keep mobile. . . . People like me can't help but value what modern surgery has done for us. If I had been born 100 years ago I simply would not have survived, I would have died soon after birth . . . and without the help of many doctors . . . and people like physiotherapists . . . and the tremendous support I have always got from my family, and from my

friends too, I could not have got where I am now, holding down a job and owning and running my own home.

These last two factors could have been simply interpreted as 'nay-saying' and 'yea-saying', but, as closer examination of the patterns of response indicate, they do both in fact indicate more complex and meaningful viewpoints.

MHLC Factor 7 was exemplified by the responses of a student who is a Hindu. Most notable was the clear distinction he made between the influence of fate and good fortune (strongly endorsed) and accident and luck (strongly rejected); and between the importance of family and friends (endorsed) and medical professionals (rejected). It became easier to make sense of the responses later when I looked at his responses on the IHI Scale.

IHI SCALE RESPONSES

Very, very rarely, and only if you are really lucky, you have the experience in research of getting data which is truly exciting, and even (in your moments of fancy) what you might describe as beautiful. These next data were the most enjoyable and thrilling I ever expect to find. The gradual and painstaking process of bringing them to life took a couple of days, and over this time my excitement grew. The best description I can give is to draw an analogy with the trick we used to play as children with a banana in its skin, and a darning needle. We used to push the needle cautiously into the flesh, and wobble it around carefully until we had sliced the banana into pieces. We would then give the banana to an unsuspecting friend or co-operative parent, and watch their face as they pulled down the skin. Voilà, a sliced banana – end of trick.

When I started to analyse the IHI Scale data, it was just like that (and I imagine the look of amazed delight on my face would have been much the same). The by-person factor analysis of the IHI data yielded eleven factors with eigenvalues greater than one, of which five were easily interpretable. The factors and summary of exemplars (including MHLC scores and, where relevant, the factor exemplified by the scale) are provided in Table 7.2. From this you should be able to see why I was so delighted, as the IHI factors deconstructed the Health Locus of Control data almost like slicing the banana.

Look first at what happens to the earlier MHLC Factor 1, which

182

Table 7.2   Factors extracted from by-person factor analysis of the IHI data

Factor	N	Average loading	Average MHLC scores			Factors from MHLC data
			I	C	PO	
1	19	.70	24.5	16.8	16.7	1
2	4	.65	29.1	12.2	9.9	1
3	2	.68	16.5	28.2	13.7	2
4	2	.74	15	29.7	9.5	2
5	2	.65	23	16.8	18.8	7
X̄			21.6	20.7	13.7	

drew together response sets expressing 'internal control'. With the IHI data they divided up into two, yielding IHI Factor 1, and IHI Factor 2. IHI Factor 1 was exemplified by 19 people's response patterns, five of whom had exemplified MHLC Factor 1. IHI Factor 2 was exemplified by four people's response patterns, all participants who had also exemplified MHLC Factor 1. So the IHI data yielded two factors which both expressed 'internality', but since they are independent, different versions of 'internality'.

Similarly IHI Factor 3 and IHI Factor 4 deconstructed 'externality'. Each one was exemplified by two people who were exemplars for MHLC Factor 2. From this point on, the 'slicing' becomes less distinct, although the results are still interesting because IHI Factor 5 was exemplified by two participants, one of whom was the exemplar for MHLC Factor 7, and thus it is possible to make better sense of that account. These data were interpreted by examining those items endorsed most strongly (I used, arbitrarily, a cut-off point of a mean = >6) in the response sets providing the exemplificatory loading.

Within IHI Factor 1 (Table 7.3) 'internality' was by no means the only focus around which the account was built.

In terms of health and becoming ill, such things as work, home circumstances and environmental influences were also seen as important determinants. However, 'internality' was primarily, by this account, to do with 'state of mind', including both positive aspects (e.g. feeling 'on top of life' is important for current health, and 'positive attitude' and 'seeking out things that make me happy' are important for improving health in the future) and negative aspects (e.g. 'my state of mind becoming negative' is cited as something very likely to engender illness).

Table 7.3   Strongest influences as identified within IHI Factor 1

Situation	Influences scored as +6 or more (Scale 0–7)
My current state of health	My state of mind My emotions Whether I feel 'on top' of life My overall lifestyle 'Taking good care of myself' My working environment The circumstances of my home life The current circumstances at work Particular events in life at the time
My capacity to become healthier in the future	Promoting a positive attitude Seeking out things that make my happy Tackling unresolved inner conflicts Taking charge of my own life Changing my day to day behaviour Giving up unhealthy habits Improvements in work circumstances
Whether or not I become ill	My body's natural defences weakened My state of mind becoming negative Working in a poor environment Stressful conditions at work Stressful, nasty or unsettling events Inbuilt weaknesses
When I am ill, how quickly I will recover	None

Within this context, stress was accorded a central role – particularly in the working environment, and in terms of the impact of stressful or upsetting events. These attributions, plus a specific endorsement of the idea that 'tackling unresolved inner conflicts' would be salient to improving health in the future, imply a psychodynamic account for health and illness. This is supported by the observation that none of the influences suggested concerning recovery receive a mean endorsement higher than 6. Psychodynamics offers a better account for illness causation than its cure.

However, this account was not just concerned with mind. Action was seen as salient too in terms of health, with 'taking care of myself' and 'lifestyle' regarded as important influences affecting current health, and capacity to be healthier in the future strongly determined by 'taking charge of my life', 'changing day to day behaviour' and 'giving up unhealthy habits' gained mean scores of 5.6 in the section about recovery from illness. Overall, then, this account was one in which both mind and actions were seen as crucial, but where external factors like events and circumstances (which, of course, will affect such things as state of mind, particularly when stressful) were also seen to play a role.

IHI Factor 2 responses (shown in Table 7.4) were much closer to the original intentions of Wallston and Wallston for 'internality', with the majority of items that gain a mean score of 6 or more being ones to do with the individual's own actions.

However, in addition the body's defences were also seen as very important for current health and recovery from illness, and conducive circumstances and medical treatments regarded as salient to recovery. Unlike IHI Factor 1, internal aspects associated with 'mind' were regarded as relatively unimportant. Examination of Table 7.4 provides

Table 7.4   Strongest influences as identified within IHI Factor 2

Situation	Influences scored as +6 or more (Scale 0–7)
My current state of health	My body's natural defences Actively taking action to be healthy
My capacity to become healthier in the future	Changing to a more healthy lifestyle Giving up unhealthy habits
Whether or not I become ill	Behaving in stupid ways Adopting unhealthy lifestyle
When I am ill, how quickly I recover	Taking responsibility for myself Looking after myself Being careful about my behaviour Making my lifestyle more healthy Giving up unhealthy habits Circumstances conducive to recovery Treatments My body's own natural defences

185

a very clear picture of 'internality' as a belief in the individual's pre-eminent capacity to control their health in all situations by what they *do*.

IHI Factor 3, like IHI Factor 1, identified an account in which a wide variety of influences are seen to play a part, as shown in Table 7.5.

The influence of luck was strongly endorsed except for recovery. 'Luck' and 'probability' were treated as synonymous, both possibly linked to the high overall salience attributed to infectious organisms and other uncontrollable agents like pollution, age and other people's stupid actions. The sense, then, is that it is not so much that some

Table 7.5 Strongest influences as identified within IHI Factor 3

Situation	Influences scored as +6 or more (Scale 0–7)
My current state of health	Good or bad luck
	Simple probability
	Exposure to infectious organisms
	My age
Capacity to become healthier in the future	Changing to a more healthy lifestyle
	Giving up unhealthy habits
	Good or bad luck
	My age
	Exposure to infectious organisms
	What happens in the future
	Exposure to substances
Whether or not I become ill	My body's natural defences weakened
	Adopting unhealthy lifestyle
	Bad luck
	Exposure to infectious organisms
	Working in a poor environment
	Exposure to harmful chemicals
	Other people's stupid actions
	Virulence of infective organism
	My age
When I am ill, how quickly I will recover	Quality of medical treatment
	Virulence of the disease
	Taking drugs or medicines
	Treatments
	'Alternative' therapies
	Seeking medical advice soon enough
	My age

malevolent or benign 'fate' was seen as operating as the sheer unpredictability of factors that are outside of the individual's control. Recovery was treated rather differently from the other situations, in that medical intervention is seen as very important (whereas none of the medical intervention or advice items score much above a mean of 4 in the other situations). While this would be interpreted as a 'powerful others' in the MHLC Scale, it reads here much more like a perception of illness as amenable to the technological procedures of biomedicine in tackling disease organisms and dysfunction rather than the agency of 'people' per se. This suggests a further dimension of 'externality', one that sites the locus of control for *illness* in the unpredictability of disease organisms and the physical environment.

IHI Factor 4 was also 'external' in focus, though what is striking was the strong distinction made between 'luck' as having virtually no influence, and 'probability' as being very important indeed. From this perspective luck seemed to be interpreted as a capricious determinant (as in 'I'm feeling lucky tonight') whereas probability was just a matter of statistical odds. Here too infectious organisms were scored as highly salient, with medicine seen as having little role other than as a preventive measure (such things as inoculations) and in its ability to bring about

Table 7.6   Strongest influences as identified within IHI Factor 4

Situation	Influences scored as +6 or more (Scale 0–7)
My current state of health	Simple probability Exposure to infective organisms
Capacity to become healthier in the future	Simple probability Seeking out preventive services
Whether or not I become ill	My body's defences weakened Simple probability Effects of poor medical treatment Exposure to infectious organisms The virulence of infective organism
When I am ill, how quickly I recover	Simple probability The virulence of the disease itself

iatrogenic illness. Examination of Table 7.6 shows that other influences (e.g. pollution, the body's defences, medical treatments) were seen as salient. Importantly, the individual was seen as having some control (e.g. 'Taking care of myself' was scored 4.6 with regard to current health). Thus although this account does provide the clearest picture of what Wallston and Wallston intended by their 'chance' construct, it would be quite wrong to say it was one of fatalism, which is all too often what happened to people gaining high 'chance' scores.

IHI Factor 5 came from the responses of the Hindu student whose responses also provided MHLC Factor 7. With opportunity to say that 'God' and other supernatural forces are influences over health, this man's understanding can be seen with much more clarity (See Table 7.7).

The strong focus on religious, cultural and kinship aspects of life portrayed an explanatory system very different from the 'powerful others' one that Wallston and Wallston built into the MHLC Scale. The second person whose responses also mapped onto this factor was a Christian Spiritualist, belonging to a church in which faith healing is practised. So this viewpoint is in no way restricted to a particular religious or cultural background. It indicates a more wide-ranging explanatory system in which supernatural powers are regarded as pre-

Table 7.7 Strongest influences as identified within IHI Factor 5

Situation	Influences scored as +6 or more (Scale 0–7)
My current state of health	Inner forces of my 'psyche' The culture within which I live God or some other supernatural power
Capacity to become healthier in the future	Improvements in family relationships God's power or influence Some other supernatural influence
Whether or not I become ill	God's will Other supernatural influences A curse or ill-wishing
When I am ill, how quickly I recover	Care from my family and friends Intervention of a spiritual healer Prayers said for me God's will Some other supernatural power

eminent. It is, in fact, far closer to the 'personalistic' system described by anthropologists (see Chapter 2).

INTERPRETING THE DECONSTRUCTION

Overall, then, the MHLC and IHI responses provide evidence about three aspects of accounting for health and illness. First, they demonstrate that although accounts vary considerably in their focus, all offer complex explanations for health and illness which are never based upon entirely 'external', 'internal' or 'powerful others' attributions. Of course, Wallston and Wallston and others who adopted their scale never claimed that this is so, but their use of these labels (often following quite crude statistical techniques, such as dividing a sample at the mean), as in any research methodology which labels individuals by averaged responses, tends to reify the concepts, so that a higher-than-average 'chance' score is used to translate an individual *into* a 'fatalist', submerging the complexity of their responses (themselves highly constrained) and ignoring the possibility that the person may have expressed strong endorsement of, say, some 'internal' items. The 'reliability' of the scale assessed over *many* individuals beguiles researchers into forgetting that any *one* individual's average score on a sub-scale can be obtained just as easily by endorsing some items strongly and rejecting others as it can be by marking all items with mild disagreement. And yet, as the fine-grained analysis made possible by the by-person factor analysis of the MHLC Scale data showed, *some* people do make very clear distinctions between ostensibly (to the scale designers) small differences in wording (as IHI Factor 4 showed so clearly in its distinction between 'chance' and 'probability'). This is particularly true when shifts across culture become involved. The participant whose data sets exemplified MHLC Factor 7 and IHI Factor 5 was socialized and lives within a culture in which the concept of 'fate' is very different from its meaning elsewhere in North American and British culture.

Second, these data have shown that the assumed homogeneity of the three constructs 'internal', 'chance' and 'powerful others', for all the reliability claimed by Wallston and Wallston for sub-scale responses, hides distinctive and different constructions. 'Internality' segments into a focus on 'my own actions and lifestyle' (IHI Factor 2) and a focus on 'my state of mind' (IHI Factor 1). Similarly, there are at least two constructions of externality, one which is predominantly 'stochastic'

(IHI Factor 4) and one in which the external attribution of control is about the infectiousness of disease organisms, and the role of biomedicine in fighting them (IHI Factor 3). 'Powerful others' splits up into at least three alternative constructions: one which stresses the role of medical professionals as 'in control', albeit within a context of multiple aetiology (MHLC Factor 4); one which sees them as 'advisers' but not in control (MHLC Factor 3); and one which stresses the role of God, other supernatural influences, culture and family (IHI Factor 5, HLC Factor 7).

This classification is not exhaustive. Even so this range of diverse constructions gives some clues about why the MHLC Scale has not been a resounding success either as a dependent or independent variable. Its 'reliability' (which even Wallston and Wallston admit seems to fluctuate quite disturbingly study by study) is much more a reflection of the homogeneity of their participant samples and the culturally restricted coverage of their item sets than the homogeneity of the constructs that operate within popular discourse.

Finally, these results demonstrate another kind of diversity – differences in the distinctions which people make between different situations. The MHLC Scale assumes that people attribute the same locus of control, irrespective of whether it is 'being healthy', 'improving health', 'getting ill' or 'getting better from illness' that is being considered. Some explanatory systems do attribute similar levels of agreement to the same influences throughout – IHI Factor 4 is a good example, in its consistent endorsement of chance/probability throughout. But in other systems strong distinctions are made between situations. IHI Factor 3 switches from 'organisms' as major determinants of health and illness, to 'medical treatment' as the major factor affecting recovery. These kinds of within-account attributional variability question the whole basis of the 'locus of control' construct – that individuals make sense of the world according to some general, consistent, causal explanatory scheme. These results suggest that explanation is instead a flexible process in which attribution is applied differently, according to a variety of situational and other demands.

Although purists would not approve of my use of by-person factor analysis for conventional psychometric tests, it has demonstrated that even without Q-sorting, pattern analysis has a lot to offer to researchers who want to discover how people make sense of their world. There is currently a growing movement in social psychology in this direction, particularly among Europeans (Areni, Mannetti and Sabino's investigation of the links between cultural schemas and contraceptive choice,

1985, and Vala-Salvador and Leite-Viegas' study of the links between value patterns and political opinions in Portugal, 1987 are good examples). However, despite the finer-grained interpretation that by-person factor analysis of these two Likert format instruments made possible, I have argued in this book that Q method offers a highly sensitive technique for investigating and describing accounts in a way that 'mindless' and disjunctive scale responding can never do. Despite their relatively faster and easier completion, because Likert format instruments lack the intentional relational linkages that Q-sorting demands, the most distinctive features of accounts remain untapped. So let us now look at what the Q-sort had to offer to the study.

Q-SORT RESPONSES

The Q-sort data yielded fourteen factors with eigenvalues greater than one, of which six were easily interpretable. A summary of factors (including the linkages to the MHLC and IHI scales) is provided in Table 7.8.

Q Factor 1: the 'willpower' account

Of the eight participants whose Q-sorts exemplified this factor, seven

Table 7.8   Factors extracted from by-person factor analysis of Q-sort data

Factor	N	Average factor loading	Average MHLC scores			Exemplification of other factors	
			I internal	C chance	PO powerful others	MHLC	IHI
1 'Willpower'	8	.73	29.5	11.3	12.1	1	2+1
2 'The body as machine'	5	.73	23.9	20.2	16.4	none	
3 'The body under siege'	3	.69	19.5	20.7	18.2	3	1
4 'The cultural critique'	2	.79	17	19	11.7	none	
5 The 'power of God'	1	.66	28.5	15.5	16	1	
6 'Robust individualism'	1	.77	14.5	34	1.5	2	4

also exemplified MHLC Factor 1, three IHI Factor 1 and one IHI Factor 2 – all 'internal' attribution accounts. The people themselves included a psychologist, the owner of a health food shop, an osteopath/ acupuncturist, a herbalist, somebody who described himself as 'a student of the arcane school', a member of a 'charismatic' Christian church, an acupuncturist belonging to the Bahai faith, an osteopath/ herbalist and an Open University Administrator who was at the time of responding engaged in a course of biogenic treatment. Not surprisingly, given these people's backgrounds, in contrast to the 'willpower account' identified in the previous chapter, here the account favoured alternative medicine. It was unconvinced about the efficacy of conventional medicine and rejected the view that illness is cured by prescribed medicines. Rather, this account stressed an individual's competence to decide for themselves on treatment, and the effectiveness of their body's self-healing mechanisms. However, the strongest theme was again a strong 'internal' conviction about personal control over, and responsibility for, their own health. This shows up in a variety of statements which expressly endorse such a commitment:

How well or badly I look after myself generally has an influence over my overall health.	+4
When I'm ill, there is very little that I can do for myself that will help me get better faster.	−5
My overall state of health has a lot to do with my own day to day actions – I can allow myself to get run down, or take steps to stay healthy.	+3
My own actions are crucial to achieving better health – it is something I have to work for.	+5
My health is my own responsibility.	+5

This commitment extended to a clear willingness to take the blame for illness and was underlined by strong and consistent rejection of any effect of luck or probabilistic influence. More unusually disease organisms were not seen as the causes of illness, neither were environmental influences, and the effect of other people – relationships, people being unpleasant, others' stupid actions and the care of others – were all regarded as negligible. However, pollution and such things as food additives were seen to have some influence. Some flavour of just how central personal control and responsibility were to this account can be seen in the comment these people wrote:

I feel there is always something you can do help your health. The very fact of taking a positive action can help by improving your state of mind. You could feel very negative waiting for 'good luck' to turn up. . . . We must be the person who knows our own body best; what exercise it needs, food it needs, rest it needs, etc. etc. No one else can take responsibility for these things, and since I believe that lifestyle has a major influence on health, we can to a great extent determine our own health. (Health food shop proprietor)

Health will usually improve if we can help the body heal itself. Health is the natural state, so luck doesn't really play a part (except perhaps in one's circumstances). (Herbalist)

I am firmly convinced that I have considerable power to influence my own health. . . . I believe that disease can often he held off – it is never purely physical. . . . One should have sufficient control over oneself to prevent one from getting ill. (Bahai acupuncturist)

There's plenty I can do, from resting, taking medicine and advice and changing those habits etc. which made me get ill in the first place. . . . It is my responsibility to eat well, exercise and have a positive state of mind and try to develop these skills. . . . My own attitude and actions are crucial, not luck. (Charismatic Christian)

Within this account personal control was pre-eminently to do with 'willpower'. It was about being fully 'in charge', by power of will, of your body, and consequently both of being healthy and recovering from illness. Although certain things (like disease organisms, environmental factors and pressures from other people) may have the potential to affect you, you are capable of resisting their influence and, indeed, duty bound to resist them. It is up to you to achieve and maintain good health, whatever the onslaughts life forces upon you.

I take actions to mean psychological effort here, as that's the type of work I think achieves health. . . . If illness only emerges as a result of psychological factors 'letting disease in' then one must try to understand and hence control them. (Psychologist)

The power of the mind is the strongest influence over my health. (Student of the Arcane School)

My state of health is often determined by whether I take on board positive or negative thoughts and feelings. Promoting a positive outlook will make me much less susceptible to illness. (Administrator)

Emotions were also considered fairly important, as were long term life pressures and, less saliently, sudden stressful life events. This was no psychodynamic explanatory system, however, but one in which the mind was seen as an active agent of the will, a means to control, not a means by which one is controlled:

Our own inner state of health nearly always determines whether or not we get infected, ill or even have accidents! (Psychologist)

I do not believe disease attacks as a separate entity in itself – symptoms express some disturbances of body function – the body can be encouraged to right itself. (Osteopath/acupuncturist)

The internal attribution was thus of the 'body' as well as the 'mind', reflected in a moderate acceptance for inbuilt weaknesses and the effects of constitution, and of the body's self-healing properties. Within the Q-sorts exemplifying this account there was some diversity of opinion about the role of God, faith healing and prayer, with the comments of some people denying any divine intervention, but a majority asserting that the spiritual aspect of health was very important indeed, albeit in different forms and from different faiths:

I believe in a sort of Karma. Illness acts as a reminder that I shouldn't take all the good things in life for granted. If I were a perfect 'Christian' person I might not be ill. (Charismatic Christian)

God has frequently answered prayers of faith for physical healing both for myself and for other people. . . . God desires that I should live in perfect health and would never instigate my ill health. Our vulnerability to sickness is caused by living in a sinful world which has, to a large extent, rejected God. . . . My health is a reflection of my lifestyle – I need to be spiritually, mentally, emotionally and physically whole to be truly healthy. I believe complete wholeness is only attainable through reconciliation with God. (Herbalist)

I believe in the healing power of one's personal prayer to God or inner spirit or whatever. . . . Attuning to the universal 'will' is the best way of shaking loose selfish tendencies which cause me to be diseased. (Osteopath/acupuncturist)

This account offered a very clear and definite description of the role of the individual's control, which appeared in the IHI data as simply 'behavioural' with some 'mind' aspects (all the exemplars on this Q Factor load positively onto IHI Factor 1). It is an 'internal' account par excellence, with external factors such as the vicissitudes of bacteria and environmental factors, and the influence of other people seen as negligibly important compared with the individual's own self-control mechanisms, either in themselves or in conjunction with a godly or universal power. There was a strong sense both of 'mind over matter' and self-determination over fate. Of the six Q factors identified it is the one which most consistently attributed locus of control, responsibility and accountability within the self, and most consistently rejected the impact of external factors, or the influence of other people. Whether an individual is ill or well is not a matter of luck, but has a reason – and that reason is predominantly found deeply within the individual themselves.

Q Factor 2: the 'body as machine' account

The five participants whose Q sorts exemplified this factor described themselves as: a secretary, a fire officer, a clerical officer, a housewife and a school student. None of their other data sets exemplified either a MHLC or IHI Factor. Whatever it is that was being expressed here was not picked up by the other instruments. It expressed a belief in multiple aetiology and influence, weaving aspects of 'external', 'internal' and 'powerful others' in a way that remains obscured within the other scales.

The individual was seen as responsible for, and able to influence their health and may need to accept some of the blame when they get ill. But this is not so much to do with living a healthy lifestyle as 'looking after myself'. Quite subtle distinctions are made between the alternative wordings of items to do with chance, luck and probability. These are probably best explained in terms of a strong belief in the role played by infectious organisms in getting ill, and environmental factors which may increase one's susceptibility to infection, such as being exposed to cold or damp.

However, the 'strongest agree' allocations were used to endorse the effectiveness of orthodox medical care:

When I'm ill enough to consult a doctor, my recovery will be faster if I comply properly with the treatment I get.	+5
I have little faith that the advice I get from the medical profession can help very much in improving my health.	−4
I usually expect to take medicine to help me recover from illness.	+3
If I were ever seriously ill, I would have a lot of faith in the ability of doctors to find a cure.	+5
When I'm ill, my recovery depends a lot on the quality of medical treatment I receive.	+5

In contrast, the influence of friends and family is seen as unimportant:

The state of my relationships with others – how well or badly I'm   −1
getting on with those close to me at a particular point in time –
has a significant impact on my state of health.

When others are unpleasant to me, or I get into conflicts, it can   −2
have the effect of making me ill.

Sometimes the stupid or thoughtless actions of others can lead to   0
me becoming unwell.

The care and support I get from others has an influence on my   −1
overall health.

The ministrations of others were, however, somewhat important for recovery. Some clues about the division made between lay and expert 'others' is provided by a neutral allocation for the item which states that 'sometimes just the chance to talk to the doctor will make me feel better' and agreement with the item that states that the body is 'rather like a machine'. These responses imply that the mechanisms involved in health and illness are predominantly seen as physical and biochemical. Within this context, medical professionals are not so much regarded as 'powerful others' per se, but more as the agents who operate a technological system of prevention and cure, and it is that system (rather than the people who operate it) which has control over health and illness. This is shown in one of the comments made by one participant, concerning items about the power of God:

> I do not think God or religion has anything to do with your health. No one but you and the mechanics of your body are responsible . . . nothing can cure you but medicine and rest. No man [sic] can perform a miracle and make you walk. (Clerical officer)

This mechanistic perspective assumed that the body has self-healing properties and that for minor illnesses it is better to let 'nature take its course' than seek out medical treatment. This stress on the physical aspects of illness was coupled with denying the influence of 'state of mind'. In particular, psychological factors such as stress, emotions and unresolved worries are mildly but consistently rejected as explanations for illness. The item about seeking deep within oneself for the reasons for illness, the most psychodynamic, was rejected the most strongly. The biological emphasis shows up particularly in strong refutation of any influence attributable to God, other supernatural forces, or indeed any 'mumbo jumbo' (as one participant expressed it) about curses or faith healing.

Overall the internal/external/powerful others dimensions are simply not all that salient to this account. Rather it is a mechanistic explanatory model of health and illness – the 'medical model' which provides the basis for biomedicine. It does include some recognition of psychosomatic processes (e.g. one participant commented that in some cases 'Smarties' would work as well as 'active' drugs), but fundamentally its perception was of illness as the simple breakdown in physical function, due to infection, pollution, injury, or degeneration, capable of being cured by the body's own regenerative and defensive mechanisms, aided by medical care and treatment. Within this model, illness is often inevitable, but can also be held off some of the time by 'taking care' of the body, and avoiding situations where it is exposed to infection or damage. One participant summarized this well in her comments:

> I think health in general boils down to you yourself leading as healthy a life as you can. If you are fat and unfit you are more likely to have illness. Although health is your responsibility in some illnesses, not all – e.g. if you break a leg you could not stop that happening – no matter how much exercise! Medicine alone will not make you completely better – your body's defences, etc., will start to work and help your recovery. For some minor illnesses, e.g. a cold, you just 'ride it out', no medicine needed. For more serious illness I would expect to take some form of medicine – if you go to the doctors, your illness was serious enough to merit you going, so you always expect something. (Clerical officer)

Q Factor 3: the 'body under siege' account

Two of the three people whose Q-sorts exemplified this factor also provided exemplificatory data for IHI Factor 1 (i.e. the 'mind' construction of internal control). They were an administrator and an unemployed man (both were psychology graduates). The other person exemplifying this factor was a psychotherapist, who exemplified MHLC Factor 3. At first sight, then, the Q analysis seems faced with inconsistency (as far as scale responses to the previous instruments are concerned), bringing these people together as exemplars. However, closer examination of their Q-sort allocations demonstrates that they are actually reconciled quite easily.

Items that relate to emotions and state of mind were consistently and often strongly endorsed, including 'state of mind' as an important influence on overall health and health improvement, that when unhappy one is more likely to be ill, emotional distress can upset health generally, and that when ill, one should seek 'deep within' onself for the reason. Although health and happiness were not regarded

197

as equivalent, emotions, state of mind and inner motivations and pressures were seen as highly salient to health status, the process of becoming ill and the process of recovery. This is consistent with the 'mind' seen as a passive object of psychodynamic forces (in contrast to its portrayal in the 'will-power' account of Q Factor 1). This was indicated by the neutral allocations to those items which refer to the individual's ability to manage their health and illness by 'willpower'. Though 'mind' itself is an internal property of the person, within this account it is not 'in control' but 'controlled'.

Other Q-sort allocations make clear the kinds of agents seen to do the controlling – all of them 'external' and all threatening. First there was the agency of personal relationships and the idea that others being unpleasant can make you ill. More specifically it is long-term pressures and stressful life events that make you ill, and, moreover, stress and 'state of mind' are seen to interact:

> I strongly believe that health or ill health is derived from factors such as environment, stress or upsets with others, and whether I'm feeling self-confident or not, all working interactively. (Administrator)

> What is going on in your life affects how you feel – 'up' or 'down' and so, I think, your susceptibility to coping with illness . . . one's day to day 'ups' and 'downs' do affect one's general health . . . economic resources are one of the major sources of feelings of security and well-being, or insecurity and stress. (Unemployed man)

All of these aspects of the account were consistent with an explanatory model in which individuals are seen as the 'innocent victims' of stressful circumstances or events. This account sites control predominantly externally, in events, circumstances and stresses that operate *upon* the individual's 'mind', leading both directly and indirectly (by lowering the body's defences to fight infection) to illness:

> I'm well aware that when personal relationships go badly (particularly at work) they affect my health – specifically severe insomnia. My state of mind all year has been depressed and dissatisfied and I rarely sleep more than 4–5 hours. I have had two episodes of illness that were likely to have resulted from long-term stresses e.g. a spate of boils during a tough 2 years, and thyroid troubles as a result of years of stress. (Administrator).

This account is about a chain of influences acting upon each other. Stresses affect emotions, feelings and psychological wellbeing, which in turn emerge as physical symptoms. There is certainly some recognition that the individual can play a part in the process (e.g. the psychotherapist described how she gives herself Mars bars when she is 'down' as a 'treat' to cheer her up and tackle her negative emotions), but there is an over-riding sense that if you happen to get caught up in a lifestyle that is distressing (e.g. unemployment) or inherently stressful (e.g. major reorganization and upheavals at work), circumstances largely out of your control, illness is likely to follow through no fault of your own.

Although psychodynamic notions were important, I have called this a 'body under siege' account because it was so pervaded by the sense of being under assault in a stressful and threatening world. Other psychodynamic notions (such as illness acting as a somatization of anger, repressed sexuality, or childhood trauma) were not expressed. It was distressing events, pressures at work (or due to the lack of it) and attacks by other people or by disease that make you ill. I will take up the analysis of this account in more detail in the next chapter.

Q Factor 4: the 'cultural critique' account

This factor was exemplified by the Q-sorts of two women, a teacher and a research psychologist, both of whom had exemplified the radical feminist version of Factor 1 accounts in the previous study. Two other women, another researcher, also a qualified nurse and a post-graduate student in literature, also had Q-sorts which gained strong loadings on this factor, but were excluded as exemplars, because their responses also loaded fairly strongly on other factors. My own Q-sort loaded most strongly onto this factor.

Given that the purpose of this study was to elucidate explanatory accounts concerning specific and personal situations in relation to health and illness (i.e. what affects 'my state of health', not 'health in general') the Q-set offered only very limited opportunities to provide a 'cultural critique' or feminist analysis. Thus this account brought out other features of the ways in which capitalism and particularly patriarchy were seen to endanger and undermine health. First, the domination of economic resources. This was the only account to agree that economic resources affect one's state of health, or that an improved environment would be necessary to improve health. Overall this account placed strong and consistent emphasis on *physical* external influences − such as housing and working conditions, pollution and food additives and the stressful, exploitative society in which we live. Participants expressed their views like this:

> I work in a clean, relatively unpolluted environment. I live in dry, uncrowded, high standard housing. All of these enable me to be healthier. If I were an industrial worker living in the North, or a third world peasant with no clean water and open sewers, or the inhabitant of a shanty town on the edge of a large city, I would not have anything like the chances of being well. (Nurse researcher)

> Looking out over my Fen in the summer sun, I realize that the farmer sprays herbicides regularly in the field next to my house, my tap water comes from surface water heavily polluted with nitrates and there's radioactive dust in my allotment. (Teacher)

The feminist perspective, furthermore, attributes the major blame for the health-threatening violence done to the physical world specifically to its *man*-made features:

> I'd add . . . patriarchal control of the noxious influences . . . my overall state of health has a lot to do with being a woman in a man's world. (Research psychologist)

Hegemonic power was once again seen as destructive to health in the way in which it constructs 'reality' in a form that seeks to shift the blame for health onto individuals. Such blame is denied:

> Telling people that if they don't pull their socks up and take responsibility for their own health is a lovely way for the Government and the bosses of industry to pass the buck. (Nurse researcher)

> the 'blame the victim' stance of 'if you're ill, it's because deep down you really *want* to be ill'. (Literature student)

This account – in marked contrast to the 'willpower account' – is wary of the notion that people have some kind of deep seated mental power either to 'will themselves well' or possibly to account for illness, resists notions of individual culpability and plays down the importance of individual action. It is 'external' to the extent that illness is seen as a 'fact of life':

> Of course. And important in terms of the rights of the physically challenged. (Teacher)

A probabilistic assessment here was in no way 'fatalism' but what was seen as a realistic appraisal of life. It was also an explicit challenge to treating health and able-bodiedness as morally superior to and more desirable than illness or handicap, since this undermines the rights and self-esteem of people who are physically challenged. The term 'physically challenged' has been adopted within the feminist movement and elsewhere (particularly among groups such as the Disability Alliance, cf. Finkelstein, 1980) to dispute the perception of disability as deviance of *sub*-normality. There was similarly a distrust of the medical profession, rejecting compliance, the capability of medicine and doctors to cure illness, and the value of advice from the medical profession. Minor illness was seen as best dealt with by the body's own defensive and curative capacities. Overall, then, this account was predominantly more concerned about the effects of capitalism, patriarchy, social inequality, than about cause, blame and responsibility:

> [My awareness of] . . . the relationship between poverty and ill health, Third World women, private health care and of the London Food Commission report, etc. . . . There are more important things to worry about than the state of my personal health, given that Man and Nature between them will eventually finish me off anyway. (Nurse researcher)

> I see the bugs and viruses as an important a part of nature as we are, and therefore find them easier to accept than the disease created by society. (Teacher)

Consequently this account rejected psychodynamic explanations of illness, not so much to deny the possibility that 'inner life' can affect health, but because it regarded such explanations as a way to shift blame onto the individual. The explicity political stance taken here rejects notions of 'internal control' in a considered and deliberate way, treating such ideas as a 'false consciousness'. Illness, in a biological sense, is a fact-of-life – even in a 'perfect' society, there would be some disease and disability. What matters is not so much what causes it, but how we respond to it.

One way of making sense of this account is to view it as a politicized, Westernized form of a 'personalistic' belief system, replacing intervention by malicious ghosts, spirits or witch doctors by the perception of illness as the result of the direct and *motivated* impact of exploitative capitalists, politicians, the medical hegemony and decision and policy makers. For example, in response to the item that 'Sometimes the stupid or thoughtless actions of others can lead to me becoming ill', the teacher wrote, in the wake of the Chernobyl incident: 'e.g. the stupid idiots who let a radioactive cloud loose over my planet'.

What this account did, overall, was to divide accounting for health and illness into two distinct domains. There is illness which is *inevitable* within a biological ecosystem, about which individuals can take some action (e.g. getting enough exercise and choosing a healthy diet), but in general there is little anybody can do. However, much more importantly, there is illness which is potentially *preventable* or *avoidable* if society were organized differently. In a more just society there would be clean water, proper drains and adequate housing available to all, poverty would be tackled, and commerce, industry and the arms race would be forced to respond to the need for ecological protection and safe, nutritious food. In a world without poverty, anomie and exploitation, people would not need to resort to tobacco, alcohol and other 'unhealthy habits', and in a world freed from the commercial greed of the profit motive, they would not be submitted to the aggressive marketing of the 'naughty but nice'. But beyond this, a truly healthy society would be freed from negative connotations about disablement, and collective living would be organized to enable the sick and the physically challenged to participate fully and autonomously alongside the well and able-bodied.

Q Factor 5: the 'power of God' account

This factor was exemplified by the Q-sort of a single individual, a homoeopathic pharmacist. A number of other people's Q-sorts loaded, though less strongly, onto it, including a lecturer in neurophysiology; the Hindu student who exemplified IHI Factor 5, a Spiritualist healer; a pensioner who described herself as 'an active church member'; and a nurse in a managerial position. Its distinguishing feature was its strong focus on the power of spiritual and religious forces in giving health and bringing about recovery from illness. God is regarded as a major positive force for promoting and caring for health:

> I believe that God has ultimate control over all of us. (Spiritualist healer)

God does not send illness nor can ill wishing or curses cause illness, but faith healing and the power of prayer can cure: 'I believe in a God who hears and answers prayer. Though an analytical scientist, I also believe as a committed Christian in faith healing' (Neurophysiologist).

	Factors					
	1	2	3	4	5	6
God has given me the means by which to improve my health	+2	−5	−4	−4	+5	−5
I believe that God watches over my health.	+1	−5	−5	−3	+4	−5
By attuning myself to nature itself − to the 'power for good' in the Universe, I can improve my health.	+2	−3	−4	−3	+4	−4

This account combined religious and spiritual faith with endorsement of conventional medical care and treatment as well as 'alternative medicine'. The account was equivocal about individual action, seen as salient to recovery and achieving better health, but not salient to overall state of health. Personal responsibility was simply not a very important concept, and blame for illness was strongly denied. This is likely to be at least in part because of an acceptance of the role of disease organisms in causing illness and particularly virulence as affecting recovery. However, although in other accounts such acceptance of the role of infection is linked to an acceptance of the role of chance, a characteristic of this account is its consistently strong rejection of luck or probability influencing health and illness. Indeed, comments about these items show a strong antipathy to what is regarded as 'fatalism': 'I do not believe in an irresponsible fatalistic attitude to illness' (Pensioner).

This was not a 'personalistic' belief system which regarded God as deliberately bringing illness. Illness arises out of 'natural' (e.g. viruses and 'bugs') and person-made (e.g. pollution) attacks upon the body, and many things are seen to influence health − e.g. physical conditions, circumstances, the body's own defence mechanisms and emotional distress. However, it is God's intervention that was seen as the ultimate controlling influence: 'It is through the Lord Jesus that we are given our health and wellbeing' (Homoeopathic pharmacist).

Q Factor 6: the 'robust individualism' account

This account was exemplified here by the Q-sort of a woman who described herself as a mother, who also exemplified MHLC Factor 2 and IHI Factor 4, indicating a 'probabilistic' construction of externality. A university lecturer's Q-sort also loaded fairly highly, but had high loadings on other factors. This account, as before, stressed the absolute pre-eminence of individual freedom, suggesting that it is this which is salient rather that aetiology:

> To me this is a moral issue, and far more fundamental than any belief I may have about, say, whether exercise is good or bad for you. It's my body, my risk to die young, my lungs, and I reserve the absolute right to decide, and not be dictated to by a doctor or so-called expert from the Health Education Council. (Mother)

> I have the absolute right to the ultimate decisions I make on matters affecting my health, whether harmful or not. (Lecturer)

Good health was seen as having more to do with living a satisfying life than being obsessive over things like exercise and diet. Here, a firm distinction was drawn between 'chance' (seen to be irrelevant) and probability (strongly endorsed): '[Agreement with these items is] . . . fundamental to anybody who construes "reality" as fundamentally stochastic . . . basic probabilistic or actuarial "truth". If not, assurance companies would go bust' (Lecturer).

It is not surprising, therefore, to find the individual not held responsible, let alone blameworthy, for any illness. Recovery was seen neither in terms of a passive acceptance of odds nor as lying in the ill person's hands alone, although infectious organisms are seen as important causes of illness. But the effects of other factors like pollution, 'inbuilt weaknesses' and constitution were played down:

> The factors that determine, at any point in time, whether I am ill or well are complex and interactive. It doesn't make any sense to me to say that it's X or Y that makes me ill, or that by doing Z I can ensure good health. That's nonsense — I could eat all the right foods, take exercise, give up smoking, and then the nuclear power station close by could spring a leak, or some idiot could mow me down with his car, and all the 'good habits' in the world wouldn't save me from the consequences. (Lecturer)

Thus, the statement 'illness is a fact of life' provides a strong key to understanding this account. While there is a strong commitment to individual autonomy, what the individual can actually do about health is seen as limited, in a world in which so many other factors are involved. Specific explanations of health and illness are not particularly salient, however, compared with the rights of the individual for self-determination. Unlike before, in the previous study, the expression of this account had less of the monetarist flavour. Here individualism seemed more independent of political overtones, a point made by one respondent: 'I am not a political animal. I'm too much of a damn bloody minded individualist.' (Mother)

OVERALL CONCLUSIONS

The sheer diversity and richness of these six accounts make the assumptions upon which the Multidimensional Health Locus of Control construct was based look simplistic and misguided. While broad internal/external/powerful others constructs had some relevance for some of the accounts identified, for others they were almost entirely irrelevant. Using an approach which was sensitive to people's 'artful use of language to give meaning to the world' (Mulkay, 1991) made it possible to find treasures entirely buried and hidden by techniques which assume that people all share common constructs that are equally salient to all. For example, the 'body as machine' account could not be identified by the MHLC Scale. The multiplicity of attributed influences simply appear there as so much 'muddy data' that would be rejected as 'too close to the mean' to be worth considering. Given the importance of the medical model upon which it is built (in orthodox medicine if nowhere else) this failure of the MHLC Scale to uncover it may provide some clues about why the scale's performance has been so disappointing.

However, even in the three accounts where the MHLC constructs were relevant, the crude division between the three constructs, reifying individuals as one or another, is grossly inadequate to classify the alternative accounts expressed. While some (e.g. the 'willpower' account) did focus quite specifically on just one construct, for others both internal and external loci of control are equally important. Furthermore, constructs which are excluded were highly salient in some cases (e.g. the 'body under siege' account's focus on stress). Indeed, the 'body under siege' account raises questions about the conceptual basis of 'locus of control'. While the locus of *agency* – the mind – is clearly 'internal', it is none the less not a 'locus of control' in the sense that either Rotter or Wallston and Wallston intended it. Control was attributed, ultimately, to onslaughts from the *outside*, such as inter-personal strife and life-stress. But these in their turn affect the emotions and the 'mind' on the inside. The distinctions between the 'willpower' and the 'body under siege' accounts illustrate that there is a crucial difference between the perceived *site* of control, and its operation – the 'mind' can be seen as either 'in control' or 'controlled'.

Explaining health and illness is a lot more complex than separating out just three loci of perceived control. However strange or unfamiliar the accounts identified, each of them is clearly predicated upon active cognition, a theory-about-the-world, or a moral system, and often a complex mixture of both. Charles Leslie (personal communication) has classified three co-existing themes in any 'medical system' accounting for illness: cosmopolitan, humoral and punitive:

> In cosmopolitan medicine the primary conceptions of the body are on an analogy with a machine, and therapeutic interventions are efforts to fix the body as a mechanic or engineer would do. The layperson asks 'What is broken? Can you fix it?' In humoral medicine the primary thinking is ecological and based upon the macrocosm/microcosm analogy. The layperson's question is 'How can things be restored to harmony and balance?' Therapeutic interventions adjust the whole system of body and social relationships. . . . In the punitive curing traditions, the primary question is 'What did I do to deserve or provoke this suffering?'. The effort, again, is to restore harmony or balance between people, or between them and the gods.

Put more generally, he is suggesting that in any account there will exist at least three levels of explanation, each one based on an over-arching model of the world either (or both) in terms of 'what is' or 'what should be'. Firstly, the machine-like analogy implies an explanatory level that is about cause and effect, reasons, agency or influence, and so on, the mechanisms and processes by which states of health and illness occur. Secondly, the harmony/balance analogy implies an explanatory level concerned with how things interface with one another – how the individual interconnects with society, for instance, or what is her or his place in the 'scheme of things' in a religious or philosophical sense; an understanding of the broader, interactive milieu within which health and illness need to be understood. Thirdly, the 'punitive' analogy (a term which I find rather inappropriate) denotes a concern with the moral and valuational system within which ideas about health and illness need to be set.

The six accounts identified by the Q-sort suggest that all three levels do indeed co-exist, but that accounts differed in relation to which of these was most salient. The 'body as machine' account concentrated on explanation in terms of cause-and-effect. The 'cultural critique' account, however, pivoted around ideas of balance and equity, and the interconnections between the individual and society. The 'robust individualism' account was not much interested in explanation, but concerned instead to assert the individual's right to freedom of choice and self-determination. But other accounts were couched, simultaneously, at all three levels. There was embedded within the 'willpower' account, for instance, an explanation of what's 'in control' (my self) a concern with balance (about my self in relation to the spiritual domain) and a moral theme (a duty to assume control and accept responsibility).

Locus of control is primarily an explanatory, cause-and-effect construct, which sites accounting in the first of Leslie's levels of 'understanding'. It emerged from a theoretical base – social learning theory – which was itself mechanistic and positivistic in its conceptual properties. As such, locus of control reflects its conceptual limitations. Put crudely, it assumed that the kind of account salient to a small group of Western psychologists at a particular historical period would be sufficiently robust and comprehensive to explain why people act in particular ways, or why they construe the world in the way they do. It was not – and is not – up to the job. The MHLC Scale, in seeking to impose this conceptual strait-jacket upon people's accounting for health and illness, failed dismally. It did so, not just because its construct validity is suspect (because of its ethocentricity apart from anything else), but because when people seek to make sense of the world, far more is involved than a simplistic attempt to explain cause-and-effect within a very limited domain of variables.

CHAPTER EIGHT

Cultural Analysis

I set out at the beginning of this book to identify and describe some of the ways in which people explain health and illness, and place them within broader contexts and wider explanatory frameworks. I also explored some aspects of the process of explaining itself. In this chapter I will conduct a cultural analysis of results which I obtained in terms of those aims and consider the theoretical and practical implications of the particular approach which I took.

ALTERNATIVE ACCOUNTS

Within the two studies, eight alternative accounts were identified. These were, in summary, as follows:

1. The 'body as machine' account, operating within the modernist worldview of science, within which illness is regarded as naturally occurring and 'real', and modern biomedicine is seen as the only valid source of effective treatment for any kind of serious illness.
2. The 'body under siege' account, in which the individual is seen to be under threat and attack from germs and diseases, interpersonal conflicts and the 'stress' of modern life acting upon the body through the agency of 'mind'.
3. The 'inequality of access' account, convinced of the benefits of modern medicine, but concerned about the unfair allocation of those benefits and their lack of availability to those who need them most.
4. The 'cultural critique' of medicine account, based upon a 'dominance' sociological worldview of exploitation and oppression

208

and a post-modernist analysis of knowledge as socially constituted and ideologically mediated.

5. The 'health promotion' account, which recognizes both collective and personal responsibility for ill health, but stresses the wisdom of adopting a 'healthy lifestyle' in order for good health to be achieved and maintained and illness to be prevented.

6. The 'robust individualism' account, which is more concerned with the individual's right to a 'satisfying life' and their freedom to choose how to live their lives, than with the aetiology of illness.

7. The 'God's power' account, within which health is a product of 'right living', spiritual well-being and God's care, and recovery from illness a matter of regaining spiritual wholeness, attained by intercession to some form of Deity or spiritual power.

8. The 'willpower' account, which sees the individual as pre-eminently in control, and stresses the moral responsibility of the individual to use their 'will' to maintain good health.

The first two of these accounts reflect Moscovici and Hewstone's (1983) assertion that within Western culture, social representations are often popularized or 'commonsense' versions of scientific, academic or professional theories, operating within everyday discourse.

The 'body as machine' account

The 'body as machine' metaphor stems directly from the discourse of science. The ability to cure the sick is presented as science's greatest gift to humankind. The technological capabilities of modern bio-medical treatments are thus regarded as almost miraculously efficacious, and medical professionals are seen as possessing the skills, expertise and knowledge that enable them to cure. This is the most specifically derivative of all the accounts, showing that the scientific tenets of biomedicine are well ensconced in everyday discourse, albeit in modified form.

Kristiansen (1985), in a content analysis study of the British press's reporting about health and illness, noted that the image of medicine most commonly portrayed by the media, even in the 'quality' press, and particularly by television, is one which stresses its scientific base, its technological sophistication and its triumphant conquering over the scourge of disease. This is an image and a story which sells newspapers and makes for exciting and entertaining television programmes, from *That's Life* to *Tomorrow's World* (Murrell, 1987, provides an excellent analysis of the construction of popular accounts of medicine and science by the latter). It is promoted by charities that seek funds for medical research and equipment, as the sponsorship for any 'Fun Run' and the advertisements in newspapers and on hoardings make evident. It is not at all surprising, therefore, to find it expressed in everyday discourse.

Murrell argued that popular science television programmes like *Tomorrow's World* are not neutral windows through which science can be viewed, but impose approving glosses on explanations and thereby construct an image of 'an autonomous science which naturalizes the "impartiality" and, in a material sense, the inevitability of the consequences of "scientific progress"' (Murrell, 1987, p. 100). Moscovici and Hewstone (1983) have argued that this kind of compelling 'isn't-science-wonderful?' message, popularized by the media and transmitted within the education system, has turned many people into 'amateur scientists'. They suggest that this second-hand knowledge enables people to fulfil psychological needs. Biomedical theorization, which turns illness into disease, and promises effective cure, gives people a sense of safety and fulfils the desire to know, for certain, of the *cause* of (and usually the suitable treatment) advised for a particular illness. Its adoption has also been functional for medical professionals, since it renders patients more compliant.

The down-side of the popularity of this account is that it also generates dependency and an unwillingness to assume responsibility, since from this perspective medicine is seen as able to patch people back together after they become ill, making preventive actions unnecessary. Consequently, as Ehrenreich and Ehrenreich have stressed (1978), this is an account which is becoming increasingly dysfunctional in modern Western society since it engenders unrealistic expectations which have led to the 'inability of (North) American medicine to deal adequately with problems that require the patient's willed participation in the cure . . . . Patients expect to be cured . . . they do not expect the doctor to impose new hardships' (p. 69)

As I will go on to argue a little later, it is this concept of medicine as all-powerful, and therefore able to 'patch up' the damage done by an unhealthy lifestyle, that the 'Health Promotion' account has been marshalled to challenge.

The 'body under siege' account

This account is, as has already been noted, a common form of traditional knowledge, evident in minority black culture in the 'Deep

South' of the USA, and in southern England, as described by Snow (1974) and Helman (1978) respectively (see Chapter 4). Whorton (1982) has argued that whereas scientific theorization assumes epistemological progress, traditional epistemology is based upon the assumption that knowledge handed down from former generations is necessarily better than new adaptations because it is 'time-tested'. Horton also drew a contrast between the 'competitive mode of theorising' which epitomizes science, and the assumed 'consensual mode of theorising' of traditional accounts. Most of our current theorization about traditional accounts derives from anthropological investigations of indigenous cultures in non-Western settings. The best known theorist about accounting for health and illness in Western culture is Foucault, particularly in his book *Naissance de la Clinique* (1963), a complex and painstaking analysis of what he called the 'architecture of medical perception' as articulated both within medical professionalism and outside it. He proposed that accounting for illness has, throughout history, been moulded by and in its turn has moulded the more general conceptualizations and discourses operating in culture. More recently Herzlich and Pierret (1985) have summed up this analysis in terms of 'a collective discourse that draws the full and meaningful picture of biological misfortune. Each person's conceptions link the nature of his [sic] bodily experience and "medical history" to the symbols and frames of reference of his group or society' (p. 146).

They note that in Western culture such symbols and frames of reference are provided both by cultural traditions and by medical progress, so that the 'traditional' accounts of today, while they incorporate biomedical ideas, are more than mere popularization of the 'medical' account. Williams (1986b) has made similar points, arguing that these include not just 'folk' theories about health and illness but also a broader range of sedimented conceptions of personhood and morality, images and ideas about such things as 'respect for neighbourliness, for authority, for perseverence and thrift'.

In the analysis of this account as identified in my study the most pervasive theme was that of the body under siege. But its articulation also demonstrated elements of a popularization and selective modification of psychodynamic theory, incorporating a number of psychodynamic concepts (e.g. unconscious motives). The transmission of such ideas into popular discourse was the first social representation investigation carried out by Moscovici (1961). But the major locus of this account is that it is *stress* which is health-threatening. Troubling and distressing life events become somatized as disease, a set of ideas

211

with clear parallels to Herzlich's discovery of 'modern life' being perceived by people as a major threat to health and cause of illness. Similarly, the 'stress' account has been extensively described and studied by anthropologists such as Blumhagen (1980) and Young (1980). Also popularized in magazines, self-help books, television programmes, lectures and advertisements for vitamins and sleep preparations, it has developed into a very pervasive and powerful account in contemporary Western society.

The stress account can be psychologically functional for people, since it allows them to attribute illness to a specific cause. Stress acquires 'thinghood' and consequently offers a focus for explaining how distressing life events or life circumstances can make people ill. However, Young argues that it also serves functions for the medical establishment, for it allows medicine to distance itself from its inability to cure and to thrust the responsibility back onto the patient to 'do something' about their stressful lifestyle. But, he argues, its entry into popular discourse and its growing salience do not simply reflect its function to doctor and patient. More perniciously, he argues, there is a congruence between the ideological content of the stress discourse in medicine and the beliefs which most middle-class North Americans hold about people's social nature. These, Young argues, combine concepts of empiricism, individualism and voluntarism.

The stress account enables people working within a Western capitalist worldview to objectify 'stress' as an immediate *biological* cause of illness which acts on the *individual*. In this way the discourse mutes any discussion of broader *social* determinants (e.g. capitalist production, structural disadvantage). To Young the stress discourse offers a means by which the cultural critique can be muted and even denied. It is not unemployment, or a lousy job, or the patriarchy that makes you ill, it is 'stress', and thus the exploitation and oppression acted out upon people is sanitized into something stripped of any moral value, thus discouraging any questioning of the social status quo.

Thus articulated within a 'traditional' frame, psychodynamic conceptions like 'stress' or the 'pressures of modern life' occupy a similar location to images of witchcraft and *'mal ojo'* (evil eye) in more magico-religious worldviews, giving 'thinghood' to the perceived threat directed towards the individual, identifying the source of threat outside the individual. In contrast to the 'health promotion' account, these images of threats against which the individual is powerless enable the person to resist exhortations to change their behaviour or their lifestyle.

The 'inequality of access' account

This account has parallels to the 'dependent' account identified by Stephenson (1963) (described in Chapter 4) and has been extensively recounted by Ehrenreich (1978), although he calls it a 'political economic critique', which, he says, 'concentrates its fire upon the inequitable distribution of health services' (p. 2). Ehrenreich's work was based very much on the North American system of 'fee for service' medicine, where inequity in provision was at that time considerably more marked than in Britain, though the march of Thatcherism has reduced the gap considerably over the last decade. Its expression in British samples is not surprising, given that the research took place during a period in which there were strong political imperatives from the then Thatcher Government to move towards privatization of health care, with consequent reduction in the levels of services provided by the National Health Service.

Ehrenreich commented that this viewpoint views modern medicine as itself essentially benign and effective. This leads to a perception of resource limitation arising out of the pressures created by the assumed ability of medical science to work 'miracle cures' and hence an overwhelming demand for medical technology. The image is of medicine as a victim of its own success. As, for instance, the capacity to treat renal failure using dialysis and kidney transplants has increased, as medical procedures become more and more effective, the medical system has to cope with growing numbers of sick people, who would previously have died, who now require continuing care. Thus demand for initial treatment grows, as expectations are raised that such illness *is* treatable. And demand for on-going care grows, as more and more people are treated.

Garner (1979) has noted that people in the West expect to receive the best medical care that is available, especially true within a welfarist medical system such as the National Health Service (NHS) in Britain, where the costs of medical treatment are effectively invisible, since patients are not expected to pay directly for treatment and are unaware of how much it costs. Whereas in the USA major surgery can decimate a person's bank balance, when the magnitude of the treatments outstrips the insurance available to pay for it, in Britain, although drug prescriptions are charged at a nominal cost, surgery within the NHS is free, no matter what its costs.

Despite this, the problems faced by the NHS in Britain are well publicized, as budgets are cut, hospital wards and clinics are forced to

213

close, waiting lists for operations grow longer and services are run down. These events are given prominence on television and in the press, especially when highlighted by charity campaigns to raise money for machinery and buildings previously funded by the NHS. In contrast, over the last ten years there has been considerable growth in the availability of and advertising for private medicine, promoted by images of luxury and freedom very different from the dingy wards and ramshackle facilities of the public sector. It is therefore not surprising to have found that 'inequality of access' is a commonplace theme in accounting for health and illness, articulated out of both the political ideology of socialism, and a broader-based expectation in Britain that the sick deserve the best of treatment, irrespective of their ability to pay.

The 'cultural critique' account

This account has been extensively described and discussed already. It is explicitly critical of the 'popularization of science' accounts, incommensurable with them and indeed constructed (predominantly by academic theorists) and polemicized as a deliberate attempt to refute the principles upon which such 'science' is based. Its articulation as a cultural critique of modern orthodox medicine is couched within the more general post-modern account which seeks to demystify essentialism, positivism and empiricism, and to deny that (in this case) scientific knowledge is, as it claims to be, 'merely mirroring the real conditions of existence' (Young, 1980) but is rather the product of social relations which reflect the social divisions of power and labour in our culture, vulnerable to historical and ideological forces.

The articulation of the cultural critique of medicine account in the Q studies was by the Q-sorting of people who described themselves as political radicals, although, as noted in Chapter 6, the account melded together quite different radical formulations, including feminist and Marxist interpretations. It is interesting as much in its refutation as its expression. Particularly in my first study, the items provided for its expression (e.g. about capitalism being inherently anti-health) drew forth, in some accounts, highly antagonistic comments from those adopting other viewpoints such as 'Must have come out of a communist manifesto'. It is interesting to speculate why this account seemed to make a number of people so obviously angry. Certainly antagonism to what is portrayed in the tabloid newspapers as the 'Loony Left' is an emerging cultural theme within the political arena in Britain today, with the label 'socialist' acquiring the status of insult within conservative thought. This analysis suggests that the people who control the media do not just sensationalize a 'good story' to sell newsprint and increase viewing figures, but act from overt and explicit political motives, seeking not just to promote certain accounts conducive to their own perpetuation, but also to distort and vilify other accounts that they regard as threatening. To the extent that this is true, the cultural critique account is suppressed from popular discourse. It tends to be a marginal and somewhat elite discourse of a particular counter-cultural 'in-group', restricted in its availability to those who seek out radical, counter-orthodox ideas by, for instance, engaging in radical politics and reading the 'radical' press; who have access to the appropriate academic literature and the motivation and intellectual skills to read and discuss it.

The basis of this account is usually traced back to the writings of Gramsci (in English translation, 1971; Bennett *et al.*, 1981, provide an excellent summary and review), smuggled out when he was imprisoned by Mussolini. Gramsci focused on the term 'hegemony' within his argument for a Marxist analysis which transcended what he saw as the 'vulgar materialism' of the notion of class domination. His thesis was that social control is acted out by powerful groups not just by their capacity to dominate in terms of their control over economic and other resources, but by their intellectual 'ethical-political' power to construct culture. Gramsci's attacks on intellectualism were specifically antagonistic to the idea that expert knowledge is either politically neutral, or should be seen as a justification for assumed superiority:

> We need to free ourselves from the habit of seeing culture as encyclopaedic knowledge, and men [sic] as mere receptacles to be stuffed full of empirical data and a mass of unconnected raw facts . . . . This form of culture is really dangerous, particularly for the proletariat. It serves only to create maladjusted people, people who believe they are superior to the rest of humanity because they have memorised a certain number of facts and dates and who rattle them off at every opportunity, so turning them into a barrier between themselves and others. It serves to create the kind of weak and colourless intellectualism . . . which has given birth to a mass of pretentious babblers . . . this is not culture, but pedantry, not intelligence, but intellect, and it is absolutely right to react against it. (Gramsci, 1977)

Gramsci argued that the Enlightenment was an emancipatory cultural movement which questioned the status quo and laid the foundations of the French Revolution. He saw the socialist critique of two centuries later as a similar emancipatory philosophy, within which new ideas do not just emerge (in some quasi-naturalistic manner) but are 'reactions against' and questionings about the established order:

> A critique implies . . . self-consciousness. . . . Consciousness of a self which is opposed to others, which is differentiated and, once having set itself a goal, can judge facts and events other than in themselves or for themselves but in so far as they tend to drive history forward or backward. (Gramsci, 1977)

Thus Gramsci was arguing that society is neither merely constructed by nor operates just in terms of material divisions, but is more fundamentally the product of the way in which different groups wield ideas. The 'cultural crtitique of medicine' account is a direct descendant of such a notion, both in the way in which it is seen by its proponents as a specific challenge to the unquestioned orthodox ideas of biomedicine as enculturated into popular discourses, and in its refutation of the assumption that knowledge is ever empirically based or value free.

The 'health promotion' account

Unlike the four described so far, this account has been institutionally promoted and popularized as a matter of social policy, to serve the explicitly defined function of creating social change. In Britain institutions like the Health Education Council were set up with the purpose of persuading people to alter their habits and lifestyles to conform more closely to those that have been defined (predominantly by sectors of the medical profession) as 'more healthy', by way of advertising campaigns and health education in schools, colleges and within the training of health professionals. In North America, where health care is privately funded and hence costs employers large sums of money (the Chrysler Corporation estimated in 1984 that employee medical insurance cost the company $373m a year and added $600 to the cost of each car they sold: Carlson, 1984), health education and promotion is being funded increasingly by large corporations and insurance companies in an effort to reduce corporate expenditure on medical care and insurance. However, as Crawford (1984) has noted, from its origins in social and corporate policy, the 'health promotion' account has been taken up commercially. Its moral desirability aspects have acquired for it an image of high social desirability, so that the promoters of 'health foods' and designer jogging suits have been able to make huge profits by exploiting its culturally sanctioned positive images. For example, 'Tesco' have attributed much of their 34 per cent (£176m) increase in profits in Britain in 1986/7 to their investment in the production of free 'healthy living' leaflets, improved labelling and introduction of new ranges of 'healthier' foods (Poulnin, 1987).

Underlying the deliberate promotion of this account is an assumption that in order to promote healthy living, people need to be informed, and to develop appropriate attitudes and motivations. Early health education strategies assumed that it was merely necessary to provide accurate information and this would be sufficient to modify behaviour. More recent health promotion strategies have assumed that attitude change is also needed: increasing the value placed on health (Kristiansen, 1985), and persuading people to adopt a more 'internal control' attribution (see Nash, 1987, for a review).

Crawford (1984) commented that as an account it has both liberatory and 'false consciousness' potentials. As publicized by right-wing politicians, it is an account which can be used, like the idea of stress, to devolve responsibility for health to the individual and to deny structural and politico-economic causes of ill health, and hence government culpability for the inequalities between rich and poor. In Britain Edwina Currie's (1987a) suggestions that northerners are less healthy because of their poor diet and lack of exercise absolved her (as she was then Junior Minister for Health) from the need to consider social and economic disadvantage as within her remit; her invectives about the effects of alcohol abuse among doctors (1987b) absolved her from the need to consider whether the demands of their professional life may need review. The impression given by such articulations of this account is that people, as individuals, need to 'pull themselves together and act sensibly'.

However, Crawford additionally argues that the 'health promotion' account also contains a message of self-empowerment which has had considerable emancipatory impact, particularly upon women in relation to its redefinition of the desirable female body image. The promotion of fitness and muscle as more desirable for women than the 'tyranny of slenderness' has reconstituted the female body from its earlier ideal (in our culture) of frailty to one of physical power and competence. He also noted that the adoption of a healthier lifestyle does improve health and wellbeing, and can provide people with a self-image of greater confidence and self-esteem. Certainly changes in lifestyle are assumed to be the reason for the reductions in coronary disease in the United States and other Western countries (a trend much less marked in Britain). It is, therefore, important to recognize that the 'health promotion' account has different potentials and meanings according to whether it is utilized by an individual to plan and 'make sense of' their own actions (where it can be emancipatory); or used as a form of 'victim blaming' to marginalize and deny the structural problems faced by the disadvantaged.

The 'robust individualism' account

This account is fundamentally concerned with a perception of oneself as an 'authentic person'. Rorty (1987) has attributed this kind of self-perception to a number of traditions (e.g. Judeo-Christianity and the Renaissance) which have constructed our modern perceptions of 'authentic personhood':

> assuring us of a certain kind of regard, to be treated as ends not means, with activities that are rational (or at least reasonable) and good-willed (or at least well-intentioned) . . . persons should be respected because they are capable of critical reflective rationality, or because they are free inventors of their lives, or because they have divinely donated souls, or because they can be harmed, frustrated in living out their life plans. (p. 57)

Rorty argued that there have been dramatically discontinuous changes in the characterization of personhood across history, and that such conceptualizations differ across and within cultures. For example, she lists conceptions of person-as-rational-being, person-as-creative-being, person as *dramatis persona* and person as socially formed 'in the eyes of others'. This account portrays a very clear perception of authentic personhood in terms of self-determination and self-definition. Rorty described this particular version as: 'primarily negative [and] defensive . . . that concentrates on fending off external interference: "Noli me tangere", or, in Amerispeak, "Don't tread on me buddy"' (p. 56).

She argued that it emerged within Enlightenment political theory as the way in which 'personhood' could be protected against tyrannical or unjust authority. It began within the Christian conception of the person as defined by the capacity for free-will. Within our secular society, where such an 'Old Order' has lost its authority, the concept of free-will has been retained, and, unfettered from the higher authority of God, has developed into our contemporary notion of the person as a constructive, self-determining legislator – the Enlightenment image of an independent, inquiring, rational self, free from the claims of any dogmatic doctrine. However, Henriques *et al*. (1984) have argued (as have many sociologists and Marxist theorists) that the emergence of this emphatically individualist image is also the product of the profit motive of industrial capitalism. McClelland's (1971) achievement motivation formulation is clearly salient in this regard, a rare but welcome example of psychological theorization which sought to explore the interplay between individual and collective features in the linkages it drew between the level of achievement endorsement of a culture within an historical era (e.g. as indicated by the themes in its literature) and its level of production (e.g. as evidenced by the number of artefacts produced). Hence, within this analysis, the value base of a competitive capitalist system is one within which rewards are earned and misfortunes deserved, wherein a class of 'self-made-men' are encouraged to see themselves as dictated to by nobody, answerable only to themselves.

Turner (1986) has traced the history of this image of personhood along similar lines to Rorty, from the philosophy of John Locke, through the impact of competitive capitalism and Calvinistic Protestantism, to its importance in the maintenance of social order within bourgeois society. However, he has taken it further towards our contemporary culture, arguing that whereas the individualistic self-perception tended, historically, to be the prerogative of the ruling classes, because there has been a democratization of the availability of lifestyles (and hence ideologies) within the period of post-war economic recovery, this kind of self-concept is now a reflection of status rather than class consciousness. Individualism is today as much the prerogative of the *nouveau* riche, the 'yuppie' and the Thatcherite property-owning working class as it is of the Lord of the Manor or 'old money'.

The comments made by people whose Q-sorts identified this account, when directed to the topic of health and illness, showed that it can be articulated in somewhat different ways. In my first study the principle of autonomy was seen to imply a conception of health as a commodity to be bought, sold, invested in and insured, endorsing 'private medicine' as a means by which people can assert their freedom by buying services. In my second study, autonomy was expressed in terms of embodiment: 'It's my body, my risk to die young, my lungs, and I reserve the absolute right to decide, and not to be dictated to by a doctor or so-called expert from the Health Education Council.' Thus the 'robust individualism' account, like the cultural critique account, is one which challenges the hegemony-derivative accounts, although the motivation is different. Whereas in the cultural critique it is the 'false consciousness' of individual culpability that is denied (i.e. hegemony is seen as a source of exploitation and oppression) here what is denied is the right of the State, or of self-defined experts, to 'interfere' (i.e. hegemony is seen as the 'Nanny State' or intrusive professional bureaucracy). The autonomy account has its exponents both from the 'New Right' (e.g. Scruton, 1986) and the 'left' (e.g. Donzelot, 1977).

The 'God's power' account

Herzlich and Pierret (1985) have traced European 'lay' accounting for illness from roots within Christianity. Seventeenth-century Christian conceptions tended to portray a wrathful, punitive God who scourged humankind with diseases as tests of faith, as punishments for misdeeds and as routes to spiritual salvation. As an example, in a prayer written in 1654, Pascal expressed his understanding of his illness thus:

> You have given me health to serve You, and I have used it profanely. Now you send a sickness to correct me. . . . Do not suffer me to use Your punishment badly. . . . Make me clearly realise that the body's afflictions are nothing other than both punishment and the image of the soul's affliction. (Quoted in Herzlich and Pierret, 1985, p. 148)

In the seventeenth century even medical professionals assumed that healing began with the purification of the soul, and that sickness was often an offer of redemption. The shift within the eighteenth and nineteenth centuries to our dominant modernist conception, according to Herzlich and Pierret, was a product of: improvements in health (and hence, illness becoming less of a mass phenomenon); the growing capability of biomedicine to offer efficacious cures; the emerging image of the person as 'worker' within a system of industrial production; and the gradual loosening of the Church's hold over society.

Up until recently most theorists investigating accounting for health and illness have assumed that spiritual and religious conceptions of health and illness have become marginalized almost to the point of extinction within contemporary Western culture. The importance of religion has continued to be recognized in 'other' cultures, including its salience in the medical systems of 'immigrants' and in indigenous cultures (such as those of Native Americans in the USA). But the sociological and psychological literature about accounting for health and illness leaves anybody reading it with a strong sense of a highly secularized culture in which religion plays a negligible part. Religious beliefs find no place, for example, in the MHLC Scale or the 'Health Belief Model'. Indeed, Csordas (1986) has argued that a similar denial of religious elements has occurred in medical anthropology. In its emergent focus upon Western culture, it has tended increasingly to ignore the problem of explaining the 'existential relation between medical and sacred realities'.

In the last few years, however, a number of researchers have begun to recognize that despite increasing cultural secularization, religious beliefs and theistic conceptions continue to play an important role within the 'lay' accounting for health and illness of 'ordinary people'. Williams (1986b), for instance, writing about the accounting of older people in Scotland, noted the salience of an

> 'invisible religion' of a world view which, often selective in doctrine and uncommitted to the church, nevertheless drew on universal statements of faith or ethics to make sense of experience, in a way which showed a number of debts to Scottish Calvinism. (p. 1)

He argued that irrespective of the Church as an instutional constructor of discourse, such an 'invisible religion' provides a competing set of ideas to indigenous concepts of an individuated self (an image of authentic personhood which reads very similarly to those described in the 'body under siege' and 'robust individualist' accounts). Several accounts within the second study I conducted included theistic elements, drawing both from conventional Christianity and from other religious creeds and ideologies, including Christian Spiritualism, charismatic Christian faith, Hinduism and the Bahai faith. Spiritual and religious concepts were woven into the following (willpower) account, but such formulations also emerged as the basis of a specifically 'God's power' account, founded upon notions of faith, 'right living' and spirituality as central to well-being, and crucial to healing.

The research which I conducted has only touched, in a very limited way, upon the salience of religion and spirituality for explaining health and illness which is central in many of the cosmopolitan medical systems such as Traditional Chinese and Ayurveda medicine. Nevertheless, the ability of Q analysis to uncover muted accounts (which other approaches to participant sample selection and data interpretation tend to submerge) does remind us that although religion may contribute little to the accounting of many people in our culture (other than as a set of ideas to be strenuously denied, as one participant described them, as 'mumbo jumbo'), for not a negligible number of people, religious belief is highly, and often centrally, salient.

The 'God's power' account assumes that God is the pre-eminent 'Powerful Other' who watches over all aspects of the individual's life, is the ultimate source of healing and wellbeing, and is the authority to whom the individual must answer for their actions. Within this account bodily health cannot be divorced from spiritual wellbeing, and the actions which promote health are those of 'right living' within religious creed:

> I believe in a God who loves and cares for me, who watches over me, and who judges me. He is my strength, and He is my guide. If I follow His commandments, then my soul will be strong, and as my soul, so too my body and my mind. (Homoeopathic pharmacist)

Rorty (1987) argued that the Christian conception defines a person as having free-will and a conscience. This was evident in the Q identified 'God's power' account, with strong antagonism to 'fatalism' or any denial of personal responsibility; but, as the IHIQ identified version of this account in the second study demonstrated, this assumption of moral responsibility is not restricted to Christianity, for it was equally salient for the Hindu student. I suspect that one of the most interesting aspects of this account, at which, so far, my research has really only been able to hint, is the different ways in which theistic accounting deals with notions of 'fate' and personal responsibility and culpability − i.e. with the moral and ethical aspects of the relationship between the person and their God(s).

The combination of submission to a higher authority and yet strong moral codes of personal behaviour and a deep sense of responsibility to that authority is one which is problematic for any simple internal/external control analysis. And yet it is evident that such a system is both highly meaningful to, and strongly prescriptive for, those individuals who found their lives upon a strong religious faith. Any attempt to model accounting or action that ignores the role of religious faith, I believe, will not only fail to account for the 'realities' of the religious, but will be inadequate to account for the wider moral 'realities' constructed by the 'hidden religion' in our culture as a whole.

The 'willpower' account

This account has been expressed within popular discourse from at least as far back as the writings of John Barlow (1843) and Daniel Hack Tuke (1872), who asserted: 'The power of the will in resisting disease is unquestionable.' More of our age, in a *Wholistic Handbook*, Miles (1978) wrote:

> nature is an interactive friend, and disease is a feedback process within the choosing system of the individual, a process which informs the individual that some life-process is off course. The individual is the only person who can discover that feedback message and act upon it. (p. 20)

In the same book Bauman (1978) counselled expressly against the 'negativity' of blaming the environment for illness. Ardell, writing at much the same time (1977), specifically stressed self-responsibility:

> All dimensions of high level wellness are equally important, but self-responsibility seems more equal than the rest. It is the philosopher's stone, the mariner's compass, and the ring of power to a high level wellness lifestyle. Without an active sense of accountability for your own well-being, you won't have the necessary motivation to lead to a health-enhancing lifestyle. (p. 94)

Crawford (1980) regarded concepts of individual responsibility and self-determination as central to the forms of 'alternative' medicine that stress wholism, and so it is therefore not surprising that four of the six practitioners in 'alternative' medicine who took part in my second study gave Q-sorts exemplifying this factor.

The kinds of context now provided by the work of Turner (1986) and Rorty (1987), concerning the historical development of concepts of 'personhood', show that even before the nineteenth century, self-determination and free-will were well sedimented within Western popular discourse. Rorty described the 'will' focus as the more positive expression of an image of self-determination which expresses the positive aspects of autonomy in two ways. The first emphasizes critical rationality and independent evaluation, portraying the person as 'capable of stepping back from his [sic] beliefs and desires to evaluate their rationality and appropriateness, . . . capable of (at least) *attempting* to form and modify his beliefs and desires, his actions, on the basis of rational evaluations' (p. 61).

The second expression emphasizes a person's capacity to be creative and 'world making', constructing their world by shaping, choosing and constructing systems of values either as a social and political domain (e.g. by participating in public life) or as a visionary-poetic domain. These two articulations are reflected, respectively, by the 'Enlightenment' theorization about human conceptualization (as argued by Voltaire, Diderot and Condorcet; before them Socrates, Spinoza and Hobbes; after them Chomsky, Lévi-Strauss and Piaget) and the 'Romantic' theorization (of Goethe and Schiller; before them the Sophists, Hume and Leibnitz; after them Levy-Bruhl, Whorf, Kuhn, Feyerabend and Geertz). Shweder (1984) provides a thorough review of this theoretical tension. The point is that although these alternative constructions portray personal self-determination in very different ways, both assume, fundamentally, that authentic personhood is bound into the capacity for the individual's *willed* self-making and self-control.

Haley (1978) and Whorton (1982) both observed that self-control is an image that has appeared in the health discourses of Western cultures throughout much of the nineteenth and twentieth centuries. In his 1984 article, Crawford argued that within contemporary culture generally, health has increasingly acquired the status of a moral imperative. Embedded within it is the expectation that being healthy requires self-control. Good health has thus become increasingly viewed as something which you must be prepared to work for:

> Health is not a given; nor is it just the result of good luck or heredity
> . . . [n]either is it believed to be the outcome of normal life activities
> . . . . Health must be achieved. . . . To speak of health in this way is
> to speak of resolve. Health as a goal necessitates the adoption of a more
> determined regime of restraint and denial – more 'perseverence'. (p. 67)

Crawford argued that this perception reflects a number of origins, including: practical reasoning (based upon the popularization of medical research about the links between lifestyle and preventable disease); a developing sense of bodily vulnerability (particularly as a result of the politicization of public health issues and media messages about the toxicity of food additives, pollution, the ill-effects of stress and so on); and the re-emergence of self-control as a cultural symbol for authentic personhood in US culture. He too traced this construction of personhood through from the nineteenth century 'work ethic', whereby 'self control became the supreme virtue of a triumphant bourgeoisie, the foundation of "character" and achievement, the bed-rock of an ideology of self-determination . . . as a guide to action and morally as a legitimation of privilege' (p 77).

He also mentioned the impact of psychodynamics as a major force in constructing oneself as subject to an unending war between biological instinct and social necessity. Thus, within contemporary American culture, he argued, to be healthy is to demonstrate to oneself and to others an appropriate concern for the virtues of self-control, self-discipline, self-denial and willpower.

This 'willpower' account was expressed within the Q studies mainly by a variety of 'alternative' medical practitioners. According to Aakster (1986), alternative medicines, while differing in their specific theory-bases and techniques, share a common conviction that individuals must expect to take sole responsibility for maintaining their own health and, when ill, for curing themselves. Alternative practitioners regard themselves as supporting (not treating) the individual, and see their therapeutic regimes as strengthening the constructive forces of healing that are present within the body and the soul.

Unlike the 'robust individualism' account, which claims the right for individuals to set their own moral standards, the 'willpower' account assumes that moral standards are set by a higher authority (usually God) and that people should judge themselves according to how well they live up to those standards. Whereas the comments from those who expressed the 'robust individualist' account repeatedly mentioned 'my rights' and 'my freedom', those who expressed this assount wrote about responsibility, duty, the need to avoid selfishness, traps of 'blaming others' and striving to be a better person: 'If I were a perfect "Christian" person, I might not be ill.'

The image conveyed is one which Mischel (1966, 1977) has termed the 'Puritan', typified by high levels of self-control, high achievement motivation and a strong sense of personal and social responsibility. Crawford (1984) asserted that a puritanical self-image of this kind is likely to become increasingly pertinent within times of economic recession, when its links to the work ethic promote its moral features, and its links to the biological status of the body allow people, literally, to 'embody' the mandate of hard work, self-sacrifice and discipline:

Our bodies, the 'ultimate metaphor', refract the general mood. We cut out the fat, tighten our belts, build resistance, and extend our endurance. Subject to forces that lie beyond individual control, we attempt to control what is within our grasp. Whatever practical reasons and concerns lead us to discipline our bodies in the name of health or fitness, the ritualised response to economic crisis finds in health and fitness a compatible symbolic field. (p. 80)

Although this account was mainly exemplified in the second study by the Q-sorts of alternative practitioners, it was identified by the factor to which the highest proportion of overall variance in the data was attributed, showing that its expression was shared by a much wider diversity of people in the participant sample. Thus the Q study which I conducted in Britain supports Crawford's assertion for North American samples, that self-control is an important theme in accounting for health in Britain today.

EXPLANATION

This final section examines the results obtained in my two studies in terms of what they offer to an understanding of the process of explanation, with respect to three themes: account sympatricity; the selection, use and production of accounts; and the links between accounting and action.

Account sympatricity

I based my work on the assumption that people have access to and utilize a range of alternative accounts to 'make sense of' health and illness. I argued that this was a more plausible understanding of what they do than claiming that there are specific, enduring personality traits, psychological mechanisms or social forces that constrain people to think in particular ways. Boyer (1987) argued a similar case for the traditions of a culture; that they should be considered as 'a text people can use, cite and manipulate', but '[W]hat is on people's minds at any moment is only a certain idiosyncratic version.' Crawford (1984, p. 81) goes further, and argues that '[L]ogically entailed in any discourse . . . is its opposite. . . . One discourse does not exist without the other . . . the interplay between them . . . [is] apparent within individuals as well as within society.' Rorty (1987) suggested a similar 'patchwork construal of our conceptualizations of personhood:

The various functions performed by our contemporary concept of persons don't hang together: there is some overlap, but also some

226

tension. Indeed, the various functions that 'the' notion plays are so tensed that distinctive attempts to structure or relate them to one another express quite different norms and ideals. Disagreements about primary values and good reappear as disagreements about priorities and relations among the various functions the concept plays, disagreements about what is essential to persons. Not only does each of the functions bear a different relation to the class of human beings, but each also has a different contrast class. (p. 56)

In this she went further than Crawford, suggesting that what each one implicates is different; that one conceptualization is not a mere opposite of another, but that they are, conceptually, topologically dislocated – they must be viewed, in Stephenson's terminology, as in a state of complementarity. It is this image of multiple, contrary and interpredicated accounts that I have tried to convey with the term 'sympatricity'. Originating in ecological biology, when applied to accounting, sympatricity allows us to portray a situation in which diverse accounts dynamically co-exist in the same 'ecological domain' within which they have evolved in competition with one another.

However, such a biological analogy has an ultimately limited range of convenience, and sympatric accounting is perhaps more broadly approachable as a process of 'making sense' of a difficult topic by reference to a variety of texts of different kinds, some on philosophy, some story books, some encyclopaedias. Like the book I am writing, the result is no mere re-exposition of just one, but the product of my searching first here and then there to weave the story that, informed by the texts, is still my own.

The accounts as described in the previous section do convey a certain library-like quality. Having read them all, one is left with a sense of different 'texts' that a person could, at different moments and in different circumstances, pull off the shelf, use where they are helpful to push the story along, thrust back when they seem irrelevant or look nonsensical – 'texts' one would cite, use, manipulate, reject. In the inherent plausibility and cohesion of each one within its own narrative, they convey the sense which one often feels when reading a particular text, that its argument is powerfully credible. But we never read texts in literal isolation, but always against the backcloth of all the other texts which we are consulting. However compelling the present argument, we continue to have the arguments of other texts 'at the back of our mind'. Nevertheless, when you come to write your own narrative, moment to moment you can pursue only one storyline at a time.

A theory of explanation based upon a notion of account sympatricity is thus one which portrays people as storymakers who weave a narrative in and out of different 'texts'. This formulation is most similar to those proffered in Cornwell's (1984) descriptions of 'private accounts' in which people continually ask the question 'What if?' and seek to answer it, and Young's perception of accounting as a narrative process which weaves explanatory models into (and out of) a fabric also made up of episodic reminiscences, comments about similarity and analogy, expectations about social relations and norms of behaviour, together with statements about emotions and feelings. Some accounts are communal, as those described in the previous section; some will be more personal (as with Young's 1982 'prototypes' and 'chain complexes'). Storymaking selects from one 'text' and then another, gradually weaving a narrative that 'makes sense' of the topic or issue in question.

The selection, use and production of accounts

Given such an analogy of person-as-storyweaver, and the assumption that one of the main functions of accounts is to enable people to explain and 'make sense' of their world and the events within it, it becomes possible to surmise the kinds of influences upon the selection of accounts at particular points in 'the story'. These are of at least three kinds:

- Ways in which they are useful for the individual themselves.
- Ways in which they serve interpersonal functions.
- Ways in which they serve collective functions.

So far as the individual is concerned, accounts are likely to be selected at least in part in terms of their explicatory power. When people ask questions like 'What do I do now?', the selection of the account to which they will turn will depend upon what kind of answer they are seeking. Asking yourself 'What do I do now?' when you have been bitten by a rabid dog is unlikely to lead to the 'cultural critique' or the 'willpower' accounts; I suspect that there are only two that would serve the purpose for most of us – the 'body as a machine' model (find a doctor, fast) or the 'God's power' account (pray, hard), and many people would draw on both. Other accounts would be better for answering 'Why me?' questions; others for 'Why now?'.

The accounts which each of us, as individuals, draw upon to 'make sense of' health and illness will also be influenced by other, broader, aspects of our strivings to explain the world, such as our political ideology, our religious beliefs (or lack of them), our constructions of authentic personhood and how we see ourselves, how we see our relations with other people; these in their turn are mediated by our experiences, upbringing, stage in the life-cycle, access to media and so on. They will also be influenced by shorter-term autodidactic world-making, such as attempts to 'pull ourselves together', 'cheer ourselves up' and so on. The use of accounts interpersonally will relate, for example, to the way in which an individual seeks to construct reality for others, for either their own purposes (e.g. to persuade them to act in certain ways, like visit a doctor, or 'take it easy') or to meet the other person's needs (e.g. to comfort or reassure them).

Many aspects of collective functions have been described already, such as using one account to deny, negate or vilify another (e.g. the use of 'body as machine' account to deny structural causes of illhealth). Smith, Bruner and White (1956) have noted that opinion expression can act to define and maintain group-membership, and Moscovici and Hewstone (1983) also stresses the function of social representations as a basis for group cohesion and solidarity, which a purpose account expression can clearly accomplish too (e.g. the expression of the 'cultural critique' at medical anthropology conferences, and of the 'God's power' account at prayer meetings). All of these may influence account selection directly (where the account explicitly constructs the desired or functional reality), by implication (where accounts say more by what they can destroy or negate than by what they explicate) and by allusion (where accounts are polysemic and their 'meaning' is as much in their subtexts as within their overt expression). Indeed, the selection of accounts and their expression will often be multiply mediated, with the account conveying a number of subtexts at different levels (e.g. personal and interpersonal).

Thus an account-selection framework for explaining offers a dialectical theory-base. Whereas the person-as-storyweaver focuses on the individual, and the image of the texts-in-the-library implies a personal search, account selection and use should be seen much more as a process of negotiation, both between an individual and their realities, and between one person and another. Explaining is communal story-weaving in which the roles of 'teller' and 'listener' are inter- and intra-personally reflexive.

The links between accounts and action

In my work I have made no general claims that gaining a better understanding of the accounts available for making sense of health and illness should, per se, enable researchers to predict which health related or responding-to-illness actions people will adopt. There are two main reasons for such a disclaimer. First, as Harré (1979) has noted, drawing upon accounts is not just about social actions, it is itself a social activity. This is more profound than saying that people respond to being the subjects of study by treating the activity as a social encounter, but conveys that explaining is always, wherever and whenever it occurs, a story-making act-in-itself. Accounts cannot be construed as lever-like 'things in the head' that trip a person into action, but rather as 'texts' from which and within which people 'make sense' of action. The second reason for caution concerning the link between accounts and action is that account sympatricity reflects the ways in which thinking is often confounded and contradictory. Within such a system, action cannot by definition, be fully predictable. People themselves, when they are 'in two minds', are uncertain what they will do until they actually do it. If actors themselves do not know what they will do up until the very moment of action, we cannot expect an external observer to do any better!

To make this point more explicitly, imagine the situation where a researcher interviews somebody concerning their 'beliefs about health and illness'. Imagine, further, that the influences stack up within the interview so that throughout most of the conversation the exposition of the 'health promotion' account becomes the most functional and socially acceptable (as negotiated by interviewer and interviewee). The interviewer returns with the interviewee neatly categorized as a believer in 'health promotion', and predicts that she or he will act accordingly. This assumption is legitimate within a theory-base that regards 'health beliefs' as fixed and singular essences. But it is quite invalid within an account sympatricity formulation, for that has to assume that in different circumstances, with different influences, other accounts (e.g. the 'robust individualist' account) may be more salient, and hence action would be predicated not upon a 'healthy lifestyle' but upon, say, 'my body, my lungs, my right to do with them as I choose'. Account sympatricity would portray this person as continually faced with dilemmas and choices, so that sometimes they would act one way, sometimes another; their actions would be, in that sense, contradictory because the accounts from which they are operating are in complementarity and hence linked to contrasted modes of conduct.

However, an account sympatricity interpretation does not deny that there can be links between accounts and actions. Accounts can relate to actions in at least three ways:

- As sources from which to plan action.
- As sources with which to predict action (one's own, or the actions of others).
- As sources from which actions (again, one's own and the actions of others) can be 'made sense of' – explained, understood and justified.

Accounts as sources from which to plan action have already been examined as the basis for answering questions like 'What do I do now?' Which account will be selected will be dependent upon the events or issues or dilemmas to be responded to. Being bitten by a rabid dog is an extraordinarily threatening event demanding fast action and rapid and clear-cut account selection, and people are unlikely to prevaricate. Deciding whether or not to give up smoking, go on 'the pill', seek out alternative healing or give money to medical research charity are more complexly instigated actions, and accounting is therefore likely to be a much-more-considered, vascillating-process. Furthermore, some accounts are more action-prescriptive than others. For example, the 'body as a machine' account contains within it specific action-plans and rules such as 'always follow doctor's orders' and 'keep taking the tablets'. Other accounts are more interpretational and less action-orientated, such as the 'body under siege' account (which denies that the sufferer is able to act purposively) and the 'cultural critique' account (which may stop you donating to medical research charities, but in its specific denial of individual responsibility, contains few action-specific prescriptions).

Treating accounts as the 'texts' from which we may be able to predict action permits two important insights. The first is providing a framework for understanding what researchers have been doing in much of their theorization. As many interpretational social psychologists (e.g. Gergen, 1982; Moscovici, 1989; Jahoda, 1986) have recognized, such theorists have not been (as they have assumed that they have been) constructing and testing theories about universal psychological processes. What they have actually been doing is utilizing their own 'implicit understandings', drawn from the accounts they share with the subjects of their experiments, as a common 'text' from which to predict action. The researchers were able to predict the actions of their experimental subjects, *not* because they had access to action-predictive psychological theories, but because the experimental subjects knew (by drawing upon the same culturally sedimented 'texts' which the experimenters used to plan the experiment) what was expected of them. It is the very combination of the taken-for-grantedness of culturally sedimented and sanctioned accounts, their prescriptive qualities (and hence their power to specify action) and the cultural homogeneity of experimenters and experimental subjects that has led so many psychologists up the primrose path, into offering their culture- and even class-specific accounts for action as universal rules to explain human behaviour.

The other insight is that action can be instantiated only (if at all) by access to the account within which it is predicated. I have a neighbour who smiles wanly each year as she comes round to my house with a collecting tin and asks me to donate to cancer research, clearly unable to understand how anybody could refuse on moral grounds. Her incomprehension is, I believe, the consequence of her having no access to my 'cultural critique' account of medicine (however hard I try to explain it). If such a complete lack of comprehension can occur between two people who ostensibly share, in any demographic analysis, a single socio-economic class, gender and age-group, how much more is it likely to occur between people whose social and cultural origins and roles differ more widely?

The eight accounts listed in this chapter should, I hope, offer food for thought for theorists attempting to understand the ways in which people account for health and illness as routes for predicting their actions. Formulations like 'Health Locus of Control' have singularly failed to predict action (see Chapter 7) because the researchers using them assumed that people would 'make sense' of health and illness only by reference to the constructs incorporated into the MHLC Scale. People who scored high on 'external control' were classified as 'fatalists'. However, while workers like Pill and Stott, Blaxter and Cornwell have avoided this simplistic assumption, they have tended to offer only singular antithetical positions (e.g. 'external control' as a realistic appraisal of structural inequality).

I hope that my descriptions of the diversity of accounts will persuade other researchers to consider that there are likely to be, for example, many different reasons for refusing to adopt a 'healthy lifestyle', and that these are not simply matters of interpersonal variation, but intrapersonal variability too. For instance, the argument that people act in particular ways as a function of self-presentation assumes that there is a singular 'self' to be presented. The strikingly different portrayals of authentic personhood embodied within the different accounts deny such singularity. To understand the role of self-presentation in explaining health and illness requires much more sophisticated analysis of the way in which people construe themselves differently according to different situations (cf. Weinreich, 1983). Similarly, the observation that different religious and ethical beliefs and ideologies are salient to explanation for many people, and the broader recognition that accounts are not just explicatory but contain moral and meaning elements as well, should, I hope, persuade researchers to move outside of their portrayals of people as mere 'rational' or even 'rationalizing' beings, and seek to understand them as feeling, moral and spiritual beings, whose values and life-plans go beyond pleasure-seeking and risk reduction. In their very different ways the people who articulated the 'God's power', 'Robust individualism' and 'cultural critique' accounts demanded to be understood as morally authentic persons, with more important life-agendas than the pursuit of physical health.

It is no longer good enough for researchers just to look within their own narrow understandings in their attempts to predict the actions of others. Before we can even begin to predict what people will do, we need to gain a better understanding about why people do what they do, based upon *their* understandings of their actions. Action-predictive studies may well need to wait until we have made a better job of that. In fact, treating accounts as the basis from which to interpret and explain actions is a growing field of interest, already engendering subtle and complex theorization. Semin and Manstead (1983) provide a thorough and clearly articulated review and analysis of this area. A number of complex typologies have already been generated in attempts to clarify the large variety of social cognitive functions that accounting can serve for the explication of action, working from Goffman's (1959) perception of interaction as an 'expressive order' within which accounting plays a crucial role, particularly when there is any fragmentation or interruption of the smooth flow of social intercourse.

Goffman himself (1971), Tedischi and Reiss (1981) and Schlenker and Derby (1981) have explored accounts as apologies; Hewitt and Stokes (1975) examined accounts as disclaimers; Schonbach (1980) sought to typologize varieties of explaining refusals to act, excuses and justifications. Semin and Manstead (1983) have drawn these together in an over-arching typology of accounting which covers such constructs as scapegoating, sad tales, appeals to religious and moral authorities and face-maintenance.

I believe that the data and theorization which I have presented have two main suggestions to contribute. The first is that although the kind of typology offered by Semin and Manstead is analytically illuminating, its list-like, 'coding-frame' qualities (quite possibly unintentionally, but compellingly none the less) portray an image of accounting strangely decoupled from any cultural or social context. The kinds of accounts described in this chapter offer an alternative portrayal, in which action-explication is a process much more like seeking out an appropriate text than each time an action demands explaining, re-constructing an articulated justification or excuse anew. It also offers a sense of the way that once one becomes 'keyed in' to a particular text in order to excuse a rule infraction or whatever, it carries with it a lot of extra conceptual baggage so that the excuse becomes a convincing 'story' in and of itself, woven around and weaving the event, its actions and its contextual elements.

The second contribution is that because Semin and Manstead have focused selectively upon social norm infraction as the kinds of actions that accounts are needed to explain, their typology, though lengthy, gives only a partial picture of explanation. It de-emphasizes biological and other 'natural' discontinuities, such as those arising from temporal features, and, in its specific concern with discontinuities, omits consideration of explaining continuity (e.g. in the case of chronic illness) and 'wholeness'. Although theorists like Harré (1979) have argued that the smooth flow of ordinary social interaction, in its taken-for-granted qualities, requires no concurrent explaining, Dingwall (1976) has argued that the social pressure to do usual, expected, normal things at usual times in usual places requires a great deal of fluency with commonsense knowledge, and that our understandings of illness are thus predicated upon our conceptions of 'ordinariness'. Hence, I would argue, we cannot gain understanding of people's explanations simply by reference to the way in which they account for discontinuity and the fracturing of 'ordinariness'. We must find out how people account for 'being ordinary' too.

I deliberately chose the topic of health and illness as a subject matter because it offers biological as well as social discontinuities that stimulate explication, and it incorporates the reflexivities of continuity/discontinuity, wholeness/dislocation. Thus the accounts which I have identified and described cover a more comprehensive field. I agree with Henriques et al. (1984) that 'whilst we should avoid founding a theory of subjectivity on a taken-for-granted biological origin, we cannot construct a position which altogether denies biology and its effects' (p. 21).

If we are to gain understanding of the role that explanation plays in social being, we need to develop a comprehensive theory of explanation that includes the ways in which people explain their biological as well as their social realities, and 'ordinariness' as well as 'disorder'. This book is offered as a contribution to that endeavour.

Appendix 1: Q-set used in Study 1

1. When it comes to medical treatment, patients should always follow their doctor's advice.
2. Disease and bodily decay are inevitable aspects of being alive – anyone who tells you different is either a liar or a fool.
3. Medicine is a science and should be based on rigorous scientific principles.
4. Many so-called 'mental illnesses' are actually forms of weakness or an inability to face reality.
5. People are born with a predisposition to be 'sickly', 'robust' or whatever.
6. Modern therapeutic achievements (like heart transplants) are important contributions to progress in health care.
7. Usually being struck by illness is just a matter of bad luck.
8. Fringe medicine is a dangerous intrusion on proper health care.
9. Doctors treat symptoms, not the underlying causes of illness.
10. Being fit and well depends as much on your state of mind as on the functioning of your body.
11. We could improve health more in Britain by providing better sports and recreational facilities than by building more and better hospitals.
12. It is very important to keep yourself and your home clean and hygenic to keep disease at bay.
13. Many forms of medical treatment today seem to do more harm than good.
14. Doctors only recommend surgery when it is really necessary.
15. When someone is seriously ill, knowing the full truth may not be in their best interests.
16. Many diseases of modern life result from the stressful, polluted, noxious environment in which we live.

17. Treating people as 'mentally ill' is often a means by which society controls those who don't conform.

18. For some people being ill becomes a way of life.

19. We will only improve the overall health of people in the world when we have found ways to overcome the fundamental injustices between rich and poor.

20. The ability of the body to heal itself is far greater than most people realize.

21. Good health is a fundamental human right.

22. Modern drugs have made a major contribution to fighting disease.

23. When deciding upon medical treatment it is better to let incurably ill people die with dignity rather than prolong life regardless.

24. Treatment which uses 'therapy of the mind' (e.g. relaxation or imaging techniques) should be used much more widely.

25. Giving birth is a natural process and should not be treated as if it were an illness.

26. Often just going to the doctor can make you feel better.

27. Being healthy is a lot more than simply not being ill – it has to do with a positive state of wellbeing.

28. A vegetarian diet is more healthy than one containing meat.

29. Our experience of 'being ill' is substantially something that we *learn*.

30. The 'will to live' can be a significant factor in whether people recover from a serious illness or serious injury.

31. It is quite possible to die of a 'broken heart'.

32. As doctors are committed to preserve life, they have a moral duty to support nuclear disarmament.

33. If people are unpleasant to me, it can have the effect of making me ill.

34. To be healthy, it is best to live as natural a life as possible.

35. Doctors don't discover diseases so much as invent them.

36. It's a good idea to see illness as a 'challenge' – something to be overcome, to fight with all the resources you can muster.

37. I can't help seeing illness as a 'weakness' in myself and in others.

38. Basically I define 'health' as an absence of symptoms. I'm healthy when I don't have to worry about my body.

39. Health in adulthood depends upon building up a robust constitution when you are young.

40. When I'm ill I feel as though in some way I'm to blame.

41. Many people suffer from illnesses caused by their own bad habits.

42. People who suffer from 'depression' are often just responding to the intolerable pressures and problems of their lives.

43. Adequate food, better housing and proper drains have done more to improve our health than all the medical discoveries of the last 100 years.

44. We are fortunate to live in a world of medical excellence – skilled surgery, highly trained professional care, etc.

45. Capitalism is inherently anti-health. It puts making profits before the wellbeing and safety of people.

46. Life is too short and too sweet to spend time worrying over much about what is 'healthy' and what is not.

47. Having good health is about the most important thing in life.

48. The worst off in our society have very little choice about the unhealthy lives they lead.

49. Health is largely a matter of moderation in all things.

50. Sometimes being struck by illness is a punishment for misdeeds.

51. When I'm ill I don't just feel pain and discomfort, I feel less of a person.

52. Lazy people are seldom really healthy.

53. Health promotion has become just another fashion – health foods and jogging suits are just more ways to persuade people to spend money.

54. A good health service is one which respects people's autonomy even if it puts people at risk.

55. Being healthy depends a lot on the food you eat.

56. Faith-healing can bring about a cure where conventional medicine fails.

57. I have more important goals in my life than the pursuit of optimal health.

58. The Government cares more about tobacco revenues than the health of its people.

59. Recent medical advances (e.g. in contraception and childbirth) have been particularly beneficial to women.

60. People should be free to damage their own health (e.g. by smoking).

61. People should take responsibility for their own health.

62. Information about improving our national diet has been suppressed because of lobbying by the food industry.

63. In the future medical science will have eradicated disease.

64. The 'work ethic' has a lot to answer for when it comes to people's health.

65. It is important that all children are given a full set of inoculations.

66. Obesity is an illness and needs to be treated medically.

67. Dental decay is more a matter of bad luck than poor care of your teeth.

68. Too much 'junk food' in childhood can be a serious threat to health.

69. Most of the things I enjoy are bad for my health in some way or another.

70. For most minor illnesses (like a 'cold') it's better to let nature take its course than seek out medical treatment.

71. Medical researchers should be encouraged to look for the underlying causes of so-called spontaneous recovery.

72. Drug companies are more concerned with profits than making people well.

73. Most people have cancer at some time in their life but their body's defences are able to overcome it.

74. More care about health in adulthood could prevent many of the illnesses of old age.

75. A lot of health problems are caused by people not following their course of treatment properly.

76. I approve of measures like fluoridation of the water supply.

77. Far too many drugs are prescribed because people need to feel that their doctor has 'done something' for their illness.

78. I would prefer to be treated by homoeopathy than by conventional medicine.

79. Technical expertise is far more important in a doctor than personal qualities.

80. We should be doing a lot more about environmental causes of disease (e.g. cancer).

Appendix 2: (a) Items used for IHI Questionnaire

MY CURRENT STATE OF HEALTH

1. The constitution with which I was born.
2. My body's natural defences.
3. My state of mind.
4. My emotions.
5. 'Inner forces' of my psyche.
6. Whether I feel 'on top' of my life, or pressured by it.
7. Everyday behaviour (e.g. getting enough sleep; eating spasmodically).
8. My overall lifestyle.
9. 'Taking good care of myself'.
10. Whether or not I'm actively taking action to be healthy (e.g. monitoring my diet, exercise etc.).
11. Good or bad luck.
12. Simple probability.
13. The society in which we live in Britain.
14. The culture within which I live.
15. The weather.
16. My relationships with family and friends.
17. The care of medical professionals.
18. Whether there is somebody 'ill wishing' me or not.
19. God, or some other supernatural power.
20. Whether or not I have been exposed to infectious organisms.
21. My home environment.
22. My working environment.
23. The circumstances of my home-life.
24. The current circumstances at work.
25. Particular events in my life at this time.

MY CURRENT STATE OF HEALTH

26. Whether or not I am being exposed at present to certain substances (e.g. pollution; additives in food).
27. My age.

MY CAPACITY TO BECOME HEALTHIER IN THE FUTURE

28. The constitution with which I was born.
29. My current state of health.
30. Marshalling my body's own strengths.
31. Promoting a positive attitude.
32. Actively seeking out things that make me happy.
33. Tackling any unresolved inner conflicts.
34. Taking charge of, and responsibility for, my own life.
35. Changing my day to day behaviour.
36. Actively changing to a more healthy lifestyle.
37. Giving up unhealthy habits (e.g. smoking).
38. The weather.
39. Good or bad luck.
40. Simple probability.
41. Improvements in my relationships with family and friends.
42. Getting advice from friends and family.
43. Getting advice from books or leaflets.
44. Seeking out preventive medical services (e.g. getting blood tests, going to a 'Well Person' clinic).
45. Getting advice from my doctor or health visitor.
46. Getting advice from a practitioner of alternative medicine.
47. Getting medical treatment.
48. My age.
49. God's power or influence.
50. Any other supernatural influence.
51. Whether or not I am exposed to infectious organisms.
52. Improvements in my home environment.
53. Improvements in my working environment.
54. Improvements in my circumstances at home.
55. Improvements in the circumstances in which I work.
56. Particular events – what happens in the future.
57. Whether or not I'm exposed to certain substances (e.g. pollution).
58. Taking vitamins or a tonic.

WHETHER OR NOT I BECOME ILL

59. The constitution with which I was born.
60. If my body's own natural defences become weakened or break down.
61. If my state of mind becomes negative, feelings of powerlessness.
62. Feeling unhappy.
63. Inner conflicts of my psyche making themselves felt.
64. Behaving in stupid ways (e.g. not getting enough sleep, working too hard).
65. Adopting a lifestyle that is unhealthy.
66. Bad luck.
67. Simple probability.
68. Rows or conflicts with family or friends.
69. Rows with people at work.
70. Lack of proper medical care.
71. The ill-effects of poor medical treatment.
72. Uncaring or unsympathetic treatment by my doctor.
73. God's will.
74. Other supernatural influences.
75. A curse or ill-wishing.
76. Something at home or work that I can avoid by being ill.
77. Whether or not I have been exposed to infectious organisms.
78. Living in a poor environment (e.g. damp or crowded housing).
79. Working in a poor environment (e.g. bad lighting or with noxious chemicals).
80. Stressful conditions at home (e.g. bad conflicts between other members of the household).
81. Stressful conditions at work (e.g. too much work, threats of redundancy).
82. Stressful, nasty or unsettling events in my life.
83. Major *pleasant* life changes (e.g. getting married, being promoted).
84. Exposure to harmful chemicals (anything from pollution to other people's cigarette smoke).
85. Other people's stupid actions (e.g. visiting me with a bad cold).
86. Inbuilt weaknesses or susceptibility to particular diseases (e.g. having a 'weak chest').
87. The virulence of the infective organism.
88. The weather.
89. My age.

WHEN I AM ILL, HOW QUICKLY AND EFFECTIVELY I RECOVER

90. Getting 'back to normal' as soon as possible.
91. Finding ways to make myself feel happier.
92. Finding ways to resolve any inner conflicts.
93. Taking responsibility for myself, and doing all I can to get better.
94. Looking after myself and taking things easy.
95. Being careful about my day to day behaviour (e.g. getting sufficient sleep and a nourishing diet).
96. Actively taking steps to make my lifestyle more healthy.
97. Giving up unhealthy habits (e.g. drinking too much).
98. Good luck.
99. Simple probability.
100. The care I got from my family and friends.
101. The quality of medical treatment I received.
102. The sympathy and understanding of my nurse/doctor.
103. The quality of any *conventional* medical treatment.
104. A curse or ill-wishing.
105. The intervention of a spiritual healer or healers.
106. Prayers said for me.
107. God's will.
108. Some other supernatural power.
109. The virulence of the disease itself.
110. An environment which is conducive to recovery (whether at home, at work or in hospital).
111. Circumstances which are conducive to recovery.
112. Particular events in my life at the time.
113. Taking drugs or medicines that are effective.
114. Treatments (e.g. surgery, radiotherapy) that are effective.
115. 'Alternative' therapies, if I sought them out.
116. The constitution with which I was born.
117. My body's own natural defences.
118. Thinking positively and seeing the illness as a challenge.
119. Following 'doctors' orders' – complying properly with the treatment I am given.
120. Letting nature take its course.
121. Seeking medical advice soon enough – not waiting until the illness becomes too serious before I go to the doctor.
122. Just the chance to talk things over with the doctor without any treatment.

WHEN I AM ILL, HOW QUICKLY AND EFFECTIVELY I RECOVER

123. The weather.
124. My age.

(b) Q-sort used for study

1. I believe I may have certain inbuilt weaknesses which make me vulnerable to particular illnesses or disorders.
2. When I'm ill enough to consult a doctor, my recovery will be faster if I comply properly with the advice and treatment I get.
3. My becoming ill is seldom, if ever, the result of exposure to noxious substances in the day-to-day environment (e.g. food additives, pollution, industrial waste).
4. To improve my health would require improvements in the environment in which I live.
5. I see my body as rather like a machine; how well or badly it is running determines my state of health.
6. When I'm ill, my recovery is influenced by the quality and comfort of my surroundings.
7. Some of the time I'm likely to be healthy, some of the time ill. At any point in my life, my state of health is often just a matter of how the probabilities stack up.
8. I usually expect to take medicine to help me recover from illness.
9. I have little faith that the advice I may get from the medical profession can help very much in improving my health.
10. When I'm ill, I usually feel as though I'm in some way to blame.
11. If I were ever seriously ill, I would have a lot of faith in the ability of doctors to find a cure.
12. My state of health at any time is considerably influenced by whether or not I've been exposed to infectious or contagious disease organisms.
13. I believe I could become ill through a curse or ill-wishing on the part of another person.

14. State of mind is a crucial part of my achieving better health – by promoting positive feelings of contentment and fulfilment in myself, I can enhance my state of physical health.
15. When I'm ill, whether I get better quickly or slowly is largely a matter of luck.
16. The physical conditions of my life (e.g. my working environment, my housing situation) *do not* affect my general state of health.
17. Try as I may, there is nothing I can do that I can be *certain* will improve my health. The best I can do is to change the odds to give myself a greater chance of becoming more healthy.
18. The state of my relationships with others – how well or badly I'm getting on with those close to me at a particular point in time – has a significant impact on my state of health.
19. God has given me the means by which to improve my health.
20. When I'm exposed to infection, my capacity to achieve better health is impaired.
21. How well or badly I look after myself generally has an influence on my overall health.
22. My ability to achieve a better standard of health is affected by whether my life circumstances are helpful or unhelpful.
23. When I feel unhappy, I'm more likely to become ill.
24. My state of overall health is in part a product of my economic resources – how 'well off' or 'badly off' I am.
25. In order to become healthier, I would need to marshal my body's own natural capacities.
26. My falling ill can be a weakness of will – I don't always have the power of mind to fight off disease.
27. I cannot improve my health by 'tonics' or taking extra vitamins.
28. If I'm going to get ill, then I will get ill – it's just the luck of the draw.
29. Illness is a fact of life – I cannot expect to go through life without ever becoming ill, or without risk of disability.
30. When others are unpleasant to me, or I get into conflicts with them, it can have the effect of making me ill.
31. The speed of my recovery from an infection depends a lot on the virulence of the disease organisms causing it.
32. It's a matter of luck whether or not my health will improve.
33. Being exposed to crowded conditions (e.g. public transport) can lead to me catching disease.
34. The constitution with which I was born has little if any influence on my day to day state of health.
35. I believe that God watches over my health.

36. Sometimes when I get ill, it's a result of long-term pressures in the circumstances of my life.
37. When I'm ill, I have faith in my body's mechanisms to promote recovery, and restore good health.
38. Sudden stressful life events (e.g. bereavement, moving house, losing my job) can sometimes have the effect of making me ill.
39. I see illness as a challenge to be overcome – a determined attitude on my part can speed my recovery.
40. When I'm ill, there is very little that I can do for myself which will help me to get better faster.
41. Emotional distress can upset my general health.
42. When my state of health is poor, it is often my own bad habits that are to blame.
43. When I'm ill, sometimes just a chance to talk to the doctor will make me feel better.
44. Recovery from illness is, as much as anything, a matter of odds – there's a certain probability I'll get better sooner or later, and a certain probability that I won't.
45. Illness is often a simple matter of being attacked by a disease – nothing more complicated than that.
46. My overall state of health has a lot to do with my own day to day actions – I can allow myself to get run down, or take steps to keep healthy.
47. My recovery from illness depends a lot on the circumstances in which I'm ill – some would help my recovery, others would make it more difficult.
48. My state of health at any point in time reflects what is going on in my life – some of the things that happen will improve it, some make it worse.
49. Maintaining my health is somewhat of an uphill struggle, given the polluted, stressful, exploitative society in which we live.
50. I feel I have the state of overall health I deserve.
51. Sometimes I get ill because of my own stupid behaviour.
52. When I'm ill, my recovery depends a lot on the quality of medical treatment I may receive.
53. My physical health and well-being are affected by my state of mind.
54. Being able to achieve a better standard of health is *not* really influenced at all by what is going on in my life at the time.
55. There may be times when God sends me ill health for reasons I may not be able to understand.
56. The care and support I receive from others has an influence on my overall health.

57. I *don't* believe that my health is very much affected by chemicals such as additives in food, or pollution.
58. My own actions are crucial to achieving better health – it is something *I* have to work for.
59. Sometimes the stupid or thoughtless actions of others can lead to me becoming unwell.
60. How well or ill I am is seldom, if ever, just a matter of chance.
61. The 'tender loving care' I get from others when I'm ill can make all the difference to whether I make a full recovery or not.
62. Often for me, feeling truly fit and well, and feeling truly happy are much the same thing.
63. There are times when I think I become ill because of deep-seated worries of which I am not consciously aware.
64. I believe that there are people with the powers of a 'healer', who could cure me were I to become ill.
65. With minor illnesses, I think that I will do far better to let 'nature take its course' than seek out medical treatment.
66. My health is my own responsibility.
67. Major stresses in my childhood have shown up as illness in my adult life.
68. I feel I have a right to choose whether or not to act in ways that harm my health (e.g. work too hard, or smoke).
69. Stress only makes me ill when I'm 'down'; when I'm feeling full of energy and/or content, I can ride it out with no ill effects.
70. Where certain forms of illness are concerned, I would seek help from competent practitioners in 'alternative' medicine.
71. No amount of praying on my part could physically affect my recovery, if I was ill.
72. When I'm ill, my ability to recover will depend very little upon other events in my life (e.g. whether there are other stresses like trouble at work).
73. Illness can be caused by the external environment – my being somewhere that is cold and damp, for example.
74. A lot of the time when I am ill, I use my own common sense to work out what to do to treat it.
75. I think good health has more to do with living a satisfying and fulfilling life than being obsessive over things like exercise and diet.
76. I believe that faith healing could work for me.
77. By attuning myself to nature itself – to the 'power for good' in the Universe, I can improve my health.
78. Being healthy is a product of lifestyle as a whole – only by living a healthy lifestyle can I ensure that I'm fit and well.

79. For me illness can sometimes be a way of withdrawing from life or my responsibilities.
80. When I'm ill, I believe I should seek deep within myself for the reason — by tackling the inner motivations and pressures, I can find ways to get better.

Bibliography

Aakster, C.W. (1986), 'Concepts in alternative medicine', *Social Science and Medicine*, 22 (2), 265–73.

Abramson, L.Y., Seligman, M.E.P. and Teasdale, J.D. (1978), 'Learned helplessness in humans: Critique and reformulation', *Journal of Abnormal Psychology*, 87, 49–74.

Ackerknecht, E.H. (1942), 'Problems of primitive medicine', *Bulletin of the History of Medicine*, 11, 503–21.

Ackerknecht, E.H. (1971), *Medicine and Ethnology: selected Essays*, Johns Hopkins: Baltimore.

Adam, B. (1990), *Time and Social Theory*, Polity: London.

Adorno, T.W., Frenkel–Brunswick, E., Levinson, D.J. and Sanford, S.J. (1950), *The Authoritarian Personality*, Harper: New York.

Ajzen, I. and Fishbein, M. (1972), 'Attitudes and normative beliefs as factors influencing behavioural intentions', *Journal of Personality and Social Psychology*, 21 (1), 1–9.

Ajzen, I. and Fishbein, M. (1973), 'Attitudes and normative variables as predictors of specific behaviours', *Journal of Personality and Social Psychology*, 27 (1), 401–15.

Alland, A. (1966), 'Medical anthropology and the study of biological and cultural adaptations', *American Anthropologist*, 68, 40–51.

Alland, A. (1970), *Adaptation in Cultural Evolution: An approach to medical anthropology*, Columbia University Press: New York.

Amanico, L. and Soczka, L. (1986), 'Why are women discriminated against at work?: A study of implicit theories', paper presented to the European Association of Experimental Social Psychology Advanced Workshop on Social and Environmental Psychology, Lisbon (September).

Antaki, C. (ed.) (1981), *The Psychology of Ordinary Explanations of Social Behaviour*, Academic: London.

Antaki, C. (1988), *Analysing Everyday Explanation: A casebook of methods*, Sage: London.

Antaki, C. and Fielding, G. (1981), 'Research on ordinary explanations', in

Antaki, C. (ed.), *The Psychology of Ordinary Explanations of Social Behaviour*, Academic: London.

Apple, D. (1960), *Sociological Studies of Health and Illness*, McGraw-Hill: New York.

Ardell, D.B. (1977), *High Level Wellness: An alternative to doctors, drugs and disease*, Bantam: New York.

Areni, A., Mannetti, L. and Sabino, G. (1986), 'Influence des schemas culturels traditionnels sur le choix de la contraception', *Contraception, Fertilité et Sexualité*, 14 (4), 347–58.

Bannister, D. and Fransella, F. (1986), *Inquiring Man: The psychology of personal constructs*, Croom Helm: London.

Barlow, J. (1843), *Man's Power Over Himself to Prevent or Control Insanity*, William Pickering: London.

Barnes, B. and Law, J. (1976), 'Whatever should be done with Indexical expressions?', *Theory and Society*, 3, 227–37.

Barrett, M. and Roberts, H. (1978), 'Doctors and their patients: The social control of women in general practice', in Smart, C. and Smart, B. (eds.), *Women, Sexuality and Social Control*, Routledge & Kegan Paul: London.

Barthes, R. (1985), *The Fashion System*, Cape: London.

Bartlett, F.C. (1932), *Remembering*, Cambridge University Press: Cambridge.

Baughman, M.K. (1978), 'The relationship of locus of control and value beliefs to health status and behaviour among clerical workers', unpublished doctoral dissertation, University of Cincinnati.

Bauman, B. (1961), 'Diversities in conceptions of health and physical fitness', *Journal of Health and Human Behaviour*, 2, 39–46.

Bauman, B. (1978), in Miles, R. (ed.) *The Wholistic Handbook*, Simon & Schuster: New York.

Beck, S.J., Molish, H.B. and Sinclair, J. (1956), 'Researches concerning thinking in schizophrenia research', *American Journal of Orthopsychiatry*, 26, 792–800.

Becker, H.S. (1963), *Outsiders*, Free: New York.

Bennet, T., Martin, G., Mercer, C. and Woollacott, J. (1981), 'Antonio Gramsci', in Bennet, T., Martin, G., Mercer, C. and Woollacott, J. (eds.), *Culture, Ideology and Sociological Processes*, Batsford: London.

Berlin, I. (1969), 'A note on Vico's concept of knowledge', in Tagliacozzo, G. and White, H.V. (eds.), *Giambattista Vico: An international symposium*, Johns Hopkins: Baltimore.

Berlin, I. (1976), *Vico and Herder*, Hogarth: London.

Berger, P. (1977), *Facing up to Modernity*, Basic: New York.

Berger, P. (1979), *The Heretical Imperative*, Doubleday: New York.

Berger, P. and Luckmann, T. (1966), *The Social Construction of Reality*, Allan Lane: London.

Berger, P. and Pullberg, S. (1965), 'Reification and the sociological critique of consciousness', *History and Theory*, 4, 198–201.

Billig, M. (1987), *Arguing and Thinking: A rhetorical approach to social psychology*, Cambridge University Press: Cambridge.

Binik, Y.M. and Devins, G. (1979), 'Personal control and end–stage renal disease', paper presented at the American Psychological Association, New York City.

Blaxter, M. (1983), 'The causes of disease: Women talking', *Social Science and Medicine*, 17 (2), 59–69.

Blaxter, M. (1990), *Health and Lifestyles*, Tavistock/Routledge: London.

Blaxter, M. and Paterson, L. (1982), *Mothers and Daughters: A three–generational study of health attributes and behaviour*, Heinemann: London.

Block, J. (1961), *The Q-sort Method in Personality Assessment and Psychiatric Research*, Charles C. Thomas: Springfield, Ill.

Blum, A.F. and McHugh, P. (1971), 'The social ascription of motives', *American Sociological Review*, 36, 98–109.

Blumhagen, D.W. (1980), 'Hypertension: A folk illness with a medical name', *Culture, Medicine and Psychiatry*, 5, 337–40.

Blumhagen, D.W. (1981), 'On the nature of explanatory models', *Culture, Medicine and Psychiatry*, 6, 137–46.

Bohm, D. (1973), 'Quantum theory and an indication of a new order in physics: Implicate and explicate order in physical law', *Foundations of Physics*, 3, 139–68.

Boyer, P. (1987), 'The stuff "Traditions" are made of : On the implicit ontology of an ethnographic category', *Philosophy of Social Science*, 49–65.

Brown, R. (1985), *Social Psychology: The second edition*, Free: New York.

Brown, S. (1980), *Political Subjectivity: Applications of Q methodology in political science*, Yale University Press: New Haven, Conn.

Brown, S. (1984), 'The subjective communicability of meta–ethics: A note on Fishkin's methodology', *Political Methodology*, 10, 465–78.

Budd, R.J., Blieiker, S. and Spencer, C.P. (1983), 'Exploring the use and non-use of marijuana as reasoned actions: An application of Fishbein and Ajzen's methodology', *Drug and Alcohol Dependence*, 11, 217–24.

Budd, R.J. and Spencer, C.P. (1985), 'Exploring the role of personal beliefs in the theory of reasoned action: The problem of discriminating between alternative path models', *European Journal of Social Psychology*, 15, 299–313.

Burt, C. (1972), 'The reciprocity principle' in Brown, S.R. and Brenner, D.J. (eds.), *Science, Psychology and Communication: Essays honouring William Stephenson*, Teachers Press: New York.

Bury, M.R. (1986), 'Social constructionism and the development of medical sociology', *Sociology of Health and Illness*, 8 (2), 137–69.

Busfield, J. (1990), 'Sectorial divisions in consumption: The case of medical care, *Sociology*, 24 (1), 77–96.

Buss, A.R. (1979), *A Dialectical Psychology*, Invington: New York.

Butler, R. and Haigh, T. (1954), 'Changes in the relation between self-concepts and ideal concepts consequent upon client-centred counselling', in Rogers, C.R. and Dymond, R.F. (eds.), *Psycho-therapy and Personality Change*, University of Chicago Press: Chicago.

Calnan, M. (1987), *Health and Illness: The lay perspective*, Tavistock: London.

Calnan, M. and Johnson, B. (1985), 'Health, health risks and inequalities: An exploratory study of women's perceptions', *Sociology of Health and Illness*, 7 (1), 55–75.

Carlson, E. (1984), 'Is our care system killing us?', *Modern Maturity*, April–May.

Carnahan, T.M. (1979), 'The development and validation of the Multi-dimensional Dental Locus of Control Scales', unpublished doctoral dissertation, State University of New York.

Cartwright, S.A. (1851), 'Report on the diseases and physical peculiarities of the Negro race', *New Orleans Medical and Surgical Journal*, 691–715, reprinted in Caplan, A.L., Engelhardt, H.T. and McCartney, J.J. (eds.) (1981), *Concepts of Health and Disease: Interdisciplinary perspectives*, Addison-Wesley: Reading, Mass.

Chassin, L., Presson, C.C., Brensberg, M., Corty, E. and Sherman, S.J. (1981), 'Predicting adolescents' intentions to smoke cigarettes', *Journal of Health and Social Behaviour*, 22, 445–55.

Cicourel, A.V. (1973), *Cognitive Sociology*, Penguin: Harmondsworth.

Clark, M. (1970), *Health in the Mexican–American Culture*, University of California Press: Berkeley, Calif.

Claxton, G. (1987), 'Beliefs and behaviour: Why is it so hard to change?', *Nursing*, 3 (18), 670–3.

Clements, F. (1932), 'Primitive concepts of disease', *American Archives of Ethology*, 32, 185–252.

Cohen, S. (1971), *Images of Deviance*, Penguin: Harmondsworth.

Collins, B.E. (1974), 'Four components of the Rotter Internal–External Scale: Belief in a difficult world, a just world, a predictable world, and a politically responsive world', *Journal of Personality and Social Psychology*, 29 (3), 381–91.

Cornwell, J. (1984), *Hard–Earned Lives: Accounts of health and illness from East London*, Tavistock: London.

Cornwell, J. (1986), 'Health beliefs in old age: The theoretical grounds for conceptualising older people as a group', in Glendenning, F. (ed.), *Working Together for Health: Older people and their carers*, Beth Johnson Foundation: Stoke-on-Trent.

Cosminski, S. (1977), 'The impact of methods of analysis of illness concepts in a Guatemalian community', *Social Science and Medicine*, 11, 325–32.

Crawford, R. (1980), 'Healthism and the medicalisation of everyday life', *International Journal of Health Services*, 10 (3), 365–88.

Crawford, R. (1984), 'A cultural account of "health": Control, release and the social body', in McKinlay, J.B. (ed.), *Issues in the Political Economy of Health Care*, Tavistock: London.

Creaser, J.W. (1955), 'An aid in calculating Q-sort factor arrays', *Journal of Clinical Psychology*, 11, 195–6.

Csordas, T.J. (1986), 'Religion and health', paper presented to the British Medical Anthropology Society/Society for Medical Anthropology Meeting, Cambridge (July).

Currer, C. and Stacey, M. (eds.) (1986), *Concepts of Health, Illness and Disease*, Berg: Leamington Spa.

Currie, E. (1987a), as quoted in national press, March–April.

Currie, E. (1987b), as quoted in *The Oxford Journal*, July.

Currier, R.L. (1966), 'The hot–cold syndrome and symbolic balance in Mexican and Spanish-American folk medicine', *Ethnology*, 5, 251–63.

D'Agostino, D. (1986), 'Q factors and developmental models: The case of changing attitudes towards nuclear weapons', paper presented at the Second Institute for the Scientific Study of Subjectivity, Columbia, Miss. (October).

De Vellis, R.F. De Vellis, B.N., Wallston, B.S. and Wallston, K.A. (1980), 'Epilepsy and Learned Helplessness', *Basic and Applied Social Psychology*, 1, 241–53.

Devereux, G (1972), *Ethnopsychanalyse Complementariste*, Flammarion: Paris.

DHSS (1980), *Inequalities in Health*, report of a research working group (The Black Report), HMSO: London.

Dingwall, R. (1976), *Aspects of Illness*, Martin Robertson: London.

DiVito, A.J., Reznikoff, M. and Bogdanowicz, J. (1979), 'Actual and intended health–related information seeking and health locus of control', paper presented at the American Psychological Association, New York City.

Doise, W. (1978), 'Images, représentations, idéologies et expérimentation psychosociologique', *Social Science Information*, 17, 41–69.

Doise, W. (1986), *Levels of Explanation in Social Psychology*, Cambridge University Press: Cambridge.

Donzelot, J. (1977), *The Policing of Families: Welfare versus the state*, Hutchinson: London.

Douglas, M. (1978), *Implicit Meanings: Essays in anthropology*, Routledge & Kegan Paul: London.

Douglas, M. (1982), *In the Active Voice*, Routledge & Kegan Paul: London.

Doyal, L. (1979), *The Political Economy of Health*, Pluto: London.

Dulany, D.E. (1961), 'Hypotheses and habits in verbal "operant condition-ing"', *Journal of Abnormal and Social Psychology*, 63, 251–63.

Dulany, D.E. (1968), 'Awareness, roles and propositional control: A confrontation with S-R behaviour theory', in Horton, D. and Dixon, T. (eds.) *Verbal Behaviour and S-R Behaviour Theory*, Prentice Hall: New York.

Dunn, F.L. (1968), 'Epidemiological factors: Health and disease among hunter-gatherers', in Lee, R.B. and DeVore, I. (eds.), *Man the Hunter*, Aldine: Chicago.

Dunn, F.L. (1977) 'Traditional Asian Medicine and Cosmopolitan Medicine as Adaptive Systems', in Leslie, C. (ed.), *Asian Medical Systems: A comparative Study*, University of California Press: Berkeley, Calif.

Durkheim, E. (1898), 'Représentations individuelles et représentations collectives', *Revue de Metaphysique et de Morale*, VI, 273–302.

Ehrenreich, B. and Ehrenreich, J. (1978), 'Medicine and social control', in Ehrenreich, J. (ed.), *The Cultural Crisis of Modern Medicine*, Monthly Review Press: New York.

Ehrenreich, B. and English, D. (1973), *Witches, Midwives and Nurses*, New York, The Feminist Press: New York.

Ehrenreich, J. (ed.) (1978), *The Cultural Crisis of Modern Medicine*, Monthly Review Press: New York.

Erikson, E.H. (1953), 'On the sense of inner identity', in *Health and Human Relations*, report of a conference held at Hiddesen, New York, Blakiston.

Fabrega, H. (1974), *Disease and Social Behaviour: An interdisciplinary approach*, MIT Press: Cambridge, Mass.

Farr, R.M. and Anderson, T. (1983), 'Beyond actor–observer differences in perspective: Extensions and applications', in Hewstone. M. (ed.), *Attribution Theory: Social and functional extensions*, Blackwell: Oxford.

Farr, R.M. and Moscovici, S. (1984), *Social Representations*, Cambridge University Press: Cambridge.

Festinger, L. (1957), *A Theory of Cognitive Dissonance*, Row & Peterson: Evanston, Ill.

Finkelstein, V. (1980), 'Attitudes and Disabled People', *World Rehabilitation Fund Monograph*, No. 5.

Fishbein, M. (1980), 'A theory of reasoned action: Some applications and implications', in Howe, H.E. (ed.) *Nebraska Symposium on Motivation, 1979* University of Nebraska Press: Lincoln.

Fishbein, M., Jaccard, J.J., Davidson, A.R., Azjen, I. and Loken, B. (1980), 'Predicting and understanding family planning behaviours: Beliefs, attitudes and intentions'. in Ajzen, I. and Fishbein, M. (eds.), *Understanding Attitudes and Predicting Social Behaviour*, Prentice Hall: Englewood Cliffs., NJ.

Foster, G.M. (1976), 'Disease aetiologies in non-western medical systems', *American Anthropologist*, 78, 773–81.

Foucault, M. (1961), *Folie et Déraison: Histoire de la folie à l'âge classique*, Plan: Paris.

Foucault, M. (1963), *Naissance de la Clinique*, Presses Universitaires de France: Paris; English translation (1973), *The Birth of the Clinic*, Tavistock: London.

Foucault, M. (1970), *The Order of Things*, London: Tavistock.

Foucault, M. (1977), *Discipline and Punish: The birth of the prison*, New York: Vintage.

Friedson, E. (1970), *Profession of Medicine: A study of the sociology of applied knowledge*, Dodd Mead: New York.

Friedson, E. (1986), *Professional Powers: A study of the institutionalization of formal knowledge*, University of Chicago Press: Chicago.

Furnham, A. and Henderson, M. (1983), 'Lay theories of delinquency', *European Journal of Social Psychology*, 13, 107–20.

Gaito, J. (1962), 'Forced and free sorts', *Psychological Reports*, 10, 251–4.

Gardner, C. and Young, R. (1981), 'Transforming television', *Screen*, 25 (1).

Garner, L. (1979), *The NHS: Your money or your life*, Harmondsworth: Penguin.

Gauld, A. and Shotter, J. (1977), *Human Action and its Psychological Investigation*, Routledge & Kegan Paul: London.

Geertz, C., 'Religion as a cultural system', in Banton, M. (ed.), *Anthropological Approaches to the Study of Religion*, Tavistock: London.

Gergen, K.J. (1973), 'Social psychology as history', *Journal of Personality and Social Psychology*, 26 (1), 309–20.

Gergen, K.J. (1982), *Towards Transformation of Social Knowledge*, Springer-Verlag: New York.

Gergen, K.J. (1986), 'Interpreting the texts of nature and culture: A reply to Jahoda', *European Journal of Social Psychology*, 16, 31–7

Gergen, K.J. and Gergen, M.M. (1981), *Social Psychology*, Harcourt, Brace, Jovanovich: New York.

Glaser, B.G. and Strauss, A.L. (1968), *The Discovery of Grounded Theory*, Weidenfeld & Nicolson: London.

Gleeson, K (1991),' Out of our minds: The deconstruction and reconstruction of madness', unpublished doctoral dissertation, University of Reading.

Goffman, E. (1959), *The Presentation of Self in Everyday Life*, Doubleday: New York.

Goffman, E. (1963), *Stigma: Notes on the management of spoiled identity*, Prentice-Hall: Englewood Cliffs, NJ.

Goffman, E. (1968), *Asylums*, Penguin: Harmondsworth.

Good, B.J. (1977), 'The heart of what's the matter: The semantics of illness in Iran', *Culture, Medicine and Psychiatry*, 1, 25–58.

Good, B.J. and Good, M.J. (1981), 'The meaning of symptoms: A cultural Hermeneutic Model for Clinical Practice', in Eisenberg, L. and Kleinman, A. (eds.), *The Relevance of Social Science for Medicine*, Reidel: Dordrecht.

Gore, P.M. and Rotter, J.B. (1963), 'A personality correlate of social action', *Journal of Personality*, 31, 58–64.

Graham, Helen (1986), *The Human Face of Psychology: Humanistic psychology in its social and cultural context*, Open University Press: Milton Keynes.

Graham, Hilary (1984), *Women, Health and the Family*, Brighton: Harvester.

Gramsci, A. (1977), *Selections from the Prison Notebooks*, transl. Hoare, Q. and Nowell-Smith, G., Lawrence & Wishart: London.

Grube, J.W., Morgan, M. and McGree, S.T. (1986) 'Attitudes and normative beliefs as predictors of smoking intentions and behaviours: A test of three models', *British Journal of Social Psychology*, 25, 81–93.

Guess, V.A. (1984), 'Comparative medical systems: An anthropological perspective', in Ruffini, J.L. (ed.), *Advances in Medical Sciences*, Gordon & Breach: New York.

Habermas, J. (1970), *Towards a Rational Society: Student protest, science and politics*, Beacon: Boston, Mass.

Habermas, J. (1983), *The Theory of Communicative Action*, Beacon: Boston, Mass.

Hack Tuke, D. (1872), *The Influence of the Mind on the Body*, John Churchill: London.

Haley, B. (1978), *The Healthy Body in Victorian Culture*, Harvard University Press: Cambridge Mass.

Hall, S. (1980), 'Encoding/decoding', in Hall, S. *et al.* (eds.), *Culture, Media and Language*, Hutchinson: London.

Hall, S. (1986), 'Where is social science going?', paper presented to Faculty of Social Science Seminar Series, The Open University, Milton Keynes.

Hallpike, C.R. (1979), *The Foundations of Primitive Thought*, Clarendon: Oxford.

Harré, R. (1974), 'Blueprint for a new science', in Armistead, N. (ed.), *Reconstructing Social Psychology*, Penguin: Harmondsworth.

Harré, R. (1979), *Social Being: A Theory for Social Psychology*, Blackwell: Oxford.

Harré, R. and Secord, P.F. (1972), *The Explanation of Social Behaviour*, Blackwell: Oxford.

Harwood, A. (1971), 'The hot–cold theory of disease: Implications for treatment of Puerto Rican patients', *Journal of the American Medical Association*, 216, 1153–8.

Health Education Council (1987), *The Health Divide*, Health Education Council: London.

Heelas, P. (1981), 'Introduction: Indigenous psychologies', in Heelas, P. and Lock, A. (eds.), *Indigenous Psychologies: The anthropology of the self*, Academic Press: London.

Heider, F. (1944), 'Social perception and phenomenal causality', *Psychological Review*, 51, 358–74.

Heider, F. (1958), *The Psychology of Interpersonal Relations*, Wiley: New York.

Helman, C.G. (1978), ' "Feed a cold and starve a fever". Folk models of infection in an English suburban community, and their relation to medical treatment', *Culture, Medicine and Psychiatry*, 2, 107–37.

Henriques, J., Holloway, W., Urwin, C., Venn, C. and Walkerdine, V. (1984), *Changing the Subject: Psychology, regulation and subjectivity*, Methuen: London.

Herriot, P. (1974), *Attributes of Memory*, Methuen: London.

Hersch, P.D. and Scheibe, K.E. (1967), 'Reliability and validity of internal–external control as personality dimensions', *Journal of Consulting Psychology*, 31, 609–13.

Herzlich, C. (1973), *Health and Illness*, Academic Press: London.

Herzlich, C. and Pierret, J. (1985), 'The social construction of the patient: Patients and illnesses in other ages', *Social Science and Medicine*, 20 (2), 145–51.

Herzlich, C. and Pierret, J. (1987), *Illness and Self in Society*, transl. Foster, E. Johns Hopkins: Baltimore.

Hewitt, J.P. and Stokes, R. (1975), 'Disclaimers', *American Sociological Review*, 38, 367–74.

Hewstone, M. (1983), 'Attribution theory and common-sense explanations: an introductory overview', in Hewstone, M. (ed.), *Attribution Theory: Social and functional extensions*, Blackwell: Oxford.

Holland, R. (1977), *Self and Social Context*, Macmillan: London.

d'Houtaud, A. (1976), 'La représentation de la santé: recherche dans un centre bilan de santé en Lorraine', *Revue International d'Education pour la Santé*, 19, 2.

d'Houtaud, A. (1981), 'Nouvelles recherches sur les représentations de la santé', *Revue International d'Education pour la Santé*, 24, 3.

d'Houtaud, A. and Field, M. (1986), 'New research on the image of health', in Currer, C. and Stacey, M. (eds.) *Concepts of Health, Illness and Disease*. Berg: Leamington Spa.

Ibañez, T. (1991), 'Social psychology and the rhetoric of truth', *Theory and Psychology*, 2, in press.

Illich, I. (1976), *Limits to Medicine – Medical Nemesis: The exploitation of health*, Penguin: Harmondsworth.

Jahoda, G. (1986), 'Nature, culture and social psychology', *European Journal of Social Psychology*, 16 (1), 17–30.

James, W. (1878), 'Remarks on Spencer's definition of mind and correspondence', *Journal of Speculative Philosophy*.

James, W. (1891), *The Principles of Psychology*, Macmillan: London.

James, W. (1909), *The Meaning of Truth*, Macmillan: London.

Janet, P. (1932), 'Les sentiments dans le délire de persecution', *Journal de Psychologie Normale et Pathologique*, 29, 161–240.

Janoff-Bulman, R. and Brickmann, P. (1980), 'Expectations and what people learn from failure', in Feather, N. (ed.), *Expectancy, Incentive and Action*, Earlbaum: Hillside, NJ.

Jones, A. (1956), 'Distribution of traits in current Q sort methodology', *Journal of Abnormal and Social Psychology*, 52, 90–5.

Jones, E.E. and Davis, K.E. (1965), 'From acts to dispositions: The attribution process in social perception', in Berkowiz, L. (ed.), *Advances in Experimental Social Psychology* (vol. 2), Academic: New York.

Jones, E.E., Davis, K.E. and Gergen, K.J. (1961), 'Role playing variations and their informational value for person perception', *Journal of Abnormal and Social Psychology*, 63, 302–10.

Jones, E.E. and Nisbett, R.E. (1971), *The Actor and the Observer: Divergent perceptions of the causes of behaviour*, General Learning Press: Morristown, NJ.

Jones, W.T. (1977), 'Worldviews and the Asian medical system: Some suggestions for further study', in Leslie, C. (ed.), *Asian Medical Systems: A comparative study*, University of California Press: Berkeley, Calif.

Kaplan, G.D. and Cowles, A. (1978), 'Health Locus of Control and health value in the prediction of smoking reduction', *Health Education Monographs*, 6, 129–37.

Kasl, S.V. (1974), 'The Health Belief Model and chronic illness behaviour', *Health Education Monographs*, 2, 433–44.

Kelley, H.H. (1967), 'Attribution theory in social psychology', in Levine, D. (ed.), *Nebraska Symposium on Motivation*, University of Nebraska Press: Lincoln.

Kelly, G.A. (1955), *The Psychology of Personal Constructs* (vols 1 and 2), Norton: New York.

Kelly, G.A. (1966), 'A brief introduction to Personal Construct theory', in Bannister, D. (ed.) (1970), *Perspectives in Personal Construct Theory*, Academic: London.

Kerlinger, F.N. (1972), 'Q methodology in behavioural research', in Brown, S.R. and Brenner, D.J. (eds.), *Science, Psychology and Communication*, New Teachers College Press: New York.

King, J. (1983), 'Attribution theory and the health Belief Model', in Hewstone, M. (ed.), *Attribution Theory: Social and functional extensions*, Blackwell: Oxford.

Kitzinger, C. (1984), 'The constructing of lesbian identities', unpublished doctoral dissertation, University of Reading.

Kitzinger, C. (1986), 'A Q methodological investigation of accounts of moral development' (in press).

Kitzinger, C. (1987), *The Social Construction of Lesbianism*, Sage: London.

Kitzinger, C. and Stainton Rogers, R. (1985), 'A Q methodological study of lesbian identities', *European Journal of Social Psychology*, 15, 167–87.

Klandermans, P.G. (1983), 'Rotter's EI Scale and socio-political action taking: The balance of 20 years research', *European Journal of Social Psychology*, 13, 399–415.

Klein, P. (1988), *Psychology Exposed: Or the emperor's new clothes*, Routledge: London.

Kleinman, A. (1978), 'What kind of model for an anthropology of medical systems?', *American Anthropologist*, 80, 661–74.

Kleinman, A. (1980), *Patients and Healing in the Context of Culture: An exploration of the borderline between anthropology, medicine and psychiatry*, University of California Press: Berkeley, Calif.

Kleinman, A. (1984), 'Clinically applied medical anthropology: The view from the clinic', in Ruffini, J.L. (ed.), *Advances in Medical Science*, Gordon & Breach: New York.

Kohlberg, L. (1963), 'Psychological analysis and literary form: A study of the doubles in Dostoevsky', *Daedalus*, 92, 345–62.

Koos, E.L. (1954), *The Health of Regionville*, Columbia University Press: New York.

Kristiansen, C.M. (1985), 'Value correlates of preventive health behaviour', *Journal of Personality and Social Psychology*, 49 (3), 748–58.

Kruglanski, A.W. (1975), 'The endogenous–exogenous partition in attribution theory', *Psychological Review*, 82 (6), 387–406.

Kuhn, T.S. (1962), *The Structure of Scientific Revolutions*, University of Chicago Press: Chicago.

Laing, R.D. (1959), *The Divided Self*, Tavistock: London.

Lalljee, M. and Abelson, R.P. (1983), 'The organisation of explanations', in Hewstone, M. (ed.), *Attribution Theory: Social and functional extensions*, Blackwell: Oxford.

Langer, E.J. and Rodin, J. (1976), 'The effects of choice and enhanced personal responsibility for the aged: A filed experiment in an institutional setting', *Journal of Personality and Social Psychology*, 34 (1), 191–8.

Lee, R.B. (1978), 'Trance cure in the !Kung Bushmen', in Logan, M.M. and Hunt, E.E. (eds.), *Health and the Human Condition: Perspectives on medical anthropology*, Wadsworth: Belmont, Calif.

Lefcourt, H.M. (1981), *Research with the Locus of Control Construct Vol 1: Assessment methods*, Academic Press: New York.

Lefcourt, H.M. (1982), *Research with the Locus of Control Construct Vol 2: Current trends, theory and research*, Academic Press: New York.

Lefcourt, H.M. (1983), *Research with the Locus of Control Construct Vol 3: Developments and social problems*, Academic Press: New York.

Lefcourt, H.M. (1984), *Research with the Locus of Control Construct Vol 4: Extensions and limits*, Academic Press: New York.

Lemon, N. (1973), *Attitudes and their Measurement*, Wiley: London.

Leslie, C. (1976), *Asian Medical Systems: A Comparative Study*, University of California Press: Berkeley, Calif.

Leslie, C. (1987), personal communication.

Levenson, H. (1981), 'Differentiating among internality, powerful others, and chance' in Lefcourt, H.M. (ed.), *Research with the Locus of Control Construct Vol. 1: Assessment Methods*, Academic: New York.

Levenson, H. and Miller, J. (1976), 'Multi-dimensional Locus of Control in sociopolitical activists of conservative and liberal ideologies', *Journal of Personality and Social Psychology*, 33 (2), 199–208.

Leventhal, H. and Hirshman R.S. (1982), 'Social psychology and prevention, in Sanders, G.S. and Suls, J. (eds.), *Social Psychology of Health and Illness*, Earlbaum: Hillside, NJ.

Levin, A. and Shulz, M.A. (1980), 'Multidimensional Locus of Control and compliance in low and high participation hemodialysis programs', unpublished Paper, University of Wisconsin.

Levin, J.S. and Coreil, J. (1986), 'New Age Healing in the US', *Social Science and Medicine*, 23 (9), 889–97.

Lewis, F.M., Morisky, D.E. and Flynn, B.S. (1978), 'A test for construct validity of Health Locus of Control: Effects of self-reported compliance for hypertensive patients', *Health Education Monographs*, 6, 138–46.

Litton, I. and Potter, J. (1985), 'Social representations in the ordinary explanations of a "riot"', *European Journal of Social Psychology*, 15, 371–88.

Logan, M.H. and Hunt, E.E. (1978), *Health and the Human Condition: Perspectives on medical anthropology*, Wadsworth: Belmont, Calif.

Lowenstein, V.H. (1979), 'The relationship between pregnant women's belief of health locus of control and reported health maintenance behaviour', unpublished masters thesis, Pennsylvania State University.

McClelland, D.C. (1971), *Motivational Trends in Society*, General Learning Press: New York.

McCusker, J. and Morrow, G. (1979), 'The relationship of health locus of control to preventive health behaviours and health beliefs', *Patient Counselling and Health Education*, 1, 479–50.

McKeown, T. (1976), *The Modern Rise of Population*, Edward Arnold: London.

McKinlay, J.B., (1984), 'Introduction' to *Issues in the Political Economony of Health Care*, Tavistock: London.

Maiman, L.A., Becker, M.H., Kirscht, J.P., Haefner, D.P. and Drachman, R.H. (1977), 'Scales for measuring the Health Belief Model dimensions: A test of predictive value, internal consistency and relationships among beliefs', *Health Education Monographs*, 5, 215–30.

Marsh, P. (1982), 'Rules in the organization of action : Empirical studies', in Cranach, M. von and Harre, R. (eds.), *The Analysis of Action*, Cambridge University Press: Cambridge.

Marsh, P., Rosser, E. and Harré, R. (1978), *The Rules of Disorder*, Routledge & Kegan Paul: London.

Maslow, A.H. (1968), *Towards a Psychology of Being*, Van Nostrand: New York.

Mead, G.H. (1934), *Mind, Self and Society*, University of Chicago Press: Chicago.

Miles, R. (1978), *The Wholistic Handbook*, Simon and Schuster: New York.

Mischel, W. (1966), 'Theory and research on the antecedents of self-imposed delay of reward', in Maher, B.A. (ed.), *Progress in Experimental Personality Research*, 3, Academic Press: New York.

Mischel, W. (1977), 'Self-control and the self', in Mischel, T. (ed.), *The Self*, Blackwell: Oxford.

Mishler, E.G., AmaraSingham, L.R., Hauser, S.T, Liem, R., Osherson, S.D. and Wexler, N.E. (1981), *Social Contexts of Health, Illness and Patient Care*, Cambridge University Press: Cambridge.

Mitchell, J. (1984), *What is to be Done about Illness and Health?*, Harmondsworth: Penguin.

Morgan, D.L. and Spanish, M.T.(1985), 'Social interaction and the cognitive organisation of health-relevant knowledge', *Sociology of Health and Illness*, 7 (3), 401–22.

Moscovici, S. (1961), *La Psychanalyse: Son image et son public*, Presses Universitaires de France: Paris.

Moscovici, S. (1981), 'The phenomenon of social representations', in Farr, R.M. and Moscovici, S. (eds.), *Social Representations*, Cambridge University Press: Cambridge.

Moscovici, S. (1985), 'Society and theory in social psychology', in Israel, J. and Tajfel, H. (eds.), *The Context of Social Psychology: A critical assessment*, Academic: New York.

Moscovici, S. (1989), 'Preconditions for explanation in social psychology', *European Journal of Social Psychology*, 19 (5), 407–30.

Moscovici, S. and Hewstone, M. (1983), 'Social representations and social explanations: from the "naive" to the "amateur" scientist', in Hewstone, M. (ed.), *Attribution Theory: Social and functional extensions*, Blackwell: Oxford.

Mulkay, M. (1979) 'Knowledge and utility: Implications for the sociology of Knowledge', *Social Studies of Science*, 9 (1) 63–80.

Mulkay, M. (1991), *Sociology of Science: A sociological pilgrimage*, Open University Press: Milton Keynes.

Murrell, R.K. (1987), 'Telling it like it isn't: Representations of science in "Tomorrow's World"', *Theory, Culture and Society*, 4, 89–106.

Nagy (1979), Personal communication cited in Wallston and Wallston (1981).

Nash, C.L. (1987), 'An enquiry into the concept of locus of control and its relationship to health', unpublished PhD Dissertation, University of London.

Navarro, V. (1977), *Medicine under Capitalism*, Croom Helm: London.

Neisser, U. (1966), *Cognitive Psychology*, Appleton-Century-Crofts: New York.

Nicholson, J. (1980), 'Childbirth events and changes in maternal health locus of control', paper presented at the American Psychological Association Meeting, Montreal.

Nisbett, R.E. and Ross, L. (1980), *Human Inference: Strategies and shortcomings of social judgement*, Prentice Hall: Englewood Cliffs, NJ.

Olbrisch, M. (1975), 'Perceptions of responsibility for illness and health related locus of control in gonorrhoea patients', unpublished masters thesis, Florida State University.

Oliver, R.L. and Berger, P.K. (1979), 'A path analysis of preventive health care decision models', *Journal of Consumer Research*, 6, 113–22

Parker, I (1989), *The Crisis in Modern Social Psychology, And How to End It*, Routledge: London.

Parsons, T. (1951), *The Social System*, The Free Press: Glencoe, Ill.

Paul, B.D. (1955), *Health, Culture and Community: Case studies of public reactions to health programs*, Russell Sage: New York.

Pellegrino, E.D. (1963), 'Medicine, history and the idea of man', in Clausen, J.A. and Stauss, R. (eds.), *Medicine and Society*.

Peritore, P. (1986), 'Field notes on the use of Q methodology in the study of the Brazilian left', *Operant Subjectivity*, 10, 10–20.

Pill, R. and Stott, N. (1981), 'Relationship between Health Locus of Control and belief in the relevance of lifestyle to health', *Patient Counselling and Health Education*, 3 (3), 95–9.

Pill, R. and Stott, N. (1982), 'Concepts of illness causation and responsibility: Some preliminary data from a sample of working class mothers', *Social Science and Medicine*, 16 (1), 43–52.

Pill, R. and Stott, N. (1985a), 'Choice or chance: Further evidence on ideas of illness and responsibility for health', *Social Science and Medicine*, 20 (10), 981–91.

Pill, R. and Stott, N. (1985b), 'Preventive procedures and practices among working class women: New data and fresh insights', *Social Science and Medicine*, 21 (9), 975–83.

Pill, R. and Stott, N. (1987), 'Development of a measure of potential health behaviour: A salience of lifestyle index', *Social Science and Medicine*, 24 (2), 125–34.

Popper, K. (1959), *The Logic of Scientific Discovery*, Basic Books: New York.

Posner, T. (1977), 'Magical elements in orthodox medicine', in Dingwall, R., Health, C., Read, M. and Stacey, M. (eds.), *Health Care and Health Knowledge*, Prodist: New York.

Potter, J. (1984), 'Testability, flexibility: Kuhnian values in scientists', 'discourse concerning theory choice', *Philosophy of Social Science*, 14, 303–30.

Potter, J. and Litton, I. (1985), 'Some problems underlying the theory of social representations', *British Journal of Social Psychology*, 24, 81–90.

Potter, J. and Wetherell, M. (1987), *Discourse and Social Psychology: Beyond attitudes and behaviour*, Sage: London.

Poulnin, M. (1987), 'Healthy Profits', *She*, August, 102.

Press, I. (1980), 'Problems in the definition and classification of medical systems', *Social Science and Medicine*, 14b, 45–57.

Pribram, K.H. (1986), 'The cognitive revolution and mind/brain issues', *American Psychologist*, 41 (5), 507–20.

Reason, P. and Rowan, J. (1981), *Human Inquiry: A sourcebook for new paradigm research*, Wiley: Chichester.

Renaud, M. (1981), 'Les Réformes Québecoises de la santé ou les aventures d'un Etat narcissique', in Bozzini, L. *et al.*, *Médecine et Société, les annés 80*, Laval: Quebec.

Research Unit in Health and Behavioural Change, University of Edinburgh (1989), *Changing the Public Health*, Wiley: Chichester.

Richards, M.P.M. (ed.) (1974), *The Integration of the Child into the Social World*, Cambridge University Press: Cambridge.

Riegel, K.F. (1978), *Psychology Mon Amour*, Houghton Mifflin: Boston, Mass.

Rivers, W.H.R. (1924), *Medicine, Magic and Religion*, Harcourt Brace: New York.

Rivers, W.H.R. (1926), *Psychology and Ethnology*, Routledge: London.

Rogers, C.R. and Dymond, R.F. (eds.) (1954), *Psychotherapy and Personality Change*, University of Chicago Press: Chicago.

Rokeach, M. (1960), *The Open and Closed Mind*, Basic: New York.

Rokeach, M. (1968), *Beliefs, Attitudes and Values: A Theory of organisation and change*, Jossey-Bass: San Francisco.

Rommetveit, R. (1980), 'On "meanings" of acts and what is meant and made known by what is said in a pluralistic world', in Brenner, M. (ed.), *The Structure of Action*, St Martin's Press: New York.

Rorty, A.O. (1987), 'Persons as rhetorical categories', *Social Research*, 54 (1), 55–72.

Rose, H. and Rose, S. (1976), '"Press freedom": A socialist strategy', in Gardner, C. (ed.), *Media, Politics and Culture: A socialist view*, Macmillan: London.

Rosenblum, E.H. (1979), 'Maternal compliance in immunisation of pre-schoolers as related to Health Locus of Control, health value and perceived vulnerability', unpublished doctoral dissertation, University of New Mexico.

Rosenstock, I.M. (1966), 'Why people use health services', *Millbank Memorial Fund Quarterly*, 44, 94–124.

Rosenstock, I.M. (1974), 'Historical origins of the health belief model', *Health Education Monographs*, 2, 328–35.

Rosenwald, G.C. (1986), 'Why operationalism doesn't go away: Extrascientific incentives of social-psychological research', *Philosophy of Social Science*, 16, 303–30.

Ross, L. (1977), 'The intuitive psychologist and his shortcomings: Distortions in the attribution process', in Berkowitz, L. (ed.), *Advances in Experimental Social Psychology* (vol. 10), Academic: New York.

Rotter, J.B. (1966), 'Generalised expectancies for internal versus external control of reinforcement', *Psychological Monographs*, 80 (1).

Rotter, J.B., Seeman, M. and Liverant, S. (1962), 'Internal versus external control of reinforcement: A major variable in behaviour therapy', in Washburne, N.F. (ed.), *Decisions, Values and Groups* (vol. 2), Pergamon: New York.

Saltzer, E.B. (1979), 'Causal beliefs and losing weight', unpublished doctoral dissertation, University of California at Irvine.

Schlenker, B.R. and Darby, B.W. (1981), 'The use of apologies in social predicaments', *Social Psychology Quarterly*, 44, 271–8.

Schonbach, P.A. (1980), 'A category system for account phases', *European Journal of Social Psychology*, 10, 195–200.

Scott, M.B. and Lyman, S. (1968), 'Accounts', *American Sociological Review*, 33, 46–62.

Scruton, R. (1986), *Sexual Desire: A philosophical investigation*, Weidenfeld & Nicholson: London.

Scully, D and Bart, P. (1978), 'A funny thing happened on the way to the orifice: Women in gynaecology textbooks', in Ehrenreich, J. (ed.), *The Cultural Crisis of Modern Medicine*, Monthly Review Press: New York.

Sedgwick, P. (1982), *Psychopolitics*, Pluto: London.

Seligman, M.E.P. (1975), *Helplessness: On depression, development and death*, Freeman: San Fransisco.

Seligman, M.E.P., Abramson, L.Y. and von Baeyer, C. (1979), 'Depressive attributional style,' *Journal of Abnormal Psychology*, 88, 242–7.

Semin, G.R. and Manstead, A.S.R. (1983), *The Accountability of Conduct: A social psychological analysis*, Academic: London.

Semin, G.R. and Rogers, R.S. (1973), 'The generation of descriptive–evaluative responses to scale-answering behaviour: A model', *European Journal of Social Psychology*, 3, 311–28.

Shank, R. and Abelson, R.P. (1977), *Scripts, Plans, Goals and Understanding: An enquiry into human knowledge structures*, Earlbaum: Hillside, NJ.

Shaver, K.G. (1970), 'Defensive attribution: Effects of severity and relevance of the responsibility assigned for an accident', *Journal of Personality and Social Psychology*, 14 (1), 101–13.

Shaver, K.G. and Drown, D. (1986), 'On causality, reponsibility and self-blame: A theoretical note', *Journal of Personality and Social Psychology*, 50 (4), 697–702.

Shotter, J. (1974), 'The development of personal powers', in Richards, M.P.M. (ed.), *The Integration of the Child into the Social World*, Cambridge University Press: Cambridge.

Shotter, J. (1981), 'Vico, moral worlds, accountability and personhood', in Heelas, P. and Lock, A. (eds.), *Indigenous Psychologies: The anthropology of the self*, Academic: London.

Shultz, A. (1962), *Collected Papers: The problem of social reality*, Martinus Nijhoff: The Hague.

Shweder, R.A. (1984), 'Anthropology's romantic rebellion against the enlightenment, or there's more to thinking than reason and evidence', in Shweder, R.A. and Levine, R.A. (eds.), *Culture Theory: Essays on mind, self and emotion*, Cambridge University Press: Cambridge.

Smith, M.B., Bruner, J. and White, R.W. (1956), *Opinions and Personality*, Wiley: New York.

Snow, L.F. (1974), 'Folk medical beliefs and their implications for care of patients', *Annals of Internal Medicine*, 81, 82–96.

Sontag, S. (1977), *Illness as Metaphor*, Farrar, Straus & Giroux: New York.

Sontag, S. (1989) *AIDS and its Metaphors*, Allan Lane: London.

Sproles, K.J. (1977), 'Health locus of control and knowledge of hemodialysis and health maintenance of patients with chronic renal failure', unpublished master's thesis, Virginia Commonwealth university.

Stacey, M. (1988), *The Sociology of Health and Healing*, Unwin Hyman: London.

Stainton Rogers, R. (1989) 'The social construction of childhood', in Stainton Rogers, W., Hevey, D. and Ashe, E. (eds.), *Child Abuse and Neglect: Facing the challenge*, Batsford: London.

Stainton Rogers, R. (1990), *Cultural Tectonics*, occasional paper presented to the Beryl Curt Fan Club.

Stainton Rogers, R. and Kitzinger, C. (1985), 'Human rights: A Q methodological investigation', research report for the European Council on Human Rights.

Stainton Rogers, R. and Stainton Rogers, W. (1986), 'The social construction of addiction: Accounts of aetiology and social policy', paper presented at the ESEP Advanced Workshop on Environmental and Social Psychology, Lisbon, (September).

Stainton Rogers, W. (1987), 'Accounting for Health and Illness', unpublished Ph.D. dissertation, Open University.

Stephenson, W. (1935), 'Technique of factor analysis', *Nature*, vol. 136, 297.

Stephenson, W. (1953), *The Study of Behaviour: Q technique and its methodology*, University of Chicago Press: Chicago.

Stephenson, W. (1962), 'Image of public health and medicine: 1', report to the Director of Public Health, State of Missouri, Jefferson City.

Stephenson, W. (1963), 'Image of public health and medicine: 2', report to the Director of Public Health, State of Missouri, Jefferson City.

Stephenson, W. (1967), *The Play Theory of Mass Communication*, University of Chicago Press: Chicago.

Stephenson, W. (1986a), 'William James, Neils Bohr and complementarity: 1. Concepts', *Psychological Record*, 36, 519–27.

Stephenson, W. (1986b), 'William James, Neils Bohr and complementarity: 2. Pragmatics', *Psychological Record*, 36, 529–43.

Stephenson, W. (1986c), 'Protoconcursus: The concourse theory of communication', *Operant Subjectivity*, 9 (2), 30–72.

Stockle, J.P. and Barslay, A.J. (1980), 'Attributions: uses of social science knowledge in the "doctoring" of primary care', in Eisenberg, L. and Kleinmen, A. (eds.), *The Relevance of Social Science to Medicine*, Reidel: Dordrecht.

Stuart, R.B. (1979), 'Locus of Control Scale: A dialogue on predictive compliance', paper presented at the American Psychological Association, New York City.

Swift, D.J., Watts, D.M. and Pope, M.L. (1983), 'Methodological pluralism and personal construct psychology: A case for pictorial methods in eliciting personal constructions', paper presented to the 5th International Conference on Personal Construct Psychology, Boston, Mass.

Taussig, M. (1980), 'Reification and the consciousness of the patient', *Social Science and Medicine*, 14b, 3–13.

Taussig, M. (1986), 'The nervous system', paper presented to the British Medical Anthropology Society Conference, Cambridge, England (July).

Tedischi, J.T. and Riess, M. (1981), 'Verbal strategies in impression management', in Antaki, C. (ed.), *The Psychology of Ordinary Explanations of Social Behaviour*, Academic: London.

Tennen, H., Affleck, G. and Gershman, K. (1986), 'Self-blame among parents of infants with perinatal complications: The role of self-protective motives', *Journal of Personality and Social Psychology*, 50 (4), 690–6.

Tolor, A. (1978), 'Some antecedents and personality correlates of Health Locus of Control', *Psychological Reports*, 43, 1159–65.

Townsend, P. and Davidson, N. (1982), *Inequalities in health: The Black report*, Penguin: Harmondsworth.

Turner, B.S. (1986), 'Personhood and citizenship', *Theory, Culture and Society*, 3 (1), 1–15.

Turner, C.F. and Krauss, E. (1978), 'Fallible indicators of the subjective state of the nation', *American Psychologist*, 33, 456–70.

Unshuld, P. (1986), 'The conceptual determination (Uberformung) of individual and collective experiences of illness', in Currer, C. and Stacey, M. (eds.), *Concepts of Health, Illness and Disease*. Berg: Leamington Spa.

Valabrega, J.P. (1962), *La Relation Therapeutique, Malade et Médecin*, Flammarion: Paris.

Vala-Salvador, J. and Leite-Viegas, J.M. (1987), 'Political culture in urban Portugal', paper presented to the Workshop on the European Consortium for Political Research, University of Amsterdam (April).

Voysey, M. (1975), *A Constant Burden*, Routledge & Kegan Paul: London.

Vygotsky, L.S. (1962), *Thought and Language*, MIT Press: Cambridge, Mass.

Wallston, B.S. and Wallston, K.A. (1978), 'Locus of control and health: A review of literature', *Health Education Monographs*, 6, 107–16.

Wallston, B.S., Wallston, K.A., Kaplan, G.D. and Maides, S.A. (1976), 'Development and validation of the Health Locus of Control (HLC) Scale', *Journal of Consulting and Clinical Psychology*, 44, 580–5.

Wallston, K.A. and McLeod, E. (1979) 'Predictive factors in the adherence of antihypertensive regimen among adult male outpatients', unpublished manuscript, School of Nursing, Vanderbilt University.

Wallston, K.A. and Wallston, B.S. (1981), 'Health Locus of Control Scales', in Lefcourt, H.M. (ed.), *Research with the Locus of Control Construct Vol 1: Assessment methods*, Academic Press: New York.

Wallston, K.A., Wallston, B.S. and De Vellis, R. (1978), 'Development of the multidimensional health locus of control (MHLC) scales', *Health Education Monographs*, 6, 161–70.

Walster, E. (1966), 'Assignment of responsibility for an accident', *Journal of Personality and Social Psychology*, 3 (1), 73–9.

Watzlawick, P. (1984), *The Invented Reality*, Norton: New York.

Waxler, N.E. (1981) 'Learning to be a leper: A case study in the social construction of illness', in Mishler, E.G., AmaraSingham, L.R., Hauser, S.T., Liem, R., Osherson, S.D. and Waxler, N.E. (eds.), *Social Contexts of Health, Illness and Patient Care*, Cambridge University Press: Cambridge.

Weber, M. (1930), *The Protestant Ethic and the Spirit of Capitalism*, Allen and Unwin: London.

Weinreich, P. (1983), 'Psychodynamics of personal and social identity: Theoretical concepts and their measurement', in Jacobson-Widding, A. (ed.), *Identity: Personal and Socio-cultural*, Humanities Press: Atlantic Highlands.

Wellin, E. (1978), 'Theoretical orientations in medical anthropology: change and continuity in the past half-century', in Logan, M.H. and Hunt, E.E. (eds.), *Health and the Human Condition*, Wadsworth: Belmont, Calif.

Whitehead, M. (1987), *The Health Divide*, The Health Education Council: London.

Whorton, J. (1982), *Crusaders for Fitness: The history of American health reformers*, Princeton University Press: Princeton, NJ.

Wiggins, J.S., Renner, K.E., Clore, G.L. and Rose, R.J. (1971), *The Psychology of Personality*, Addison-Wesley: Reading Mass.

Wildman, H.E., Rosenbaum, M.S., Framer, E.M., Keane, T.M. and Johnson, W.G. (1979), 'Smoking cessation: predicting success with the health locus of control scale', paper presented at the Association for the Advancement of Behaviour Therapy, San Francisco.

Williams, R. (1981a), 'Logical analysis as a qualitative method I: Themes in old age and chronic illness', *Sociology of Health and Illness*, 3 (2), 140–63.

Williams, R. (1981b), 'Logical analysis as a qualitative method II: Conflict of ideas and the topic of illness', *Sociology of Health and Illness*, 3 (2), 165–85.

Williams, R. (1983), 'Concepts on health: An analysis of lay logic', *Sociology*, 17 (2), 185–205.

Williams, R. (1986a), 'Images of age and generation', paper presented to the British Sociology Association Conference, also forthcoming in Bryman, A. and Bytheway, W. (eds.), *Life-Cycle Perspectives*, Macmillan: London.

Williams, R. (1986b), 'Religion and other resources in coping with illness', paper presented to the Joint Conference of the British Medical Anthropology Society and the Society for Medical Anthropology, Cambridge (July).

Williams, R. (1990), *A Protestant Legacy: Attitudes to death and Illness among older Aberdonians*, Clarendon: Oxford.

Wong, P.T.P. and Sproule, C.F. (1982), 'An attribution analysis of the Locus of Control construct in the Trent attribution profile', in Lefcourt, H.M. (ed.), *Research with the Locus of Control Construct Vol 2: Current trends, theory and research*, Academic: New York.

Wortman, C.B. and Dintzer, L. (1978), 'Is an attributional analysis of the learned helplessness phenomenon viable?: A critique of the Abramson–Seligman–Tearsdale reformulation', *Journal of Abnormal Psychology*, 87, 75–90.

Young, A. (1976), 'Internalising and externalising medical belief systems: An Ethiopian example', *Social Science and Medicine*, 10, 147–56.

Young, A. (1980), 'The discourse on stress and the reproduction of conventional knowledge', *Social Science and Medicine*, 14b, 133–46.

Young, A. (1981), 'When rational men fall sick: An inquiry into some assumptions made by medical anthropologists', *Culture, Medicine and Psychiatry*, 5, 317–35.

Young, A. (1982), 'The anthropologies of illness and sickness', *Annual Review of Anthropology*, 11, 257–85.

Young, A. (1983), 'Rethinking ideology', *International Journal of Health Services*, 13 (2), 203–19.

Young, A. (1987), 'Peace-time and past-time in the clinical construction of combat-related post-traumatic stress disorder', paper presented to the Royal Anthropological Institute Conference on 'Time in Sickness and Health', Windsor, England (February).

Zola, I. (1972), 'Medicine as an institution of social control', *Sociological Review*, 20, 487–504.

Index

Labelling of feelings as illness
- medical model leads us to
make this jump rather than
say we are just 'unhappy'
Symptoms are symptoms of
illness because we
define them as such

medicalization means that the medical
model has become the dominant explanatory
→ legitization (remember Sunday?) model
article on alternative medicine) - desire
requirements of scientific proof.